Babies and Y

A GUIDE FOR PAREN1

CW00400479

Ronald Illingworth
M.D., F.R.C.P., D.P.H., D.C.H., D.Sc., F.R.P.S.
Formerly Professor of Child Health, University of Sheffield

Cynthia Illingworth
M.B., B.S., F.R.C.P.
Consultant in Paediatric Accident and Emergency,
The Children's Hospital, Sheffield

SEVENTH EDITION

CHURCHILL LIVINGSTONE
EDINBURGH LONDON MELBOURNE AND NEW YORK 1984

CHURCHILL LIVINGSTONE
Medical Division of Longman Group UK Limited

Distributed in the United States of America by Churchill
Livingstone Inc., 1560 Broadway, New York, N.Y.
10036, and by associated companies, branches and
representatives throughout the world.

First Edition 1954
Reprinted 1956
Second Edition 1960
Third Edition 1964
Fourth Edition 1968
Fifth Edition 1972
Reprinted 1974
Sixth Edition 1977
Seventh Edition 1984
    Reprinted 1990

ISBN 0-443-02970-9

British Library Cataloging in Publication Data
Illingworth, Ronald S.
    Babies and young children — 7th ed.
    I. Child rearing
    I. Title   II. Illingworth, Cynthia M,
    649'.122   HQ769

Library of Congress Cataloging in Publication Data
Illingworth, Ronald Stanley, 1909-
    Babies and young children.
    Includes index.
    1. Infants — Care and hygiene.   2. Children —
    Care and hygiene.   3. Children —
    Management.   I Illingworth, Cynthia
    M.   II. Title
    RJ101.138   1983   649'.122   83-7358

Produced by Longman Singapore Publishers (Pte) Ltd
Printed in Singapore

Preface to the Seventh Edition

In preparing this new edition we have read and reread several times every word of the previous edition, bringing it right up to date, and completely rewriting many chapters and sections. We have considerably amplified the chapter on Common Symptoms of Childhood, so that parents can know which symptoms are important, demanding the doctor's opinion, and which are merely normal variations not requiring medical advice.

We have tried to cover all questions, problems and anxieties which hundreds of mothers have asked us about over the years — and we have always made a note of any question put to us if it has not been discussed in the book.

We have included important sections on the prevention of infection, and discussed the controversy about the risk of immunisation, particularly for whooping cough. We have greatly amplified the section on the prevention of accidents, and the vitally important question to which every good parent wants the answer — how to bring the best out of a child, how to help the development of his mind, and in particular how to help him not just to be a clever person but a nice person.

Such a comprehensive book can only be written by a paediatrician. As practising paediatricians we have based this book on many years of personal experience — in hospital and outside, in baby and child health clinics, and in a busy hospital Casualty Department — and with experience of our own family. We have seen *all* the behaviour patterns described in the book — many of them hundreds of times. Scores of books have been written by psychologists about children, but few of them give parents practical down-to-earth advice about the causes and management of common behaviour problems. We have tried in all cases to explain how the various behaviour problems arise. We have tried to provide a practical guide to overall management of babies and young children, including infant feeding and nutrition and to discuss all the various features of physical growth, such as teething, tongue tie, smallness of weight or stature, overweight, and the question of circumcision. In addition we have given an outline of normal development, covering such skills as sitting, walking, talking and control of the bladder and bowel, with a detailed discussion of the normal variations which occur.

Sheffield, 1984   R.S. Illingworth
                                                                C.M. Illingworth

Acknowledgements

All the sketches are by Mary How. Plate 1 is by Peter Miles, Plates 2, 4 and 10 by Elizabeth Vago, Plate 9 by Doris Pinney, Plate 14 by Suzanne Szasz, Plate 17 by Josef A. Schneider, and all are reproduced with the permission of Camera Press Ltd. Plates 15, 26, 40 and 42 are by Graham Portlock, and Plates 6 (top), 12 and 19 (bottom) by Alan Tunstill, Photographic Department, United Sheffield Hospitals. Plates 16, 25, 32 and 34 are reproduced with the kind permission of Barnaby's Picture Library and Plates 27, 33, 37 and 38 with the kind permission of PAF International Press Service Ltd. With the exception of Plates 5, 6 (bottom), 11, 13 (bottom), 18, 19 (top), 20, 28–30, 35 and 36 the remaining plates are the author's own.

Preface to the First Edition

It was with considerable trepidation that we decided to write a book on a subject concerning which so much has been written by others. Between us we have had many years' experience of trying to answer questions posed by anxious parents about their children, and as a result of carefully noting these queries over a period of years we felt that we had a good idea of the sort of guidance which parents need. We have therefore tried to give as complete an account as possible of the management of the child in his first five years, though, of course, it is impossible to cover every difficulty which may arise. We have discussed in particular detail such matters as infant feeding, crying, sleep problems, a poor appetite, toilet training, lateness in talking and walking, toys and play, and the prevention of infection and of accidents. We have included a chapter on common symptoms in children, with the sole purpose of indicating when medical advice should be sought from the family doctor without delay. We have made no attempt to discuss the treatment of the various infections and illnesses which occur in children, and for which the help of the family doctor will be sought. The book is up to date, and incorporates what seems to us to be the best teaching of the leading experts in this country and the United States.

The book is intended for parents and is written in non-technical language without medical terms — except when these are fully explained. It is not intended for doctors, for whom one of us had already written a book* concerning problems of the first five years — a book which inevitably overlaps to some extent with this. We hope that this book will also prove useful to all those, other than doctors, who are responsible for the care of young children.

For the sake of brevity we have throughout the book referred to a child as 'he' or 'him'. Our remarks, of course, apply equally to girls.

It is impossible to give due acknowledgement to the writers of the many hundreds of papers and books which we have read in the preparation of this text.

Sheffield, 1954   R.S. Illingworth
                                                               C.M. Illingworth

*R.S. Illingworth (1953) *The Normal Child. Some Problems of the First Five Years and Their Treatment*. London: Churchill. Eighth Edition (1983).

Contents

1

Planning and preparations for a child

On planning to have a baby

Some couples on getting married decide not to have a baby for some time, either because they lack financial security, or merely because they want to enjoy themselves and to be free from family ties. We think that this must depend on the age of the couple. A good age to have the first child is around 21 to 26; if the couple is younger than this on marriage, there is something to be said for postponing conception; if the couple is much older, it would be wise if possible to shorten the gap between marriage and conception. Though the advent of a child cannot be expected to unite a couple in which relations are extremely strained, there is no doubt that the arrival of children does much towards increasing the bond of love between parents. It is not easy after several years without children for a couple to adapt themselves to the ties of family life. Not only is it better for a woman to have children when she is young, and better for the children to have young parents, but the chances of conception are better, for fertility slowly decreases with increasing age.

It is unwise to have children with short intervals between births, for it is bad for the mother, who has little chance to regain her strength fully after one pregnancy before starting a second one, and it is bad for the child. The mother is unable to give as much time as she would like to the first child, especially if he has not learnt to walk, or to the second child, if the first is still occupying much of her time. On the other hand births should not be separated by too long an interval, if this can be avoided, for children are better playmates and companions for each other if the ages separating them are not too great.

The ideal interval between births is about two years. This is long enough to allow the first child to acquire a measure of independence before the second is born, but not too long to reduce the companionship between the two children.

If you want advice about the best method of spacing births in this way, you should seek advice from the Family Planning Association, which has centres in all large towns.*

*The central address is: 27 Mortimer Street, London, W.1.

Looking after your own health

In this section we do not propose to discuss the maintenance of good health during pregnancy, except only to mention certain special conditions which are of vital importance to the baby.

All girls should be immunised against german measles (rubella) at the age of 11 to 12 years, unless blood tests show that they are immune to it because they have already had it: the girl's statement that she has had german measles cannot be accepted, because the diagnosis may have been wrong. If you are pregnant and have not been immunised or tested, all you can do is to try to avoid any known contact. The first three or four months of pregnancy are the most important in this regard. It is extremely rare for chickenpox or other common infectious disease to damage the fetus.

You should be under the supervision of your family doctor and antenatal clinic; you will be advised about the importance of proper nutrition, because unwise efforts to keep the weight down may have a harmful effect on fetal development.

Unless they are really essential, it is wise to take no medicines in pregnancy (except perhaps vitamin supplements), for scores of drugs or medicines can occasionally damage the fetus. We do not want to alarm you or to exaggerate the risk: it is only rarely that the commonly used drugs do any harm; but do avoid medicines if you can.

Drugs of addiction, like nicotine (smoking) or alcohol can do serious harm to the fetus. It has been calculated that smoking in pregnancy costs the lives of around 1500 babies a year in Britain; it increases the risk of stillbirth; commonly lowers the birth weight of the baby and affects his subsequent physical growth, and may be a factor in causing troublesome overactivity and learning problems in later childhood. Heavy alcohol drinking in pregnancy causes the same problems, but in addition the child may have a characteristic face (enabling the expert to make the diagnosis just by looking at the baby), and increases the risk of mental subnormality, cleft palate, congenital heart disease, kidney disease and abnormal finger nails and elbow movements.

You should report any blood loss, swelling of the ankles or feeling of being unwell, in order that the cause can be established and the proper treatment instituted. It is particularly important that anaemia should be corrected, for not only will anaemia make you tired and probably irritable as a result, but it will cause your baby to become anaemic some months after he has been born, for he will not receive an adequate supply of iron from you.

You may be surprised to know that around 200 diseases can be diagnosed in the fetus before birth — by examining the amniotic fluid, X-ray and other means.

Equipment for the baby

A baby's needs in the matter of clothes and equipment are really quite simple.

He should, if possible, have a room of his own. In the first few weeks, as long as he is demanding a night feed, he may share your bedroom, but as soon as possible after that it is better for him and for you that he should sleep in his own room.

A great deal of money is wasted on equipment which is unnecessary or only of limited use. For instance, the special suites of furniture, with a small sized chest of drawers, dressing table, wardrobe and bed, decorated with nursery motifs, are highly expensive and soon outgrown. It is more sensible to purchase equipment which will be of lasting value, and which will form a useful beginning for a pleasant bedroom or bed-sitting room. The nursery atmosphere can be supplied in the form of curtains and pictures which can easily be changed later without much expense. You should think of the future, and plan to make his room as attractive as you can. Do not feel that any odd bit of furniture 'will do' if you can possibly avoid it. His room will be important for moulding his tastes. When he is older you will teach him to take care of his room and to enjoy it, so that when he grows up he will make the surroundings in which he and his family live as pleasant as possible.

The baby will need a cot. It should be a well-made one with a drop side and good quality firm mattress. It is worth while to look at the catch which has to be fitted in order to let the cot side down. This should not be too easy to operate, for if it is, your young son, not long after his first birthday, may discover the trick of letting the cot side down, or his elder brother may show him how to do it. The sides must not be solid, for he will want to see out of it. The bars of the cot should not be more than three inches apart, for fatalities have occurred as a result of babies getting their head caught between the bars. An ordinary cot is suitable for even the youngest baby. He can be protected from draughts by a screen or by a blanket pinned firmly round one side of the cot. We see no point in buying an expensive crib.

No pillow is necessary for the cot. He will be safer without one. You will need a waterproof sheet to cover the mattress, and an ample supply of cot sheets, which can be cotton, linen or flannelette; if necessary they can be made from remnants of partly worn sheets. Several light wool blankets will also be needed.

The portable cot (carrycot) is useful for journeys by train or car, but otherwise it is not essential. If necessary, the baby can sleep in this at night for the first few months. You will find that it is useful during the day in the house, as something into which to put him — in the kitchen, sitting room or elsewhere. If a stand is used for a carrycot, the cot must fit firmly into the stand, or must be firmly attached to it. The carrycot, containing a baby, should never be placed on the table or chest of drawers. If the cot slides in the stand, and the straps are not absolutely secure, the baby may cause the cot and stand to fall over. Some of the stands for carrycots are unsafe. Check them carefully before buying.

It should not be forgotten, if money is short, that expensive equipment such as cot, pram and play-pen, can be obtained secondhand by advertisement in the local paper. Naturally, you will see that they are thoroughly cleaned before use.

You will want two plastic buckets preferably with lids, to hold wet and soiled napkins. Another essential is a small tray for the bathroom, to hold cotton wool swabs, baby lotion, baby cream, powder, soap and safety pins.

There are several types of plastic baths, but such baths are unnecessary, for the baby can be washed in the wash basin or in a large bowl. If he is washed in the wash basin, it is essential to see that it is absolutely clean before he is bathed in it, and that he cannot be scalded accidentally by the hot tap and that he does not bump his head on the tap. At a few months of age he can more easily be bathed in the ordinary adult bath.

Prams. There are well designed light-weight prams on the market. In some the body can be lifted off the base which then folds for storage. Whatever sort of pram you buy, you must see that the brakes are efficient. The safest and most useful sort of basket for the pram is one which fits underneath the body, so that heavy parcels do not cause it to overbalance.

The pram is usually supplied with a kind of pad on which the baby can lie, but it is desirable to buy a proper mattress, for the baby will spend a great deal of time in his pram. A waterproof sheet will be necessary, covered by a blanket and some lightweight warm blankets or pram rugs. A firm pillow will be needed when the baby reaches the stage of being propped up (at about three months), but not at first. The pillow must be firm, so that there will be no danger of suffocation if he turns over and sleeps on his stomach. A safety harness should be supplied with the pram. It should fasten over the shoulders as well as round the waist, for a single strap round the waist is useless. The baby must not be able to kneel or stand up with the harness in place. It is possible to buy a harness which can later be used as walking reins.

You will need a push chair. Some people have the extraordinary

idea that a push chair is "bad for the back" of a young baby. This is nonsense. There is nothing wrong with using a push chair as soon as you like — when he is a month old if you want.

A chair will be needed. This will be used long before he uses it for meals. It should have a broad base and be very firm so that there is no danger that it will be rocked over, for active babies perform remarkable acrobatic feats when strapped in high chairs. It should have safety straps going round the shoulders and waist, so that he cannot fall over the back of the chair; there should be a central bar between the baby's legs to that he cannot slip through. It is safer to buy a low chair than to risk accidents with a top-heavy high one. The tray of the chair should be as large as possible and have rounded corners which are easily kept clean. Some chairs have a device which holds a baby propped up, even when quite young. A large piece of plastic material placed under the high chair will avoid a good deal of mess and damage to carpets when he is learning to feed himself.

One piece of equipment which, while not essential, is extremely useful, is the Safe Sitter made by Mothercare and similar ones made by other manufacturers. Many babies, even when very young, are more content when they are propped up so that they can see something going on and this device is excellent for the purpose. It is made of plastic, can be adjusted to differing angles of height, and has plastic covered cushions which can easily be cleaned. It can be useful for a baby who tends to vomit if laid flat immediately after a feed.

The so called 'baby bouncers' are popular with mothers, and

babies seem to like them. They give good exercise and help to strengthen the legs. They are not essential, and injuries have resulted from their use.

A play-pen is useful for the older baby, but its usefulness may be short-lived, for some babies will not tolerate it for more than a month or so. Most babies, however, use them for several months. They learn to pull themselves up to the standing position in them, and to walk while holding on to the edge. We doubt the value of the type of play-pen which has a solid wood base or floor. These play-pens take up more room and are heavier than the simple folding variety. A useful plastic base is now available for play-pens. It protects the carpet and makes it more difficult for the child to push the play-pen around. It is possible to buy a play-pen which fits into the corner of a room, and so occupies a minimum space. Some play-pens have 'doors', but the danger of these is that an older child or the baby himself will open the door when the mother thinks it is securely closed. We do not recommend them. If you have a car, you will need a safe car seat for the child (Ch 24).

Equipment for the older child
When the time comes for the child to graduate from a cot to a bed, you should get a full-sized bed. We recommend a low divan, for on the rare occasion on which he falls out of bed, the fall will only be a small one. The child will also be able to get in and out of bed himself in order to attend to his toilet needs. We do not think that a small bed with side rails is of value, for its period of usefulness is a short one. The risk of the child falling out of bed is small, and can be

obviated by placing a chair with its back to the side of the bed.

As soon as the child is old enough to use it, a bedside lamp may be provided. It will give him more independence and it will help to dispel night fears.

If he is not able to have a room of his own, he should at least have a definite place in which he can keep his possessions.

Clothes for the baby

In the years since this book was first published, there have been enormous developments in the range of 'easy-care' clothes for babies. There are now specialist shops (such as 'Mothercare') which cover the whole range of needs, so that the choice is now largely a matter of taste. You will have little spare time with a new baby, and you may be tired, so buy things which are easy to look after and which do not need ironing.

The stretch 'coverall' type of garment can be used both day and night (except in unusually warm weather). They stretch as the baby grows, and do not need ironing.

Nappies are mainly of two types — gauze squares (e.g. 'Harrington squares'), and Turkish Towelling. The former are easily dried, quite absorbent and softer for the baby, but it is useful to have a few of the Turkish towel type as an outer cover for night-time and for travel.

Many types of disposable nappies are now on the market. The most satisfactory are usually those made of cellulose wadding with a thin layer of cotton wool which prevents flaking of the wadding next

to the body. Most will be used in special types of plastic holders but some are triangular in shape and can be used with the more usual type of protective baby pants. There are special types of nappies which can be put inside an ordinary nappy and remain reasonably dry — allowing the moisture to pass through to the outer one. The Marathon and Drinaps are examples. They have to be washed in the usual way. Disposable nappy liners are useful: they are placed inside the ordinary towelling nappy. A recent development is the 'one-way' sort which acts in the same way as the Marathon type.

Many mothers no longer use nightgowns for the child. The useful stretch 'coverall' type of garments which grow with the baby and do not need ironing may be used during the day in cooler months instead of dresses. Mittens or bootees should not be made of nylon or contain nylon, as the filaments of nylon are extremely tough, and if they become twisted round a finger or toe, they can cause serious damage.

Clothes for the older baby and young child
This is largely a matter of personal taste but the important thing is to provide clothing which will enable him to enjoy his activities with the minimum of restriction. Children should be allowed to get dirty and be suitably clad for the purpose. Do not dress them so that they have to have frequent warnings not to get dirty and reprimands when they forget to be careful.

In the early days of self-feeding, plastic feeders with sleeves and an ordinary absorbent towelling feeder on top will save much soiling of clothes.

When young children are becoming independent and try to dress themselves, choose clothes which are easy for them to get off to attend to their own toilet needs and which have easy fastenings. The 'Velcro' type of fastening which closes by light pressure alone is useful for young or handicapped older children.

Shoes. Well-made and properly fitted shoes and socks are vitally important in preventing future foot troubles. You should look for a shop where the feet are carefully measured, and you should have your children's shoes checked at frequent intervals in order to ensure that they are sufficiently large in both width and length.

You should not allow any shop to use an X-ray machine for checking the size of his shoes. These machines may be dangerous, because of the irradiation.

Washing woollies. There are still some who do not know that woollies should not be washed in hot water. Hot water ruins them. Only tepid water should be used, with a mild soapless detergent or a good soap powder. After washing they should be thoroughly rinsed in water of the same temperature as that in which they have been washed. Thorough rinsing is essential. They should not be rubbed. Spin dryers are safe for woollies.

Washing nappies. It is a matter of opinion whether nappies should be boiled or not. We think that it is sufficient to wash them thoroughly in really hot water with a detergent, such as Stergene, or with soda-free soap flakes, such as Lux, making sure that they are thoroughly rinsed after, for any remaining soap would irritate the baby's skin. Many mothers use 'Napisan' or similar solutions. The soiled nappies are put immediately into the Napisan solution. Next day they are thoroughly rinsed out and dried.

For those who can afford one, an automatic washing machine and a spin drier or tumbler-drier is a great help when there are young children. Most people are near a Launderette if they cannot afford to buy their own equipment.

Home help. If you have no domestic help, and no relative who can help you on your return home from hospital, you should remember that you can obtain a 'Home Help' through the Local Authority. She will tide you over the first few weeks after delivery, and will be supplied free if necessary, but normally a small sum of money has to be paid, the amount varying with the financial status of the applicant. Your district nurse, midwife, local Town Hall, or Police Station will tell you how to obtain the service.

The newborn baby and his care

Establishing the bond between parent and child

Many paediatricians and psychologists feel that it is a good thing for a mother to handle her new baby as soon as he is born. Many (but not all) mothers want to be fully conscious at the time of the child's birth and feel the urge to put him to the breast as soon as he is born. The immediate contact of the naked baby with the mother's breast and body increases the bond between mother and baby, and helps to promote breast feeding. It is likely that this urge corresponds to the fact that many animals such as the goat or sheep have the instinctive desire to lick their newborn as soon as he is born: if they are prevented from doing this, and yet the baby animal is returned to his mother in four hours or so, she will reject the baby; the goat will kick the kid to death. Furthermore, lambs and other animals separated from their mother at birth grow up and behave abnormally, and when they mature, they are bad mothers and there is a high mortality amongst their offspring. There is a considerable literature on this subject.

We believe that the right place for a newborn baby in a maternity hospital is at the mother's bedside, unless he is ill, so that he can be picked up and cuddled and fed as the mother wishes. A baby picked up in this way tends to be more alert than babies just left lying in a crib: he responds to the mother and the mother to him. We believe that the Intensive Care Unit should be used only for the ill or preterm baby who needs constant supervision — and even then we feel that the mother should be allowed and encouraged to handle the baby in the incubator or crib and help to look after him. The mother will certainly be expected to wash her hands thoroughly and wear a gown before handling the baby, but we know of no evidence that the presence of a mother in the Intensive Care Unit increases the risk that the baby will acquire some infection. We regard the separation of a mother from her new baby to be most undesirable, for it interferes with the establishment of a firm bond between mother and baby: such separation is particularly liable to occur in the case of the very small preterm or handicapped baby. Obviously if the baby is ill or very premature he will have to be separated from her so that he can have constant supervision on the Special Care Unit. Otherwise we see no justification for separating mother and baby, day or night.

It is important that a firm bond should also be established between the baby and his father. As soon as possible, certainly as soon as the baby is taken home, the father should handle the baby, help to look after him, talk to him — and do most things for him other than breast feeding. If later the child is ill, it is normal and important that the father should help to look after him, and visit him just as much as the mother if hospital treatment is necessary.

Some features of the newborn baby

Most babies have a soft swelling over the part which was born first — and therefore normally over the top of the skull — the 'caput'. It disappears in a day or two.

An occasional baby has a longer-lasting swelling on the head, called a 'cephalhaematoma'. This is usually found on the top of the head, to one or other side of the midline. It is due to a small bruise under the skin — not the result of mishandling during the delivery, but to stretching of the veins of the scalp before he was born. It is harmless and disappears without treatment. Often you will feel a rim round the edge in three to four weeks, on top of the ordinary bone of the skull. The swelling usually disappears in two or three months, but sometimes a hard bony swelling persists for much longer, but it is of no significance.

The baby is found to be covered on delivery by a greasy substance called 'vernix'. This is normally washed off in his bath within a few hours of birth, but it does no harm if left on the skin for some days, if it is thought better not to bath him. It is unwise to attempt to remove the vernix with dry cotton wool, for the skin may be damaged.

Many babies have a red staining of the skin on the inner end of the upper eyelid ('Storkbites'), on the forehead just above the nose and on the back of the head where the skull joins the neck. All these marks disappear without any treatment by about a year of age.

A few days after delivery, the skin, especially of the hands and feet, may peel. No treatment is necessary. It is common for hair to fall out after a week or two. It will be replaced by new hair.

Most newborn babies develop innumerable whitish yellow pin-head-sized spots on the nose and surrounding parts (milia). These are merely obstructed sebaceous glands. They open without treatment.

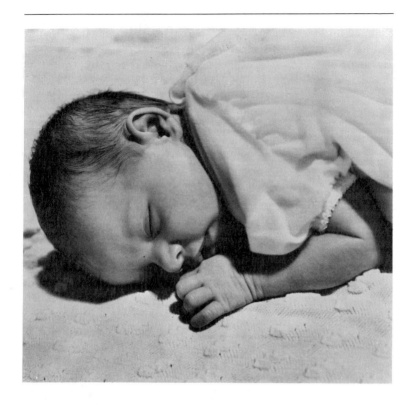

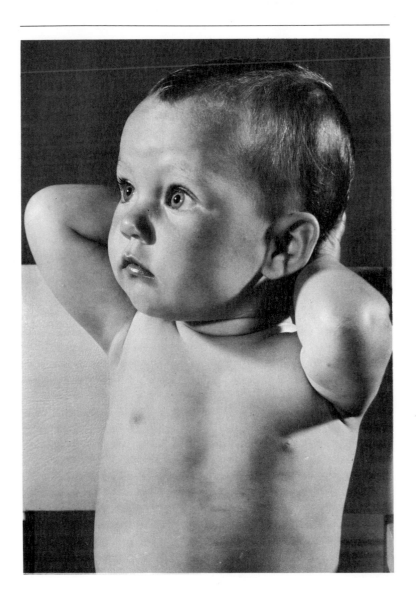

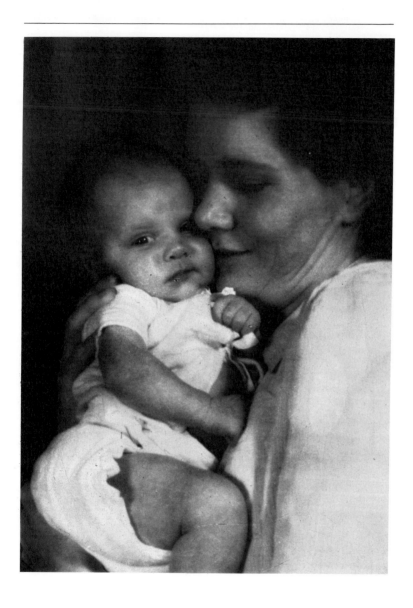

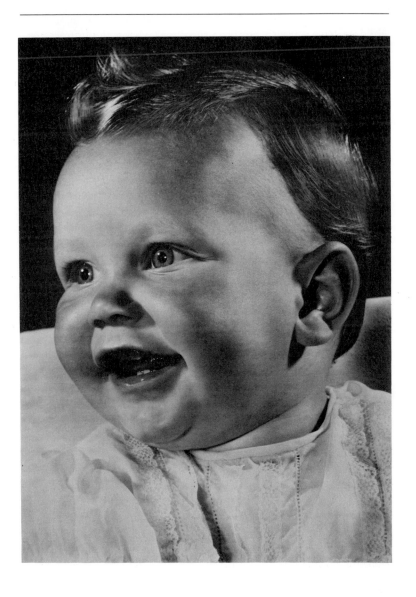

Virtually all coloured children, most Eskimos and some white children have a bluish patch on the upper part of the buttocks and adjacent back, and sometimes on the front of the ankle, shoulder or arms: it is called mongolian pigmentation: it is normal and disappears in two or three years. Some villagers in the Middle East regard it as a sign of Allah's favour.

There is sometimes a small dimple at the extreme upper end of the cleft between the buttocks (congenital dermal sinus): only if it is a very deep hole is any treatment needed.

At least half of all newborn babies develop jaundice on the latter part of the second or on the third day. It is termed "physiological jaundice" and is normal: it clears up in three or four days (or longer in the case of a preterm baby), and no treatment is required. Jaundice on the first day is nearly always due to blood group incompatibility, and treatment is urgent. If any baby with jaundice becomes unwell, your doctor should see him forthwith. For breast milk jaundice see p 22.

About half of all newborn babies, whether boys or girls, have some swelling of the breasts, starting two or three days after birth, and reaching a maximum in the second week. It is not found in small preterm babies. The breasts usually secrete milk for up to two months, and a small swelling may persist for six to 12 months or so, especially in girls. No treatment is required, and no attempt should be made to squeeze the breasts. When pregnancy begins the breasts of the mother enlarge as a result of chemical substances from the ovary. Some of these substances pass into the baby's breasts.

Some girls a few days after birth have a small amount of thin discharge from the vagina, and slight bleeding with it. This is due to similar chemical substances from the mother, and does not call for treatment. Many boys and girls have a small spot, 2–3 mm in diameter, on a line between the nipple and the middle of the pubis: you may be surprised to know that it is an accessory nipple.

You need not bother to examine your baby's tongue for tongue tie. It is never necessary to do anything about so-called tongue tie until the baby is over a year old, and the condition is extremely rare then. The fold of tissue under the tongue is attached near the tip of the tongue in newborn babies, but as they get older the tip grows forward. Exceptionally the tip fails to grow forward, so that the baby is unable to put his tongue out or to touch the roof of his mouth. This is most unlikely to interfere with his speech. A paediatric or plastic surgeon will cure it by a simple operation.

On the roof of the mouth or palate you will notice two pale grey areas. These are of no significance. Some babies are found to have a small cyst on the gum: it disappears without treatment.

The baby may not pass any urine in the first 24 hours. That is normal, but he should pass a stool of black meconium in the first 24 hours.

Babies in the first few weeks hiccough frequently, especially after a feed. Do not think that your baby has indigestion if he does this: all babies do it. All young babies sneeze frequently — and make their mothers fear that they have acquired a cold. They often make a grunting noise when they breathe, especially when they are awakening. During feeds most young babies gag and choke a little — especially if the breast milk is flowing rather quickly — but it does not seem to do any harm. They get out of it as they grow older.

Some babies, on the second day after delivery, suddenly develop a high temperature. This is called 'dehydration fever' and is not due to infection. The baby is well but the mouth and tongue are dry. It coincides with the weight loss experienced by all babies at this time. The exact reason for the fever is unknown, but it is certainly harmless and does not call for treatment. Your doctor will advise you about this. If you wish you may give the baby additional boiled water between breast feeds.

You will notice the jaw of the bably trembling at times. It only occurs in young babies. It is normal.

Your baby will startle when there is a sudden noise, or when he or his bedclothes are moved. At times you may see him startle spontaneously, but the sudden jerk is not a fit.

Circumcision

In male babies the question of circumcision arises. Circumcision was originally a ritual, and at one time it was used as a method of branding slaves. It is allied to tribal markings by burning and cutting in certain parts of Africa. It was practised thousands of years before Christ. In Moslems and Jewish children it is carried out shortly after birth, while in parts of Africa and elsewhere it is done shortly after puberty.

It seems to be a common belief that it should be possible to pull the foreskin of the penis back at birth, and that if it is not possible to do so circumcision should be performed. Others seem to think that if the foreskin is a long one, it should be removed. There is no ground for these beliefs. The foreskin cannot be retracted in more than 1 in every 20 babies at birth. In about half of all babies it can be retracted by the age of a year, and in 9 out of 10 by 3 years. It is hardly reasonable to suppose that it is 'abnormal' if a foreskin cannot be retracted at birth when retraction is not possible in 19 out of 20 babies at that age.

Circumcision is unnecessary in the new born period. We are not referring here to ritual circumcision in Jewish babies. In the Jessop Hospital for Women in Sheffield, where there are over 3000 births every year, the operation has not been performed at all in the last 20 years, except in Jewish babies. Most doctors perform the operation under anaesthetic, and it is undesirable to give a general anaesthetic to anyone unless it is really necessary. Some doctors think that the operation should be done without an anaesthetic. We feel that that is cruel.

No one has provided any satisfactory evidence that routine circumcision is of any advantage to the child. Some raise the argument that it is impossible to keep the part behind the glans of the penis clean unless circumcision is performed. It is not necessary to do anything about this in the first two or three years if the foreskin cannot be retracted. We are not at all in favour of unnecessary operations.

It is true that occasionally circumcision has to be performed in older babies, because of an infection or scarring from a repeated or long continued napkin rash. This is most exceptional.

Our advice to you is that you should make no attempt to retract the foreskin in the first two years at least, unless it retracts easily. In that case you will include the washing of the glans of the penis in your ordinary bathing of the child. If the foreskin is not retractable at two years, you may try gently at intervals to get it further and further back, without applying any force. You will be likely to make it bleed if you try hard. If it is not retractable by the age of 3 or 4, you should ask your doctor to do it for you. He may separate some small adhesions which will enable full retraction to occur and then apply petroleum jelly to protect it. There is no hurry about it even then, but it is wise to keep the glans clean by regular washing after that age, because of the accumulation of malodorous, cheesy material called smegma if it is not washed. You should not try to force the foreskin back against resistance. If you do, you may not be able to return it to its normal place, and swelling of the penis will then occur, necessitating an urgent visit from your doctor.

The bath and toilet

There are many who feel that daily bathing of the baby should be avoided in the first week of life. In some hospitals the baby is not bathed at all in the first seven days. The small premature baby should not be bathed for quite a long time after birth — until he weighs 4½ lb (2.04 kg) or more. We feel that if the full term baby is well when born, he should be bathed then and not again until the umbilical cord has separated. The cord is likely to separate sooner if it is kept dry. Thereafter the baby is bathed daily. It does not matter whether he is bathed in the morning or evening. It is a matter of convenience.

There is no hard and fast rule about how often the hair should be washed. We suggest that it would be reasonable to wash it every other day.

It is important that he should be thoroughly dried after his bath. This may appear to be obvious, but in fact it is easy to forget to dry behind the ears or even in the armpits and groin. These parts readily become sore if they are not properly dried. Baby powder should be sprinkled in the groin after thorough drying, but do not put so much on that it forms thick cakes of powder when moist with sweat. It is important that the baby should not inhale the talc powder, for it may cause lung troubles. The baby is dried by patting rather than rubbing, for the skin of the newborn baby is very delicate.

When he has soiled his nappy, you should avoid the temptation of rubbing the stool off his buttocks with it. You may damage his skin by doing this, especially with the Turkish towel type of napkin, which is relatively rough. You can do this when the baby is older, say after five or six months old, but not when younger. You should keep cotton wool or disposable tissues for this purpose and wash the buttocks with warm water. They are then dried by patting rather than rubbing, and a baby cream or lotion is applied. When the baby is older it is unnecessary to apply baby cream unless the buttocks are sore.

It is necessary to keep the baby's nose clean, for otherwise it may become blocked and a young baby does not know that he must keep the mouth open when the nose is blocked. The nostrils are cleaned at each bathtime by means of wisps of cotton wool, about an inch long, which have been moistened in warm clean water. These are gently inserted into the nostril, rotated and then destroyed. There is no need to attempt to clean the mouth, and damage may be done by attempting to do so. However careful you are with the skin of the face, your baby will probably develop small spots around the mouth and below the ear. Some of them are probably due to irritation of the skin by acid from the stomach which has been posseted by the baby, and by saliva which has dribbled out of the mouth and trickled down below the ear. Some mothers call it a milk rash, though in fact it has nothing to do with milk. A baby cream protects the skin to some extent, and should be used if spots are troublesome.

The finger nails should be kept short. They often grow rapidly in young babies, and have to be cut every three or four days. If left to grow long, the baby will scratch himself with them and may develop sore places. The nails are sometimes hollow; this may be a feature in one of the parents.

The umbilicus (navel) must be kept absolutely clean and dry until it has fully healed. Do not attempt to remove the remains of the umbilical cord, for they separate spontaneously. The umbilicus must be kept covered up after powdering it with baby powder. After it has healed, there is no need to have an abdominal binder. Binders serve no useful purpose.

Sometimes the umbilicus remains a little moist or a frank discharge may arise from it. Sometimes, after the baby is two or three weeks old, you may notice that there is a reddish lump, of the size of a pea ('granulation' or 'polyp'), embedded in it. Do not interfere with it. In either case you should consult your doctor or welfare clinic, so that it can be properly treated.

For the treatment of umbilical hernia, see Chapter 26.

Clothing

Do not allow a blanket to chafe the neck of a newborn baby. It will irritate the skin. Woollies if next to the skin may cause an annoying rash in some babies.

It is impossible to lay down hard and fast rules about how many clothes a baby should wear. The baby must be kept warm, but not too warm. The best way of judging whether he has the right amount of covering on him is simply to slip your hand under his clothes and feel his chest or abdomen. If he is sweating he has too much on him. It is far commoner to find a baby overclothed than underclothed. Even the smallest babies feel the heat as much as adults do. It is unnecessary in fine weather to put the hood up and the waterproof cover and rain guard in position. The waterproof cover is not porous and the blankets under it will soon become damp with condensation. It should only be used when absolutely necessary in bad weather. Overclothing of babies, especially in hot weather, is extremely common. Overclothing should be avoided for many reasons. It is unpleasant for the baby, and he may become drowsy and suck badly. He will gain weight badly, because he loses so much fluid in perspiration, and for the same reason he may become constipated. He may develop annoying sweat rashes. We have seen severe 'prickly heat', an intensely irritating skin condition in the tropics, as a result of overclothing.

In hot weather the young baby needs nothing but a cotton vest over the skin, for he must be protected from the direct rays of the sun. The older baby need have no covering at all as long as he is not exposed to the sun, and is not in a draught.

Fresh air and sunshine

The newborn baby should be put out of doors a week or two after birth, provided that it is not foggy or damp, and not excessively cold. After the first month or two, it does not matter if it is cold, as long as the baby is well wrapped up and protected from draughts. As far as possible he should have all his daytime naps outside.

Care must be taken to avoid exposing him too much to the sun, especially in the summer. This does not mean that he should be kept entirely out of the sun. His eyes should certainly not be exposed to its glare as he lies in the pram. We do mean that you should expose him to the sun gradually, so that he gets used to it. We suggest that you should begin by letting his legs lie in the sun for five minutes, and then gradually increase the amount of skin exposed and the time for which you expose it. You have to be particularly careful at the seaside not to expose babies and children too much, for severe sunburn and even illness may result from carelessness in this respect.

Keeping him warm

In cold weather it is important that the baby, especially the young one, should be sufficiently warm in his bedroom or wherever else he is. It may be necessary to have an electric convector radiator in his bedroom at night during cold weather. In cold spells children's

hospitals and children's wards admit babies dangerously ill because they have been inadequately protected against the cold.

Letting the father help

It is a good thing to let the father help in looking after the child. It gives you welcome relief when you are tired, and it is good for him to become accustomed to handling the baby, and for the baby to become accustomed to being handled by someone other than the mother.

Medical supervision of the baby's health

You should not fail to let your family doctor or child health clinic supervise the health of your baby from the earliest possible time. Do not wait for something to go wrong before you seek advice.

If your baby was born at home, your midwife will advise you about the care of the baby. If he was born in hospital, a health visitor will come and see you in your home, or be available to come if you have any difficulty.

On taking the baby's temperature

We recommend that you should take the temperature in the groin or armpit of the small child, making sure that the thermometer is kept in place for a full three minutes, even if the thermometer is called a 'half-minute' one. It is not safe to put the thermometer under the tongue until the child is about five years old, because of the danger that it will be broken in the mouth. We do not think that it is wise or necessary to take the temperature in the rectum. It is possible to damage the rectum by doing so if one is not used to taking the temperature there. If the temperature is properly taken in the groin or armpit, it is reliable. The normal temperature, except immediately after a hot drink, is not above 98.4°F (37°C).

Prone sleeping

Some babies prefer to sleep on the abdomen. Some paediatricians recommend that it should be encouraged, on the grounds that it is safer for the baby.

3

Breast feeding

Advantages of breast feeding

Nine out of every 10 mothers can fully breast feed their babies. In the pages to follow we shall describe the important aspects of the management of lactation which will enable you to breast feed your baby.

There are many who claim that artificial feeding is as good as breast feeding. Some doctors and nurses have no clear idea of the advantage of breast feeding, and are only too ready to advise a mother to put her child on to the bottle in the face of the most trivial difficulty. It is true that when a baby is properly fed on a cow's milk mixture or on dried cow's milk, he will thrive and grow up to be a healthy normal child. You have no reason to feel, therefore, that a major disaster has occurred if you have failed to breast feed your baby and been compelled to put him on to the bottle. Neither should you feel guilty about it, and think that you have let your baby down by not being able to breast feed him. On the other hand, there are important advantages of breast feeding, and it is as well that you should know them.

The first and most important advantage of breast feeding is that it is safer for the baby. Young babies, particularly in the first six months of their life, and more especially in the newborn period, have little resistance to infection. They acquire colds and bowel upsets readily. Not only do they get them readily, but they are liable to be more ill with them than are adults. Colds, for instance, are rarely followed by complications in adults, but in babies complications may occur.

It has been shown by numerous doctors that fully breast-fed babies get fewer infections, such as colds, coughs and diarrhoea, than bottle fed ones, and that breast-fed babies who do get infections tend to get them in a milder form. It has even been shown that babies who have been fully breast-fed for the first six months are less likely than artificially fed babies to acquire these infections in the second six months — at a time when they are on an ordinary mixed diet.

The most dangerous of all infections in the young baby is gas-troenteritis (diarrhoea and vomiting). A common cause of this is the accidental introduction of infection into the cow's milk, whether dried or otherwise, or into the teat or bottle, before the baby sucks. Apart from that, there are numerous factors in breast milk, as distinct from cow's milk, which protect the baby against diarrhoea; many of those factors are destroyed if the breast milk is heated. Severe gastroenteritis is practically unknown in fully breast-fed babies. We have never yet seen a case, but we have seen it in scores of bottle-fed babies. A striking fact emerged from Chile — that the mortality of upper class babies, predominantly bottle fed, was three times greater than that of lower class babies, who are mainly breast fed (because the mothers cannot afford anything else).

Eskimos in Alaska, North Canada and Greenland suffer a high incidence of serious middle ear disease: the incidence is 5 to 10 times greater in those put onto the bottle in the first month of life than it is in breast fed babies.

There are other advantages of breast feeding. Fully breast fed babies are less likely to develop eczema than those fed on cow's milk. It is said that even a single daily bottle feed increases the risk of allergy. Breast fed babies are less likely to become sore around the anus: this is surprising, because one would have thought that the much more liquid stools of the breast-fed baby might be more irritating to the skin than the more solid stools of the bottle-fed baby.

For reasons not yet known, breast-fed babies are less liable to sudden unexplained death (cot deaths).

There is evidence that women who have breast-fed babies are less likely to develop carcinoma of the breast.

Another important advantage of breast feeding is that it is easier for the mother than bottle feeding. There are no bottles or teats to boil, and no feeds to mix and get to the right temperature. There are no quantities to worry about. These are important factors at any time. They are particularly important if one is visiting friends, travelling by car or train, or on holiday.

Breast feeding acts as a mild contraceptive, provided that no complementary bottle feeds are given and provided that the breast feeds are fairly frequent. The longer the breast feeding lasts, the later is the onset of menstruation.

In developing countries the decline of breast feeding has had immense financial consequences. In Tanzania it is said that a 10% decline in breast feeding cost over £4 million in foreign exchange for

the import of artificial feeds and animal foodstuffs.

Other advantages are not so tangible or definite. Psychologists say that breast feeding is of psychological advantage to both mother and child — particularly to the latter. We think that it increases the bond between mother and baby. She knows that her baby is utterly dependent on her. If the baby is crying because of hunger, she alone can soothe him. This utter dependence on the mother has its drawbacks. It makes it difficult for the mother to get away from her baby for long. If she goes out shopping, she feels to be in a hurry to get back, and is worried if anything occurs to delay her. It is thought by some, admittedly on uncertain evidence, that breast-fed babies are less likely to develop arterial disease in later years. They are less likely to become too fat in infancy, and that is important because an overweight baby is more likely than others to be fat in later years.

It is notable that in Britain, America and Scandinavia there is much more breast feeding in the upper social classes than in the lower ones. In one study 67 per cent of mothers in social class 1 breast-fed their babies, as compared with 29 per cent in class 5.

Disadvantages
If the mother is well, there are few disadvantages of breast feeding, except that it ties her. Breast milk always suits the baby except in certain extremely rare diseases; and it never causes indigestion. There is no reason to believe that breast feeding tires the mother. There is a tendency to advise a mother to put her baby on to the bottle if she is tired or unwell. This advice is nearly always wrong, for it means that she will have all the extra and unnecessary labour of preparing the artificial feeds — a much more tiring occupation than

putting the baby on to the breast. There is no reason to believe that the production of milk tires the mother or weakens her provided that she is taking proper food. Admittedly, a breast-feeding mother is more tied.

The stools of the breast fed baby are very loose, so that the cleaning-up process after a motion is more troublesome. We suspect that evening colic is more common in breast fed babies (Chapter 8), but it is certainly no indication that the baby should be put onto the bottle, for it would be quite likely to continue unchanged.

At least half of all babies, breast or bottle fed, develop what is termed physiological jaundice about the third day, losing it in four or five days: it is normal and harmless. It may be much more obvious and longer lasting in breast fed babies, and is then termed "*breast milk jaundice*". It may last for six weeks or more, but usually disappears sooner. It is harmless, and it would be totally wrong to put the baby onto the bottle because of it. The precise reason for this jaundice is not yet known, but we do know that no treatment is required (and no treatment makes any difference).

It has been said that breast feeding spoils the figure: we do not believe it. It is true that breast fed babies are more likely to suffer underfeeding, but that is easily diagnosed by regular weight checks, as advised on p 88. Soreness of the nipple is painful for the mother (p 40).

The anatomy of the breast
The nipple is composed of special tissue which enables it to erect when the baby sucks, so that he can obtain milk from it more easily.

The dark area around the nipple is called the areola. The baby gets his jaws around or behind the areola in sucking.

The breast tissue is composed of about 20 segments which converge upon the nipple. Milk is produced in the cells of these segments, and passes into passages or ducts which open on the surface of the nipple. You will notice milk coming out of these minute openings in various parts of the nipple.

Nature's preparation of the breast
Many mothers notice that their breasts enlarge at the time of each menstrual period, the enlargement lasting for three or four days and then subsiding. In pregnancy the breasts enlarge at the time of the first missed menstrual period, but then continue to enlarge. This is due to the action of certain chemical substances or hormones.

In the last 12 weeks or so of pregnancy the breasts secrete a clear colourless fluid called colostrum. This changes to a yellow colour

and then to milk two or three days after the baby has been born.

Within four or five days of the baby being born, and usually about the third day after a first pregnancy, the breasts fill up, often rapidly. The milk is said to 'come in'. It is common for the breasts to feel uncomfortably tight at this time, and in a few women they become painful and 'over-distended'.

The draught reflex
Many mothers, about a month after delivery, experience a peculiar sensation in the breast as soon as the baby begins to suck. This is termed the 'draught reflex'. In cows and other animals it is called the 'let-down reflex'. Mothers who have had previous babies may begin to feel it a few days after delivery. The usual description given by mothers is this. About half to one minute after the baby has begun to suck they have a slightly uncomfortable feeling in the breast, almost like pins and needles. They may suddenly feel thirsty, and the eyes may feel dry. The breast feels tighter and milk often leaks out of the breast opposite to that on which the baby is sucking. Some mothers even feel this when they are preparing to feed the baby, or when they think about feeding him, and at certain other times. It is due to the filling of the ducts or passages in the breast tissue with milk so that it will be ready for the baby to suck.

In the first few days after delivery you may find that as soon as the baby begins to suck you feel cramps in the lower part of the abdomen. This is because the uterus (womb) contracts when the baby sucks at your breast. It is an advantage, because it helps the uterus to shrink to its normal size more quickly.

The leaking of milk
Milk often leaks out of one breast when the baby begins to suck at the other. Milk may leak out of both breasts when they become a little distended, as in the night, when the baby first misses a night feed. It is harmless and normal, but it does necessitate the wearing of a pad of cotton wool to avoid soiling the clothes. It does not necessarily mean that there is a superabundance of milk.

How does the baby get the milk?
The baby does not get the milk just by sucking. If you watch your baby carefully when he is sucking, you will see that his jaws push the milk forward into the nipple from the ducts behind, and with his tongue he pushes the milk out of the nipple which is pressed against the roof of his mouth. In addition, the breast tissue contains muscle cells which help to expel the milk. When he stops sucking for a moment and removes his jaws, you may see the milk squirting out of your breast. When it is a little distended, as it often is after a good night's sleep, the milk may pour out of your breast so fast that the baby nearly drowns in it and has to gulp it down.

The regulation of the supply of milk
The chief factor which regulates the amount of milk produced is the demand. A big baby has just as much chance of being fully breast-fed as a small one — because he takes more milk from the breast, and therefore more milk is produced. The best stimulus to milk production is the emptying of the breast. In fact we recommend mothers to express the milk routinely for the first seven to ten days after the baby has sucked, giving the baby the milk, if he will take it. This stimulates the breast to produce an adequate amount of milk, and it reduces the risk of over-distention. If this has not been done from the beginning, and there is not sufficient milk, the amount of milk can be increased by emptying the breast after each feed by manual expression.

Wet nurses used to be able to supply enough milk for many years: it is known that one wet nurse produced milk continuously for 35 years.

Worry and anxiety has a bad effect on the milk supply. A mother lying in a Maternity Hospital, worrying about those at home, may be unable to produce sufficient milk to feed her baby while in hospital, but the supply improves as soon as the source of worry is removed and she returns home. Worry about the baby or anything else will decrease the milk supply. Many of us feel that a mother in hospital should have her baby at her side, as in the Sheffield Hospitals, for she may worry about the baby if he is placed in a nursery and she is allowed to see him only at feed times.

Good nutrition during pregnancy and during lactation is important for the milk supply. Meat, fish, eggs, greens and fruit are of particular importance.

Breast feeding by virgins and grandmothers

It has been the practice in numerous parts of the world, and still is, for grandmothers to feed babies on the breast, long after their own children were born. It is a common practice in New Guinea, Central Africa and elsewhere. It was practised by refugees in Vietnam, Bangladesh and India. It is not so well known that women who have never had children of their own can breast feed; the baby sucks at the breast and stimulates it to produce milk. Mothers adopting children have successfully breast-fed their adopted babies.

Preparation for breast feeding

If your nipple is normal and protrudes normally, there is no need to do anything to it. Even if the nipple appears to be retracted, you should remember that the nipple includes erectile tissue, and a nipple which looks to be unsatisfactory erects when the baby sucks, so that he manages perfectly well. Some books wrongly advise mothers to try to harden the nipple by applying spirit and by scrubbing it with a scrubbing brush. This must be unpleasant, and it is unwise. The aim is to reduce the risk of soreness of the nipple developing when the baby begins to suck. But hard skin cracks easily and readily becomes sore. Our advice is that you should leave the nipple alone, apart from keeping it clean, unless it is very hard, when the daily application of lanoline will help.

Method of expressing milk from the breast

The method of expressing the milk is as follows. In the first place, the whole breast is compressed between the hands, starting at the outer margin of the breast tissue, continuing the pressure almost as far as the nipple. This is repeated 10 to 12 times. This drives the secretion forward towards the nipple. The breast tissue just behind the nipple is then firmly, rapidly and repeatedly compressed between the forefinger and thumb of one hand. The pressure is released and reapplied about 50 times per minute. The skin is not rubbed, for the finger and the thumb moves with the skin, not over it: and pressure must be deep, in order to empty the milk ducts. The milk squirts out if the procedure is performed properly. When expressing colostrum, the movement is carried out only sufficiently to express a few drops. If you have difficulty, your midwife or antenatal clinic will show you how to do it.

When should the baby first be put on the breast?

There is no rule about the time at which the baby should first be put to the breast. Provided that the mother has not had a general anaesthetic and that the baby is full term and well, we recommend that as soon as he is born he should be brought into contact with his mother's bare breast. If he begins to suck at the breast or lick the nipple, let him. It is felt that this immediate skin contact helps in the establishment of lactation.

After that the baby should be at your bedside — and definitely not in a nursery — so that you can pick him up and cuddle him when you want, talk to him and give him a feed as soon as he wants it.

We firmly believe that many more mothers would breast feed their babies if doctors, nurses and relatives interfered less with the mother's natural instincts and allowed her to use her common sense. Rigid ideas about the timing of the first or subsequent feeds, determination to secure a rapid weight gain, rigid feeding schedules and separation of the baby from the mother by putting him into a nursery, all conspire to lead to bottle feeding.

Some points to note in breast feeding

The baby should be comfortable — and so should you. If you are sitting on a chair, you should choose one which is sufficiently low down for you to rest your feet comfortably on the ground while feeding him — unless you have a foot stool, which serves the same purpose. Normally the baby's body is in front of yours, but if you or the baby prefer it, his body can be at your side, with his legs behind you, as in the position in which twins are fed simultaneously (p 49). When his body is in front of you, his head is supported in the bend of the elbow, and your hand supports his buttocks. He lies on your right arm when you are feeding him from the right breast, and on your left arm when you are feeding him on the left side. He should be half sitting up, not lying down, and you should lean forward a little, or lie on your side, for it is important that the nipple should lie easily in his mouth, without his having to suck it in. It is thought that soreness of the nipple may be caused by lack of attention to the mother's position when breast feeding.

It is unwise to rock the baby during the feed, for it may put him to sleep. If the breast is pendulous, you must see that he can breathe when sucking, and you may have to support the breast with one hand or keep some of the breast away from his nose by a finger; but otherwise you should do nothing to alter the natural position of the breast. Try to leave the baby's limbs free to move; and try to avoid sudden loud noises, which are likely to stop him sucking.

Most babies know perfectly well how to obtain the milk. A few, however, need a little guidance in getting the jaws well behind the nipple. If babies suck at the nipple, they will make it sore and fail to get the milk. You should see, therefore, that the baby gets his jaw well back.

There is no need for you to push the nipple into his mouth. Sheep and other animals do not have to do this with their young. The baby will 'root' around for milk as soon as his cheek touches your breast and will find it. It is wrong to try to force the baby to suck by holding his head. There is no more certain way of making him cry. He can smell the milk — a fact which you can easily check when he is brought near to your chest, without his touching it; he begins to root for the milk.

You should use both breasts at each feed. The reason has already been given, for if the breasts are not emptied sufficiently frequently the milk supply will fail. If you are feeding a baby about four-hourly, and you give him only one breast at a feed, it would mean that each breast is emptied only every eight hours. If the baby is awkward, and goes to sleep after the first breast, it is usually wise to empty the other breast by your hands.

You should alternate the breasts. In other words, if the baby sucks the left breast first at one feed, he should begin on the right breast at the other feed. This is because he may have emptied the left breast better than the other breast. He certainly will have done so if he fell asleep after sucking the second breast for a minute or two. This alternation ensures the adequate emptying and stimulation of both breasts.

The nipples should be kept clean and you should be sure that clothes do not rub them, but we do not think that it is necessary to wash the nipples after every feed.

The breasts should be supported between the feeds by a properly fitting brassiere. This will not only help to preserve your figure, but it will make you more comfortable.

Should the wind be brought up half-way through his feed?
We think that this depends on the baby, and it does not matter what you do. On the one hand it is wrong to insist on it if the baby objects

— and many babies object violently to being kept away from the second breast, feeling that they are being starved if they are kept waiting. On the other hand, if a baby does not object, there is something to be said for it, for he is likely to take the second breast better if his wind has been brought up, and therefore to be less likely to fall asleep before he has emptied it.

The best way to bring the wind up is to lift him up to your shoulder, which should be duly protected from possets, with his stomach pressed gently against the upper part of your chest. You can pat his back if you like. It is unnecessary to give him any medicine to bring his wind up, for it would not help; he merely swallows air in taking it, and so has more wind.

How long should each breast feed last?

No hard and fast rules can be laid down about the duration of each breast feed. Milk is obtained from some breasts more quickly than from others. Milk may be obtained more quickly in the first feed in the morning, when the breast is perhaps a little distended, than later in the day. Some babies suck more quickly than others, and a baby may suck more quickly at one feed, when he is hungry or thirsty, than at another. Babies suck more quickly as they grow older.

It is the common practice to advise mothers to allow their babies to suck for only a short time at the breast in the first three days, before the milk comes in, because it is felt that if they suck longer they may make the nipples sore. We do not know whether this is true, but we doubt it. Some advise that the baby should be allowed only three or four minutes on each breast for the first day, but this refers to time actually sucking. This is important, for babies often spend quite a time in 'breast-play', licking the nipple, and sucking for a minute and then withdrawing, and the irritable type of baby spends a considerable part of his time at the breast in screaming.

After the second or third day it is customary to advise mothers to feed the baby for ten minutes on each breast. For the reasons stated, however, no rigid rules are possible. It is true to say that the baby should not usually spend more than ten minutes in actual sucking. But some babies in the first few weeks need longer than ten minutes at each breast. If you do not allow them to have longer they will not be satisfied, the weight gain may not be satisfactory, and they may cry excessively; but some babies go to sleep long before they have had ten minutes on the second breast. Such a baby may defy all your efforts to awaken him. If you do manage to awaken him, he is likely to suck for a mere minute or two before falling to sleep again. If you should manage to keep him awake and he sucks after he has had what he wants, he is likely merely to swallow air instead of milk, and so he will have all the usual symptoms of wind. If he is not sucking milk, he may suck on the nipple and make it sore. If you make a baby suck a full 10 minutes on the first breast, and he has obtained all the milk there is in 5 minutes, he may become so sleepy that he does not take a full feed from the second breast.

This may sound confusing to you, but it is better that you should know the consequences of not allowing the baby to suck long enough, and of making him suck too long. How then can you tell how long to let him suck? You will have to go by the baby's responses. You will probably find that when he has got what milk there is in the first breast, he will slow down suddenly in the speed at which he sucks. When he has had what he wants in the second breast, he will fall asleep, if he is a young baby, or stop sucking and look thoroughly pleased with himself, if he is an older baby. Experienced mothers, in fact, do not attempt to time the feeds. They just observe the way the baby behaves. Until you are experienced, however, it is better to keep an eye on the clock, and avoid, as a rule, allowing the baby to suck more than 10 minutes on each breast, breaking the rule only if you are sure that he wants more and that there is more for him. In our experience no feed should take more than half an hour in all — except in the case of the irritable baby, to be discussed on page 45.

When the baby is older, say 2 or 3 months of age, provided that he was not born prematurely, he is likely to want very much less time on the breast. It is common to find that the baby obtains all the milk there is, and all that he wants, in three or four minutes at each breast. This is all right, and no attempt should be made to try to cause him to suck longer. A kid was found to have taken a pint of milk from his mother in 70 seconds. Even a young baby, 2 or 3 weeks old, can occasionally get all the milk he needs in 3 or 4 minutes per breast, but that is unusual. If you try to make such a baby suck longer, he will be cross with you, or he will merely swallow air and have wind.

How often should he be fed?
Our advice is that you should abandon any fixed rigid ideas about the feeding schedule and use your common sense, so that you adjust the feeding schedule in large part to the baby's needs, and in part to your own needs. In other words, we advocate a reasonable self-demand schedule.

There are many who advocate a strict feeding schedule, arguing that a strict schedule is essential for teaching the child regular habits, and that an irregular schedule teaches bad habits. They argue that if the schedule is not a strict one, the mother will never know when the next feed will be wanted, and she will never be able to get any work done, neither will she be able to tell when the baby is hungry, with the result that she will feed the baby every time he cries.

There is not the slightest evidence that good habits are produced by a fixed schedule or bad habits by an elastic one. If babies are fed more or less when they are hungry, they adopt a regular schedule by about a month of age, if not sooner.

As for the difficulty in deciding whether the baby is crying because of hunger or for other reasons, it is true that occasionally difficulties do arise on that score. Most mothers, however, know perfectly well whether the baby is hungry or not. The causes of crying are discussed in Chapter 8. One point is important, that the crying of hunger is not stopped by picking the baby up. To put it another way, if the baby stops crying when he is picked up (and does not start again in a minute or two while in his mother's arms) that crying is not due to hunger. We have known mothers make the mistake of putting the baby to the breast every time he cries. Others make the mistake of thinking that the baby wants feeding every time he sucks his fingers. That is not true.

The argument that the mother will not be able to get any work done because she will never know when the baby will want his next feed is unsound, for babies who are fed when they are hungry adopt a regular schedule by the time they are about a month old. It is true that you will have to adjust your domestic routine, up to a point, to fit in with the needs of your baby.

A rigid feeling schedule suits many babies, if it happens to fit in with their body needs. But a rigid schedule presupposes that all babies are the same. They are not. A rigid schedule often leads to much unnecessary and prolonged crying. Some babies, like some adults, get hungry sooner than others. We cannot see any point in leaving a baby howling for food because the alarm clock has not yet said that it is time for him to feel hungry. The baby knows much better than any clock when his stomach is calling out for food. Neither can we see any reason for awakening a baby for a feed when he is sleeping peacefully and giving the mother a pleasant respite — unless there is a good reason for awakening him, such as the parents' bedtime.

It seems obvious that there should be some elasticity in the feeding schedule to fit in with the baby's needs. It is reasonable to aim at an approximately 3 hourly schedule for a small baby, and an approximately 4 hourly schedule for a bigger baby. But if your baby awakens and howls for food before that, you should feed him. Do not feel that you must drop everything the moment he opens his mouth. It wil do him no harm to cry for a quarter of an hour while you finish some vital cooking. That is a different matter from deliberately leaving him crying for prolonged periods. If he is asleep 3 or 4 hours after his last feed, leave him, unless you want to go out or to go to bed. There is no harm in trying to awaken him for a feed if you want to do so. But do not feel that you must. Unfortunately, it is not always so easy to awaken a young baby. You may try your utmost to awaken him at 10 p.m., because you are tired and want to go to sleep, and find yourself defeated. It is most annoying after such a failure to be awakened by his screams for food half an hour later.

When you allow your baby to have food more or less when he wants it, you may find that between about the fifth and the ninth day he wants very frequent feeds. That is a nuisance, in that it does not give you much rest, but it is only a temporary phase.

It is important to note that an ill child, a premature baby, or a baby in the newborn period who is unusually drowsy should not be fed on the self-demand schedule, for he may not demand feeds. He should be fed by the clock.

If you would strongly prefer to feed your baby by a rigid schedule, you will do no harm by doing so, but he will cry quite a lot if the schedule does not suit him. It is sensible to adjust the schedule as far as reasonably possible to the baby's needs, rather than to adhere to a fixed timetable.

After 3 months or so the need for a self-demand scheule has gone. Although any sensible mother will adjust the feed times a little to the baby's needs, she will give the baby his feeds at regular times which suit her convenience. As babies grow older, they can wait longer for a feed. By 6 months the baby's feed times will coincide largely with those of the parents. There is no place for a self-demand schedule after that.

Should he be fed in the night?

The definition of a 'night feed' is a matter of opinion. We suggest that a feed between about 11 p.m. and 4 or 5 a.m. may be termed a 'night feed', at least as far as the discussion below is concerned.

The majority of babies in the first few weeks awaken in the night and demand a feed. Most babies want two feeds in the night in the first three or four weeks. Thereafter most of them want a night feed until about the age of 10 weeks, when they sleep through, much to the relief of the mother.

There are still people who say that it is wrong to feed the baby in the night, because it will cause a bad habit. This idea is wrong. When babies are given a night feed if they ask for it, they invariably drop the night feed when they are ready — usually by about ten weeks, and often sooner. It is cruel to leave a baby crying for hours on end in the night. It certainly does not lead to a 'good' habit, for he will repeat the performance night after night for weeks if he is not fed. Eventually he becomes old enough to do without a feed in the night. If a baby is left to cry for a prolonged period, he sucks less well when eventually offered a feed, because he is tired, and his stomach is liable to be distended with wind, for crying causes the swallowing of air. We do not think that it is a good idea merely to offer him water in the night. A few babies may got to sleep after it, but most will not.

It is certainly reasonable to try to get the baby to take a feed at your bed time — if you can. Otherwise there is nothing which you can do to stop him asking for a feed in the night. He will get out of it.

Do not think that if the young baby does not awaken in the night that you must awaken him to feed him. Let him sleep through, by all means, and consider yourself lucky. He will thrive and gain weight well without a night feed. Probably one in 20 mothers is lucky enough to have such a baby.

If he continues to demand night feeds after 10 weeks, the problem is not so easy. If, when he wakens, he will settle down again when his nappy is changed, he should be allowed to do so. Adjustment of the late evening feed is not likely to help. It sometimes happens that although there is quite enough breast milk for the baby during the day, there is not enough last thing at night, with the result that the baby awakens within 2 or 3 hours and cries for food. If, therefore, crying for feeds at night continues after the baby is ten weeks old, you should consider this possibility. You could try giving the baby a bottle containing, say, five measures of modified milk powder and 5 ounces (140 ml) of water, after the breast feed (see Chapter 4). It is better to do nothing else until he is say 12 weeks old, when you will have to be firm and leave him to cry. It would be desirable, however, to have him in his own bedroom. Babies at this age awaken more easily than they do in the new-born period, and may be disturbed by their parents. It may be enough merely to put him into a room of his own.

Occasionally an older baby will demand a feed in the night. It may happen for a few nights when he is first being weaned. We do not know why this happens. It may happen for a night or two in the convalescent period after an acute infection, such as diarrhoea. Naturally, any child may become thirsty in a hot night. But otherwise the older baby does not require feeds in the night and should not have them.

What should be done if the baby wants frequent feeds after the first fortnight?

The first thing is to be sure that the baby is really hungry. He may be crying because of loneliness, boredom or colic. If he is merely lonely, he will be perfectly content when he is your arms. If he is merely bored, he will be happy if he is in a pram in the room in which you are working.

A possible reason for excessively frequent demands after the first fortnight would be excessive loss of weight or slow gain in weight in the first 10 days or so of life — perhaps owing to the milk coming in unusually slowly. Such a baby may then demand frequent feeds to catch up to his 'expected' weight — the weight one would have expected him to have reached at that age. In the same way a baby sometimes demands frequent feeds when he has just recovered from an infection.

Another common cause of excessively frequent demands for feeds is underfeeding. This is diagnosed largely by the defective weight gain.

There remain a small number of babies who are gaining weight satisfactorily, and who demand frequent feeds up to about a month or so of age. The common trouble is that they seem to fall asleep unduly easily on the breast, often before they are put on to the second breast. It is common for young babies to fall asleep after sucking for two or three minutes on the second breast. They cannot obtain an adequate supply of milk in the time, and so they waken up after about 2 hours and demand another feed. They are a nuisance, and nothing can be done about it, but it is only a short-lasting problem, for when they grow older — certainly by 2 months — they fall asleep less easily in a feed and so take better feeds and sleep longer. Attempts to awaken the baby who has fallen asleep on the breast are likely to be doomed to failure. An occasional cause of this — making the baby suck longer than he needs on the first breast — has already been mentioned.

Sometimes a baby falls asleep on the breast, and then when his wind has come up and he is put back into his cot he demands more food. This, too, is only a problem of the young baby. It may sometimes be prevented by getting his wind up half-way through his feed as well as when the feed is finished.

What should be done when the baby demands only three feeds in the 24 hours?
An occasional baby, even as young as 1 or 2 months, demands only three feeds in the 24 hours, and yet thrives and gains weight well. If he is a bottle fed baby, it does not matter, but if he is a breast fed baby these infrequent feeds will not serve as a sufficient stimululs to the breast and will leave the breasts unemptied for prolonged periods. They are then liable to stop producing milk. There are two ways of dealing with the matter. One is to awaken the child and try to get him to take feeds at more frequent intervals. This is probably the best way. The other is to express milk in between the feeds, so that the breast is emptied five or six times per day.

Should he have water as well in the first few days?
Opinions differ on this matter. Some feel that it is better not to give the baby anything at all but breast milk. In most hospitals the baby is given some boiled water or sugar water in the first two or three days. In our opinion it does not matter much. If it is hot weather, or if the baby appears to be thirsty or has lost a lot of weight, or if the milk is slow in coming in, then the baby should be given boiled water or sugar water (1 teaspoonful in 4 oz (112 ml) of boiled water) until the mother's milk supply is adequate. Otherwise there is no need for the additional fluid, but it will not do any harm if it is given — as long as the water is freshly boiled and the spoon with which it is given has been boiled for the purpose.

After the newborn period, if he is thirsty, it is probably better for him to be given an additional breast feed than to be given water or orange juice between feeds. The reason is that the giving of additional fluid between breast feeds may cause him to suck less well on the breast. There is also a small element of risk that the additional fluid may be improperly prepared, so that it infects him.

What is a 'freedom' bottle?
This refers to an occasional bottle of a cow's milk mixture given to the baby between breast feeds, to enable the mother to go out (e.g. in an evening). These may do harm. Firstly, the breast is likely to remain unemptied for a long period, and this may affect the supply of milk. If the 'freedom bottle' is only used occasionally, this risk is negligible. The other objection is the fact that artificial feeds are much more likely to infect the baby, on account of careless preparation, than a breast feed. However, if the proper precautions are taken, the risk should only be a small one. For the reasons stated, we feel that the 'freedom bottle' is undesirable, at least until breast

feeding is well established, when the baby is three to four months old.

Vitamins

In obstetric units the baby, especially if breast fed, is given an injection of vitamin K to prevent a bleeding tendency. Though rickets is extremely unlikely in a breast fed baby, it is wise to give vitamin D, as clinic drops or other preparation, after the first month or two. If the mother is taking fruit and greens in reasonable quantities, the baby will receive sufficient vitamin C (to prevent scurvy) from her, and there will be no need to give orange juice, rose hip syrup or other preparations.

How will you know if he is getting enough?

The baby will be contented — unless he has colic (Chapter 8) or wind, or cries for company: his weight gain will be satisfactory and his stools will be normal. Conversely, if he is not getting milk, there are various ways in which you can discover the fact. If there is only a slight insufficiency of milk, the only way you can tell is by a defective weight gain. It is surprising how a baby who is not getting enough may be happy and contented, sleeps after his feeds, and seems well. His stools are normal, and without regular weighings you would never have the least idea that all is not quite as well as it should be.

With a slightly greater deficiency of milk you may find, in addition to a defective weight gain, that he is not sleeping long enough between feeds, and is therefore demanding feeds too frequently. This does not always happen, but it may do. We have made it clear, however, that frequent demands for food are not necessarily due to underfeeding. With still more deficiency of milk, the baby is not satisfied after his feed. The young baby does not fall asleep after the feed, and he may cry a little before going to sleep, but not all babies, in spite of adequate feeding, go to sleep after a feed.

Signs of more marked insufficiency of milk include the withdrawal of the baby from the breast and crying after sucking for only 3 to 4 minutes, wind, colic, vomiting and abnormal stools. Underfed babies get wind because they are likely to suck at the breast when there is no milk there, and so they swallow air. Wind in baby or adult is air which has been swallowed, for it is not produced in the stomach. When the baby's stomach is distended with wind he has pain and so screams, and the crying is not stopped by picking him up. The distension of the stomach may cause vomiting.

When there is really severe starvation, the baby may become

drowsy and too weak to cry and demand food. Whether he is breast fed or bottle fed, he has loose, green frequent stools which have little odour. It is a common mistake to suppose that such a baby has diarrhoea.

If you are in doubt as to whether your baby is getting sufficient milk or not, because his weight is not satisfactory, you should carry out 'test feeds'. If you have no scales in the house (and we recommend that you should not) you can borrow scales for a day, or the hospital in which your baby was born will carry out the test feeds for you, or the health visitor may be able to help you. These consist of weighing the baby immediately before and immediately after every feed in the 24 hours, leaving the nappy on in each case but without clothes. The difference in the weight tells you how much milk he has obtained from you in each feed. If you add these together, you will find how much milk the baby has obtained in the 24 hours. An average baby after the first two weeks requires about 2½ oz of breast milk for each pound (150 ml per kg) of his 'expected weight'.

The expected weight is calculated on the basis of a weight gain of 6 oz (170 g) per week in the first three months. A baby, therefore, whose birth weight was 8 lb (3629 g) and who is now 6 weeks old, should have gained not less than 6 oz (170 g) in each of the six weeks, or 36 oz (1021 g). His expected weight is therefore just over 10 lb (456 g). Such a baby would require 10 x 2½ oz (70 ml) of breast milk per day, or 700 ml. If he obtains more, it does not matter. If he obtains less, it does, and the steps to be taken will be discussed in the next section.

You must not assume that because he is gaining 6 or 7 oz (170 to 198 g) a week, his crying cannot be due to hunger. It can, because for him a 'normal' weight gain is better than the average, and he would like a bigger quantity than that which satisfies many other babies.

It should be noted that test feeds as carried out above do not show how much milk you have in the breast. They only show how much milk the baby has obtained from you. The amount of milk which you are producing is easily found by expressing all remaining milk from your breast after each test feed, measuring the quantity, and adding it to the amount the baby has gained. This may be important, because an irritable, cross baby may gain weight badly at first because he is sucking badly, not because you have not got enough milk.

There is another way in which a baby can be underfed, in spite of the fact that you have enough milk. You may not be allowing him enough time on the breast, because you are limiting him strictly to 10 minutes on each breast.

A baby does not obtain 2½ oz per lb (150 ml per kg) of body weight per day until he is 10 days or so of age, for the milk does not come in all at once. At the seventh day he is not likely to obtain more than 1¾ oz per lb (108 ml per kg) — an adequate quantity at that age.

The baby's requirements are calculated on the expected weight, because babies who have been underfed have a compensatory increase of appetite until they have caught up to the average weight for their age and birth weight.

We must remind our readers that in this section we are referring to breast fed babies only. Bottle-fed babies are frequently made too fat by overfeeding (or, more precisely, wrong feeding — making the feeds too concentrated and adding cereals to feeds).

The overfeeding bogey

There are still some doctors and nurses who ascribe all manner of evils to so-called overfeeding. They advocate careful frequent weighing in case the baby should be found to be taking too much. They ascribe every little symptom — posseting, wind, and so on, to overfeeding. It is a condition which we rarely see. It is certainly so rare that it can safely be ignored. The baby should be allowed to take as much as he wants, without any fear that he will take too much. It would be wrong to cut down the time on the breast because a child's weight gain is above the average. It will only lead to crying and achieve nothing. Overfeeding does not cause vomiting, colic, wind, or any of the other symptoms commonly ascribed to it.

How much fluid should be taken by the nursing mother?

You should take what you want, and you need not take more. It is a widespread custom to advise mothers to drink large quantities of fluid when breast feeding. Studies at the Jessop Hospital for Women at Sheffield have shown that additional fluid makes no difference to the milk supply. Nature has equipped human beings with a delicate mechanism — namely thirst — which ensures that they take enough fluid. Mothers often notice that at the moment the baby touches the nipple or begins to suck, they feel intense thirst, and have to drink to quench it. This is nature's method. If you take what you feel that you want, you will be taking enough, and you will gain nothing by taking more.

What foods should you take and what foods and drugs should you avoid when breast feeding a baby?

Just as you did during pregnancy, you should go out of your way to take a good nourishing diet, including plenty of greens, fruit, meat, fish, eggs, milk and cheese. You will find that when you are breast feeding your baby you have a big appetite. You may be worried about your weight, knowing how commonly women gain weight in this period. Greens and fruit are not likely to cause you to put on weight. Starchy foods, such as bread and potatoes, sweets and fried foods may, and they may have to be cut down. You should cut out all sweets and chocolates. But do not try too hard to diet yourself when breast feeding your baby. You can slim when you have got the baby off the breast.

There is no particular food which you should avoid taking when breast feeding a baby. It is exceedingly unlikely that any food which you take will upset him. We have heard it said that if a mother takes a large amount of fruit, the baby may be upset, but we are not sure whether it is true. Many mothers have taken great care to determine whether any food taken by them aggravates or causes the so-called 'three months' colic', but a study of such babies has left us unconvinced that any food makes any difference (Chapter 8). It is customary to advise mothers to avoid taking onions and pickles, but it is doubtful whether these really affect the baby. It is known that cow's milk tastes unpleasant if the cows eat garlic, onions, acorns, bracken or certain other plants.

Several drugs when taken by the mother are excreted in the milk, but only a few are excreted in amounts sufficient to affect the baby. Bromides and iodides taken by the mother may cause rashes in the baby. Nicotine is excreted in the milk in small amounts when large numbers of cigarettes are smoked, but it is uncertain whether there is enough of it to affect the baby. But your smoke may irritate the baby: and we know that children of parents who smoke experience more chest infections and coughs than do children of non-smokers. It tends to reduce the milk supply. It is often said that senna, rhubarb or cascara taken by the mother may cause colic, but that is doubtful: but other substances, such as liquid paraffin, would be safer. Alcohol passes in small amounts into the milk, but not usually in sufficient quantities to affect the baby, though one mother did make her baby drunk by drinking a whole bottle of port. Phenobarbitone (and other barbiturates) pass through into the milk in small quantities and it is just possible that it could make the baby drowsy. Thiouracil, used in certain cases of goitre, affects babies. Ergot, which is sometimes given to mothers shortly after delivery, may affect the baby. Anti-coagulant drugs except Warfarin, taken for a venous thrombosis, may pass into the breast milk; so may lithium, taken for depression.

Other drugs taken by the mother, and which could theoretically, but only rarely, harm the baby, include amphetamines, cancer drugs, metronidazole, methysergide, diazepam, tolbutamide, theophylline, indomethacin, phenylbutazone and reserpine. The contraceptive pill may reduce the milk supply.

Breast feeding and menstruation
Menstruction often does not begin when the baby is being fully breast fed, but when it does, mothers often wonder whether they should continue to breast feed the baby. There is no reason at all to take the baby off the breast under these circumstances. The majority of babies are unaffected during the mother's period, but some mothers have thought that the baby seems a little irritable at the time. This may be due to the mother's imagination, or it might be due to a slight falling off of milk during the period. Numerous studies and analysis of milk at the time of menstruation have shown that the milk is normal and suitable for the baby.

What illness in the mother should lead to the baby being placed on the bottle?
Each illness has to be considered on its merits, and no hard and fast rule can be laid down. It must always be remembered that bottle feeding will cause the mother more work than breast feeding.

If you acquire an acute infection, such as influenza, you can take the baby off the breast for three or four days, and keep breast feeding going by expressing the milk at every feed time. If you do not empty the breast in this way, the milk supply will stop. For a mere cold, we think that such an action is usually wrong. The mother is almost bound to have such frequent contact with the baby that it would be futile to take him temporarily off the breast in an attempt to prevent him becoming infected. The baby may have to be taken off the breast if he has the very rare metabolic diseases galactosaemia or lactose deficiency. It is unnecessary to take him off if you have mastitis.

The one certain indication for taking the baby off the breast is tuberculosis. If you have that infection in the lungs, you should take the baby off the breast immediately and consult your doctor about how you can prevent your baby acquiring the infection (Chapter 25).

If a new pregnancy starts, it is wise to take the baby off the breast.

If you have to take the baby off the breast permanently on account of some illness, such as tuberculosis, the breasts are likely to become distended and uncomfortable. You should consult your doctor about the prevention of this, in order that he can give you some medicine (stilboestrol or a similar compound) which will stop the milk forming.

When a baby has to be removed suddenly from the breast, he may be difficult about taking the bottle. He may scream and refuse to take it. All one can do is to be patient and try. One should be sure that the hole in the teat is a large one so that he obtains the milk easily. One can even try giving it by cup or spoon. The majority of such babies capitulate when they become really hungry.

What should you do when your milk looks watery?

You should do nothing, for your milk is normal. The first part of the milk which comes often looks watery, but if the whole of the milk from your breast were to be analysed, it would be found to be normal. The reason is that the last milk which leaves the breast has the highest fat content, and it is the fat content which gives milk the familiar opaque appearance. Farmers know that the last part of the milk to be obtained from a cow (the 'strippings') is the richest in fat.

Soreness of the nipple

Many mothers find that their nipples become uncomfortable after the baby has been sucking for two or three days. Sometimes the trouble arises later. We do not fully understand the reason for this in all cases, though several reasons are known. The importance of the mother being in the right position for breast feeding has already been mentioned.

Some babies suck hard as early as the first day or two and the mother feels that the nipple is being pulled on by the baby. Some babies make matters worse by biting the nipple and really hurting. When the mother tries to take the baby away from the breast, he seems to stick to it, and it hurts her. It is because he has sucked the air from around the nipple and created a vacuum. This is dealt with by inserting the little finger into the angle of the mouth, when it will be found that he comes away easily. In other cases the mother notices that each time the baby sucks, the nipple hurts more and more, especially at the beginning of each feed. If she continues, it becomes agonizingly painful. Many babies are taken off the breast altogether and put on to the bottle as a result of mismanagement of this condition.

The soreness may be due to depression of the nipple, which the baby finds difficult to suck from. It may arise from allowing the baby to suck when the breast is distended in the first few days after delivery. It may be due to allowing the baby to suck too long at the breast; he sucks at the nipple, long after he has obtained all the milk. Some feel that it arises from allowing the baby to suck too long in the first two or three days, before the milk has come in. More often than not, there is no discoverable cause. It is more common in blondes and redheads.

Some have thought that the practice of washing the nipple with soap and water after every feed may do harm by washing off a protective covering of grease. If the nipple is hard, softening with lanoline may help.

If the nipple becomes sore and painful when the baby sucks, there is only one course of action for you to take. What you should not do is to persevere and try to put with the pain. What you should do is to take the baby off the affected breast, express the milk from the breast at every feed and give it to the baby, apply a cream to the nipple or other preparation advised by the doctor, and when it is better, which is in three or four days, put the baby back to the breast. If you try to persevere when the nipple is painful, the nipple may become badly cracked, and take a lot longer to heal. It is far better to treat it early.

We do not think that nipple shields help in treating this condition, and the baby finds it difficult to obtain the milk though them.

Too large a nipple

Sometimes the nipple is so large that the baby cannot get his jaws round it, or at least cannot get his jaws far enough back to obtain the milk. In this case the milk should be expressed entirely and given to the baby by bottle.

A depressed nipple

It is difficult for a baby to obtain the milk if the nipple is depressed. He may become cross when sucking, or even fail to get the milk at all. Usually, however, he is able to obtain it, but only with difficulty. If the baby really cannot get the milk you will have to express the milk completely and give it to the baby by bottle.

Overdistension of the breast

It often happens that a few days after delivery the breasts become uncomfortably tight and distended. In most cases the distension is not severe, and is rapidly relieved when the baby sucks. It is well to have the baby on a self-demand schedule, but to encourage him to have frequent feeds — not less than three-hourly — if he does not show a natural inclination to do so. If the breasts should become a little uncomfortable between feeds, they can be relieved by expressing milk.

If the distension is more marked, you may find that there is a lot of discomfort, and that after the baby has sucked, or after you have emptied the breast by expression, it rapidly fills up again and becomes uncomfortable. You should consult your doctor immediately. He will help by giving some tablets (stilboestrol) which slows down the coming in of the milk. The condition settles in two or three days and there is no further trouble. It sometimes happens that the baby finds it difficult to obtain the milk, because the breast is so hard. In that case the baby is taken off the breast, and if you or the midwife can express milk it should be given to him. In hospital a breast pump may be used. He may have to be kept going by boiled water or a cow's milk mixture. If the overdistension is severe, you will not be able to express milk, and you will have to be patient for two or three days, when with the help of stilboestrol the trouble will settle. In severe cases there is a risk that the breast has remained unemptied so long that the milk supply will fall off, but this by no means always happens. Belladonna plasters are useless.

Later on, when the baby is 2 or 3 months old, you may find that the breast becomes uncomfortable in the night if the baby misses the night feed. It is unwise to awaken the baby for a feed, and the best thing is just to express enough to make your breast comfortable. If you express more, it will stimulate the breast to produce more milk, and you will have the same trouble on other nights.

It sometimes happens that a small part of the breast becomes painful and tender. Provided that you feel well and your temperature is normal, this is likely to be due to a partial obstruction of one of the ducts in the breast, so that the affected part of the breast is distended. It may be due to lying on it in a particular way. It settles down rapidly without treatment, but you may try to express the affected part. You should then make sure that the breast is properly supported by a well-fitting brassiere which does not nip it. If it does not settle down within a day, or if it gets worse, you should consult your family doctor immediately.

Mastitis is due to an infection of the breast tissue. The infection may have started from a sore nipple. The breast is tender and painful, and perhaps red. There is an elevation of temperature, with shivering, aches and pains and headaches. It may be particularly painful when the baby begins to suck. The family doctor should be consulted immediately.

Insufficiency of breast milk

We have mentioned some of the factors which militate against breast feeding, such as failure to establish the bond between mother and baby, rigid feeding schedules and separation of the baby from the mother. Mismanagement of sore nipples, worry about a baby's irritability or the converse, drowsiness, may lead to unnecessary bottle feeding.

Before concluding that you have insufficient milk for the baby, you must be sure that the diagnosis is correct, for almost any of the symptoms commonly ascribed to insufficiency of breast milk, and particularly crying, may be due to other causes. The diagnosis of insufficiency should only be made when the weight gain is defective, and the diagnosis has been confirmed, if necessary, by test feed.

When the milk comes in unusually slowly, the baby must be supported by boiled water or by a 'complementary feed'. By a complementary feed we mean a feed of cow's milk, dried or otherwise, given immediately after the breast feed, in order to make up the baby's requirements. Complementary feeds are avoided as far as possible in the first fortnight, because of the risk that they will indirectly cause a reduction in the supply of breast milk. If the baby is satisfied with a good feed of cow's milk, he will suck less well at the breast, and the breast will then be less well emptied, with the result that it produces less milk. Some feel that babies who are given complementary feeds in a bottle may come to prefer the bottle to the breast, and so refuse the breast. They therefore insist that complementary feeds should be given by a spoon instead of by bottle. That is time consuming, and we do not recommend it. If you do give a complementary feed, the important thing is that you should also stimulate the breast by emptying it by expression after the baby has fed from it. If you do that, the complementary feed will do no harm to your milk supply. Naturally, you will give the baby the milk which you have expressed, and that may be enough to make additional cow's milk unnecessary. You should therefore express your milk into a basin which has been boiled, and the milk can then be given by a spoon, which has also been boiled. It often happens that a mother has plenty of milk in the morning, but less in the late afternoon. If milk is expressed in this way, it can be kept until the later afternoon, boiled before use, and then given to the baby after the breast feed. The baby is thus kept on breast milk throughout the day.

The other essential is that if a complementary feed is given, it must be given immediately after the breast feed. If there is a deficiency of milk in only one or two of the feeds, the complementary feed is offered only after those feeds. One can often discover which feed is not enough for the baby by observing his behaviour. He may be contented after most of the feeds, but cry after one or two of them.

It should be exceptional to give a complementary feed before the fifth day, though boiled water can and should be given if the milk is coming in slowly. If there is no milk by the end of the fourth day, the baby should be given a cow's milk mixture (see artificial feeding), but it is only rarely that the mother has no milk at all by then.

It is common to find that the milk supply falls off slightly when the mother begins to get about her ordinary work again, about the tenth to the fourteenth days. Many babies are taken off the breast unnecessarily as a result. If the milk supply does fall off at this time, you should stimulate the breast to produce more milk by expressing the breasts after every feed — giving the milk to the baby. If the baby is still not satisfied, you should give him complementary feeds of, say, 3 measures of a modified milk powder in 3 fluid ounces of water (84 ml), letting him take what he wants. Ass soon as possible you get him back on to full breast feeding.

When insufficiency of milk occurs later, provided that it is not time to wean the child (say, 3 or 4 months of age), the same principles hold. If the shortage is only slight, merely express milk after feeds. If it is greater, give the baby complementary feeds immediately after the breast feeds, and also express the breasts after the feeds.

If at any time after the first fortnight, there is a severe shortage of milk, you may have to put the baby fully on to the bottle. You would not do this unless you are unable to supply him with as much as half of his calculated requirements (2½ oz per lb (150 ml/kg) of expected weight per day). If you have to give complementary feeds at every feed, the time taken by breast feeding, expressing and giving the bottle is too much, and you will then have to take him off the breast altogether — unless you particularly wish to carry on partially breast feeding him.

When there is a shortage of milk, you should try to get all the rest you can, but usually rest during the day is impossible. You should in addition make sure that you are giving the baby long enough on each breast. It may also be a good thing to increase the frequency of the feeds, e.g. to give them about 3 hourly, instead of 4 hourly — but not more frequently than 3 hourly. Otherwise no measures, other than those mentioned above, will help. No proprietary preparation obtainable from a shop or elsewhere will increase the supply of milk.

No medicines of any kind will make any difference. Hot and cold applications to the breast will not help and should be avoided. Massage to the breast is useless. You will achieve nothing by drinking large quantities of fluid which you do not want.

One thing which you should never do when there is a shortage of milk is to give the baby a 'supplementary feed' — that is a bottle of milk between feeds. That will cause defective emptying of the breast and the milk supply will fall off still more.

Steps to take if you have failed to breast feed previous children
The advice we have to offer under these circumstances is as follows:

1. Ignore comments from your friends and relatives that you will not be able to feed your baby on the breast.
2. Express the milk from the breast after every feed for the first seven to 10 days, giving the baby the milk by spoon if he will take it.
3. Let the baby feed when he wants to.
4. Avoid giving a bottle feed at least for the first four days, unless on the fourth day there is virtually no available breast milk. He can be given boiled water, if the weather is hot, but cow's milk (fresh or dried) should be avoided unless it is absolutely essential.
5. Try to take adequate rest during the day.
6. Do not conclude that your baby's crying or vomiting is due to insufficiency of milk unless, after a week, the weight gain is defective. (Most babies should regain the birth weight about the tenth day).

Crying in the newborn period when put to the breast
Some babies make themselves thoroughly awkward in the first 10 days of life by screaming when put to the breast. This behaviour usually begins in the first day or two. However hungry the baby is, he sucks for a minute or so, or merely touches the breast with his lips, and then withdraws and screams, or else he seems to refuse the breast altogether. He may even hurt the mother by biting the nipple. Any attempt to hold his limbs or head and to force him to take the breast merely makes him worse. Each feed may be an agony. Unless the mother is patient he may not obtain enough milk, and so he will not gain weight well, even though the mother has plenty of milk in her breast. This will certainly happen if an attempt is made to limit the feed to 10 minutes on each breast, for a feed may take up to an hour. He is sucking only for a fraction of that time, probably not more than 15 or 20 minutes, but he cries so much that the whole feed may take much longer.

No one knows the reason for his behaviour. The mother naturally assumes that her breast milk is not suiting the baby, and we have known dozens of babies put on to the bottle for that reason. This idea is always wrong, and the baby may behave just as badly on the bottle. If only his mother is patient he will begin to take the breast easily, so that by about 10 days of age there is no difficulty. Some have thought that the irritability is due to the baby's nose being obstructed by his upper lip during the feed, or by the breast tissue. This can easily be looked for. Sometimes the trouble lies in a depressed nipple which the baby finds it difficult to get hold of. The mother is often afraid that he will hurt her when he sucks, and she jumps back as soon as he starts. This annoys the baby and he cries. It is easy to assume that the mother has not enough milk. This seems to be confirmed by his defective weight gain, and a test feed may show that he has taken little milk. The mother has plenty of milk, however, for a lot can be obtained by expressing it after each test feed. If only he can be tided over a few days by careful handling, there is no reason why he should not continue to be fully breast fed. It is likely that the bad behaviour is related to his personality. Such babies, in our experience, do not often turn out to be placid children.

All efforts to force the baby to take the feed should be avoided. That will only make him worse. It is often better for the nurse to leave the baby alone with the mother, for the feed often goes more easily without others trying to help. The essential thing to realize is that there is nothing to worry about. It is not due to disease. It is not due to anything in the breast milk or to insufficiency of milk. The difficulty will disappear at about 10 days of age. Nothing but patience will help. He should be fed when he wants it and not kept waiting for a feed. He should be cuddled and given all the love he wants.

It is a difficult problem, which requires all the patience and courage which the mother can muster. For the mother this type of baby can be terribly tiring and a great strain. She can be helped enormously by those around her giving her encouragement in her difficulties, and preserving as unemotional an atmosphere as possible. In the days immediately following the birth of a baby, the woman readily becomes depressed and alarmed if anything seems to go wrong, especially with the baby.

The baby with a sore mouth
Sometimes a baby screams when put to the breast because his mouth is sore. The common cause of this is thrush, an infection which enters the baby's mouth in various ways. You will see patches of

white on the tongue and inside the cheeks, looking like milk curds, but adherent. It is easily treated by drops of nystatin, which your family doctor will prescribe. Gentian violet used to be used for the purpose, but it has a disastrous effect on shawls and clothes by staining them and the the stain cannot be removed: we never prescribe it now. Sometimes it arises from vaginal thrush in the mother.

The poor sucker
Some babies, for a few days after birth, are drowsy and do not bother about food. They show no signs of hunger. They suck slowly and badly.

There is no particular reason for this behaviour in the majority of cases. Babies may be drowsy because they are cold, or because they are too hot, but usually there is nothing wrong with them. They must not be fed on a self-demand schedule, for they will not demand food. They should be fed by the clock — at about 3 hourly intervals. If you have a baby like this, you will have to do your best to persuade him to take feeds, but it will not be easy. It is a temporary thing only, and after a fortnight or so, if not sooner, you will find that he will take his feeds better.

Wind
We do not believe in the story that there are 'windy babies' — unless the term means that babies suffer excess of wind if certain faults in feeding occur.

Though 'wind' is a troublesome thing and all young babies suffer from it to some extent, we are sure that crying is often thought to be due to wind when in fact it is due to something else.

All 'wind' in babies is air which they have swallowed. It is not produced in the stomach. Young babies have more wind than older ones, largely because they are not able to get their lips tightly round the breast or the teat of a bottle, and each time they swallow, they swallow some air. Older babies get their lips tightly round the breast, and so are little troubled by wind. If a baby sucks at the breast after he has obtained all the milk, he will swallow air, and so one of the chief causes of excessive wind lies in allowing the baby to suck too long on the breast, or in insufficiency of milk. He may obtain all the milk there is in 3 or 4 minutes, and in the remaining 6 or 7 minutes which he is allowed on the breast he merely swallows air.

A baby may swallow wind because he is gulping the milk down too quickly. Such a baby is usually described as being a 'greedy' baby, and some doctors have advised that such babies should be given a

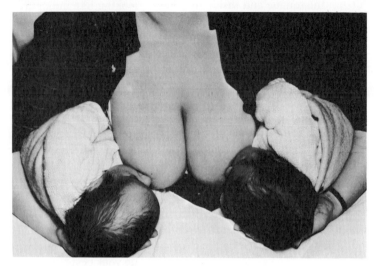

Twins being fed simultaneously on breast.

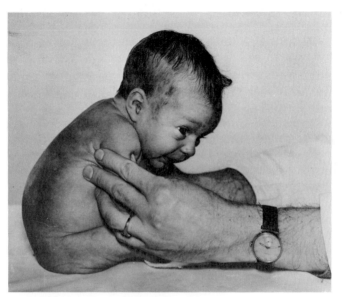

Sitting position. 1 month. Head held up slightly.

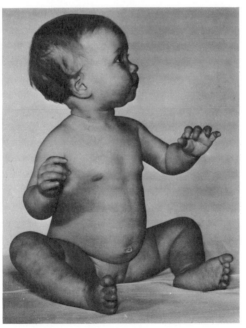

Sitting position. 9 months. Setting unsupported, securely.

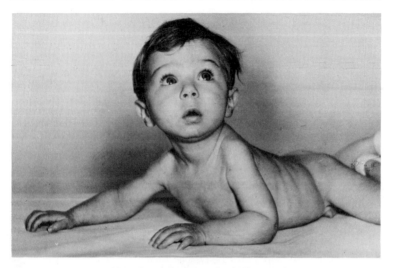

10 to 12 weeks. Plane of face almost reaches angle of 45° to couch.

drink of boiled water before the feed so that they do not suck so quickly. In fact the gulping is due to a rapid flow of milk from the breast. It is particularly likely to occur at the first feed in the morning, when the breast is a little distended. The milk flows so quickly that the baby is nearly drowned in milk and can hardly keep up with it. It is treated either by expressing a little before the baby sucks, or by trying to compress the ducts a little, by holding the breast between finger and thumb behind the nipple, so that the milk flows less quickly. The former treatment is probably the easier.

Normally the wind is brought up without trouble. Some babies, before it comes up, experience pain with it, go pale, and emit high-pitched shrieks, different from the ordinary crying such as one sees in a hungry baby. The crying stops when the wind comes up. Some bring wind up, but then scream when placed in the cot. This is naturally put down to wind, but it is not necessarily so: it may be due to a desire for more milk, or to his annoyance at being separated from the mother, or at the light being put out. Crying half-an-hour or more after a feed is unlikely to be due to wind. It is much more likely to be due to a desire for company, to boredom, or to a wet nappy. It may be due to discomfort from overclothing. It may also be due to 'colic' (Chapter 8).

Excessive wind is a common cause of vomiting (Chapter 26).

The method of bringing wind up is described on p. 27. It is never necessary or profitable to give medicines for the purpose.

Refusal of one breast

An occasional baby refuses to suck from one breast. Often there is no apparent reason for this behaviour. Sometimes it is because the nipple on one side is depressed, and he finds it difficult to obtain the milk. If there is no obvious cause, it is worth while trying a different position for him, so that his body is at your side, with his feet behind you instead of in front of you. Failing that, you can express milk from the breast which he refuses, and give it to him by spoon or bottle.

Refusal of the breast by the older baby

It sometimes happens that an older baby — anytime after four months of age — suddenly and without any apparent reason refuses the breast. He should be given the cup or bottle, preferably the cup, and weaned.

It often happens that when weaning has been carried out gradually, and the baby is still receiving about two breast feeds a day, he suddenly decides to have nothing more to do with the breast.

Unsatisfactory weight gain

The most likely cause of an unsatisfactory weight gain is under-feeding.

One has seen babies who are gaining weight unsatisfactorily even though there is an abundance of milk. This may be due to not allowing the young baby long enough on the breast. He would like to suck more, but it has not been allowed. Sometimes the unsatisfactory weight gain is due to the baby falling asleep before he has had enough milk.

A possible cause of defective weight gain is prolonged separation from the mother, with resultant loneliness. Babies treated like this may gain weight slowly.

A common cause of defective weight gain in the summer is over-clothing. The child loses so much fluid in perspiration that he gains little weight, although taking enough milk.

A child who is vomiting or has any infection, even a trivial skin infection or a cold, will not gain weight satisfactorily.

Twins

Some mothers are able to feed twins simultaneously. It is quicker than any other method. The mother has to support the head of each twin with one hand, and the bodies of the children are at her side — supported on a pillow or cushion. The feet are behind her.

A self-demand schedule is out of the question, unless both twins oblige by demanding food more or less at the same time. If they are not fed together, one may be angry at being kept waiting. All one can do is to feed them at the time which most nearly suits both of them.

It is difficult to decide what to do when there is not enough breast milk for both. The question is whether to give one nothing but breast milk and the other nothing but the bottle, or whether to let them alternate between breast and bottle. The latter is usually done, but if one twin is much smaller than the other, there is something to be said for giving the smaller one nothing but breast milk. It would take too long to feed both on the breast and then to give both complementary feeds.

When twins are born it is wise to express milk from the breasts after every feed in order to increase the supply. This should be done for two or three weeks.

For how long should the 10 p.m. feed be given?

It depends on the baby. Few babies awaken spontaneously for a feed in the late evening after the age of about four months, but some continue to do so for a few more weeks. When your baby is asleep in the late evening you will have to decide whether to try to awaken him for a feed. Up to the age of 3 months it is unlikely that if he is not given a feed then, he will sleep through the night. Some babies do, but they are unusual. When the baby is over 3 months of age (or sooner if you wish) it is worth while trying the experiment of letting him sleep through. If he awakens in the night, you should merely accept the situation and repeat the experiment in another two or three weeks. It is a matter of trial and error. Many mothers make the mistake of not trying the experiment at all, and as a result the baby is still having a 10 p.m. feed when he is seven or eight months old.

How long should breast feeding continue? When should weaning begin?

There is no hard and fast rule about this, but there is good reason for suggesting that you should begin to wean your baby by the age of 4 to 5 months, or 16 lb (7.26 kg) in weight. The reason for suggesting weaning by 4 to 5 months is the fact that the longer you postpone weaning after that, the more difficult he may be about taking new foods. If you postpone weaning to 9 or 10 months of age, he may become anaemic. The figure of 16 lb is mentioned, because a 16 lb baby is likely to want about 2 pints (1110 ml) of milk a day for an average weight gain, and it is undesirable to allow a baby to take much more than that from his mother.

If you want to introduce cereals and puréed vegetables or meat, etc., before the age of 4 months, you can do — by 2 or 3 months, or sooner, if you wish.

If there were a shortage of breast milk after a few weeks on the breast — say 2 months — we would introduce a variety of thickened feeds then, rather than give complementary feeds of cow's milk.

It is thought by some (but not all) that it is better not to introduce cow's milk or other substances until about four months, because of the very slight risk of allergy — probably in the form of eczema. This is certainly a factor to consider when there is a strong family history of allergy (e.g. eczema or asthma in a parent or previous child) but in many cases, when there is insufficiency of breast milk, one cannot avoid introducing other foods.

If fairly rapid weaning from the breast becomes necessary for any reason, there is no reason to believe that it will do the baby psychological harm. There is no evidence for this.

4

Artificial feeding
Full-term baby

Equipment

The equipment needed consists of feeding bottles, funnel, teats, half-pint graduated glass or jug, bottle brush, and medicine glasses to cover the teats when the feed is made up and in the bottle.

The bottle and teat and anything else coming into contact with the milk must be absolutely clean and sterile before use, because with artificial feeding there is the ever-present risk of infecting the baby by careless handling of the food or feeding equipment, and so causing gastroenteritis (diarrhoea and vomiting). This cannot be overemphasized.

Feeding bottles and teats may be sterilized either by the hypochlorite (Milton) method or by boiling. Both are safe and satisfactory, but the Milton method is somewhat safer. The teat is scrubbed in salt and rinsed, and the cleaned rinsed bottle is left submerged in Milton, ½ oz in 2 pints of water (14 ml in 1120 ml water) until ready for use. The bottle and teat are not rinsed out before the milk is put into the bottle: the small amount of residual Milton is harmless. The Milton solution should be changed every 24 hours.

If the boiling method is preferred, the teat and bottle must be rinsed thoroughly after a feed. Milk comes off the surface of the bottle and teat much more easily if it is washed off immediately. The inside of the bottle is then thoroughly scrubbed with a bottle brush, washed in a detergent and thoroughly rinsed. The teat is turned inside out and thoroughly washed, water being squeezed through the holes in it. The bottle is then placed in a pan along with the medicine glass, completely covered with water, and boiled for 10 minutes. Several bottles and glasses can be boiled at the same time. They are kept in the pan with the lid off until required. It is wise to boil the teats separately for 3 minutes and to pour the water off after boiling, for they will last longer if treated in this way. The bottle brush is kept specially for this purpose, and should be boiled frequently. It should not be used for anything else.

Before preparing the feed the hands must be thoroughly washed.

If dried milk is used, it is important to put the lid on the tin immediately after use. The powder is removed from the tin by the measure provided, which is kept in the tin. A spoon is too inaccurate a measure, because spoons vary so much in size. The powder is then mixed in the measuring glass or jug which has been boiled for the purpose. It is mixed with boiled water from the kettle, taking care that no lumps are left. The mixture is then poured into the bottle, and the teat is attached, taking care that the hands are clean, and the medicine glass is placed over the teat. The bottle is then placed in a cool place, and then in a refrigerator, if there is one, to await use. It is customary to warm milk before giving it to the baby, by warming the milk in a pan of warm water, but it is not necessary. Babies do not object to cold milk.

If cow's milk is used, it must be boiled before use, but there is a danger in prolonged boiling. It makes it too concentrated by evaporation. Boiling should be limited to two minutes. It is then poured direct from the pan into the bottle, which has been boiled as above, and sugar and boiled water are added and mixed.

Before the feed is given, it is essential to ensure that the hole in the teat is sufficiently large. By far the commonest cause of excessive wind in a bottle-fed baby is too small a hole in the teat. All wind which babies have is air which they have swallowed; the 'wind' is not produced in the stomach. Hence the longer the feed takes the more air is swallowed. If the hole in the teat is not large enough, the feed takes a long time and so he gets a lot of wind — and may vomit as a result; he may become tired with the long period of sucking and so not get enough.

The teat readily becomes blocked with dried milk mixture, and the hole must therefore be tested before every feed. It is tested simply by holding the bottle upside down. If the hole is big enough the milk should drop out, without any shaking and certainly without squeezing the teat, in almost a stream. If the hole is too small, it should be enlarged if made of rubber by a red hot needle whose other end is inserted in a cork.

Too large a hole may cause the baby to gag and choke in trying to swallow the milk. A bottle feed should not take more than about 10 to 15 minutes: the most likely cause of the baby taking longer than this is too small a hole in the teat. We have seen numerous 'windy' babies whose feeds were taking 45 to 60 minutes.

Choice of food

The milk of many animals has been used for the feeding of babies. They include the cow, ass, goat, camel, llama, caribou, bitch, mare, sheep, reindeer and water buffalo. The milk of the ass is most like that of the human, and was used extensively in Paris in the last century. In some countries babies used to feed direct from the ass or goat, various restraining devices being used in order to prevent the baby being injured. In the Middle Ages babies were fed on bread soaked in milk, broth or even beer — but nearly all the babies died.

In England the only artificial feed used for babies for whom breast milk is not available is cow's milk. This is satisfactory for babies if it is made up properly, but nearly all mothers prefer a dried milk preparation, because it is easier to store. The choice of dried milk is wide and therefore confusing for mothers. In our opinion there is nothing to choose between the various dried milks, and it is *never* necessary to change from one dried milk to another to find one which suits the babies. Some mothers insist that milk A did not suit the baby, while milk B does: others say the exact opposite. The differences are so trivial that they all suit the baby. Admittedly prices vary, and some mix perhaps more easily than others. You will not make a mistake whatever milk preparation you choose. Commonly used preparations are SMA, Cow and Gate and Ostermilk — all made up in the strength of one measure to each fluid ounce of water, without added sugar.

Making up the feed

There are important differences between cow's milk and human milk. Cow's milk contains three times more sodium (salt) than human milk, and it is important not to divert from the instructions in the tin and to make it up too strong. The new baby's kidneys are immature; ordinarily they get rid of the sodium in the urine, but if there is a chest infection, diarrhoea or fever the baby may lose so much fluid by other routes that there is not enough fluid to get rid of the excess sodium through the kidneys. Sodium thus accumulates in the blood and may cause dangerous symptoms, including brain damage. Another result of excess salt in the milk is excessive crying due to thirst; a mother is liable to interpret the crying as due to hunger, give more milk, and therefore increase or prolong the crying.

On no account must the measure supplied with the tin or packet be heaped, and on no account must the milk powder be compressed in the measure; having filled the measure one should just scrape the top off the powder so that the surface of the powder in the measure is flat. The correct proportion of milk powder to water is a measure to each fluid ounce: it is dangerous to increase the amount of powder per fluid ounce.

Undiluted cow's milk should not be given to babies under six months of age, because it may cause indigestion and constipation. It is different in chemical composition from human milk, and in contact with acid in the stomach it forms a bigger curd than human milk and occasionally forms an inspissated mass which obstructs the intestine. The milk, therefore, is modified in various ways, so as to make it more digestible. The drying process is one method. Another method is to dilute ordinary cow's milk with water and add sugar. Table 1 shows how feeds should be made up so as to constitute feeds closely similar to human milk, and well tolerated and digested by the baby.

We have done our best to explain that infant feedings is not complicated, but certain steps must be taken in order to work out a suitable feed for your baby. These are as follows:

1. Find the expected weight for your baby — that is, the average weight for babies of his age who weighed what he did at birth. This is worked out by adding to his birth weight 6 oz (170 g) for each week of his age for his first three months, e.g., if a baby weighed 8 lb (3629 g) at birth, his expected weight at 7 weeks would be 8 lb + 6 oz (170 g) for each of the seven weeks = 10 lb 10 oz (4819 g). In order to make the next part of the calculation easy, and make sure that he gets enough food, use the next round figure above that: for example, in the case above, say 12 lb (5443 g) instead of 10 lb 10 oz (4819 g). There is no need for greater accuracy.

2. Consult the table below for the method of making up the feeds. All these feeds give the same food value if made up in accordance with the quantities given in the table. The table shows the quantity of milk (or milk powder), and water per pound of expected weight per 24 hours. Table 1b shows the usual quantities of milk likely to be wanted for a baby of 6, 8, 10 or 12 lb (2722, 3629, 4536, 5443 g). All babies are different; some will want more than these quantities and some less.

How will you know if the baby is getting enough?

Firstly, he will not want any more food than you have offered him. He will be contented, though we must emphasize that a baby may cry because of wind, colic, loneliness and other causes. His weight gain will be satisfactory. His stools will usually be normal.

The baby who is not getting enough milk may swallow air as a result of excessive crying, and suffer from wind and even vomit. Usually, however, the main indication of underfeeding is defective

Table 1a Usual quantity per lb per day.

	Milk	Sugar	Water
Human Milk	2½ oz (71 ml)	—	—
Cow's milk	1¾ oz (49 ml)	1 teaspoon (3.6 g)	¾ oz (21 ml)
Modified Dried Milks			
S.M.A.	2½ measures		2½ oz (71 ml)
Cow and Gate	2½ measures		2½ oz (71 ml)
Ostermilk	2½ measures		2½ oz (71 ml)

Note 1 kg = 2.2 lb

1 measure = approximately ⅛ oz dry powder.

Use the measure supplied with the tin for measuring the quantity of milk powder.

Table 1b Quantity of milk, sugar and water likely to be required for each of five feeds in 24 hours.*

	Weight of baby			
	6 lb (2.7 kg)	8 lb (3.6 kg)	10 lb (4.5 kg)	12 lb (5.4 kg)
Modified Dried Milks (See Table 1a)	3 measures in 3 oz of water	4 measures in 4 oz of water	5 measures in 5 oz of water	6 measures in 6 oz of water

These quantities are approximate only, and only intended as a guide. If he wants more, he should have it.

weight gain and constipation, with the passage of hard stools. A starved baby passes loose green stools containing little but mucus — as does the starved breast-fed baby.

Overfeeding

You may overfeed him if you depart from the advice given — e.g., by giving heaped measures of milk powder, compressing the powder, or making the feeds up too concentrated. You are much more likely to overfeed him if you add cereals, rusks or other starchy foods in his early weeks. The result may be an excessive weight gain, which is undesirable. It would be most unlikely that the overfeeding would cause vomiting or diarrhoea.

If his weight gain is excessive, try to give him less milk, making the feed up more dilute (e.g., 4 measures of powder in 5 ounces (140 ml) of water, but not more dilute): avoid cereals and starchy foods, as far as possible: give him puréed meat, puréed vegetables and puréed fruit, prepared by yourself if you can, because the commercially available tins of puréed foods, especially puréed fruit, have a high cereal or carbohydrate content. In any case, it will be much cheaper to prepare the feed yourself.

Should the baby have water or other drinks between the feeds?

We indicated that a fully breast-fed baby should not normally be given water or other drinks between feeds, unless it is particularly hot weather. In the case of a bottle-fed baby we feel that there is no harm in giving him a drink of orange juice or boiled water between feeds if he wants it.

In warm climates, such as Egypt, babies want more fluid than babies in England, and they should be given additional fluid, such as fruit juice, between feeds. If they are not given additional fluid they may be unduly irritable, constipated and fail to gain weight well.

The way to give the feed

First, make sure that the feed is not too hot. The usual way to test it is to pour some on to your own arm. In fact, although it is customary to warm feeds for babies, it has been shown to be unnecessary. Secondly, test the hole in the teat, to see that it is big enough. Then give it to the baby. Avoid the mistake of having him lying down during his feed. It is difficult to swallow liquids when lying down. Have him propped up in a comfortable position. You must see that the teat is kept filled with milk. If the bottle is not tilted sufficiently your baby will suck air as well as milk and suffer from wind. Your baby will at intervals suck all the air out of the bottle, creating a vacuum. The teat will become flat, and it will be impossible for him to obtain any more milk. If he continues to suck when the teat has flattened, he will merely swallow air and so have symptoms of wind. As soon as the teat becomes flat, or preferably just before, withdraw the teat from his mouth, in order to allow air to bubble into the bottle, then put the teat back into his mouth. After the feed let him bring his wind up by holding him up to your shoulder.

The baby should never be left to 'feed himself' — sucking from the bottle which has been propped up on a pillow; the reason is that he is likely to suck the air out of the bottle and so create a vacuum in it: the teat will become flat and he will be unable to get the milk. Neither must he be left to suck after the bottle has been emptied, for if he does he will merely swallow air.

The milk must never be kept warm in a vacuum flask; it is dangerous because of the risk of infection: organisms may thrive in it. If you want to give him a warm feed in the night, keep boiled water warm in the flask, and mix the feed when you are ready to give it.

Windy bottle-fed baby

The causes of excessive wind in the bottle-fed baby have already been mentioned. The chief one is too small a hole in the teat, or a hole which has become blocked. The others consist of failing to tilt the bottle sufficiently to keep the teat full of milk, failing to let air bubble into the bottle when a vacuum has been created, and leaving the baby to suck when he has emptied the bottle.

Excessive air swallowing may be due to the baby's inability to get his lips sufficiently tightly around the teat. If you see that this is the trouble you can sometimes help by gently holding his cheeks so that his lips are kept more tightly round the teat.

Just as in a breast-fed baby, wind may result from air swallowing in excessive crying.

Unsatisfactory weight gain

By far the commonest cause of unsatisfactory weight gain is under-feeding. It has already been explained that it may be due to overclothing or to giving too little fluid, especially in hot weather. It may result from excessive posseting or vomiting. It may result from using a teaspoon to measure the dried milk instead of the measure or scoop, for a teaspoon may be smaller than the measure supplied. It may be due to the hole in the teat being too small so that he finds it difficult to get enough milk. It may be due to measuring the water wrongly, making the feed too dilute by putting too much water in the feed. The amount of water should be measured in a proper measuring glass. Some mothers make the mistake of using a tablespoon, thinking that a tablespoon measures half an ounce. Tablespoons vary, and many measure ¾ oz (21 ml) or more. If this method of measuring fluid is used, the feeds will be too dilute.

In some babies the weight gain is unsatisfactory even though the quantities given in Table 1 are rigidly adhered to. Some babies require more than these quantities for an average weight gain, and if your baby will take more, you should give him more.

There remain a small number of babies who gain weight unduly slowly in spite of taking as much as they want of a properly consti-tuted feed as often as they want. Sometimes this is due to mere loneliness. It is well known that sometimes babies in hospital fail to gain weight well in spite of being given proper feeds. They thrive as soon as they get home to their mothers. Not all babies, however, who are gaining weight at less than the usual speed are suffering from loneliness. It may be due to the fact that the baby is not taking the usual amount of milk. Do not feel concerned if he takes less than the average amount of milk, as indicated in the table, provided that his weight gain is satisfactory. It is disconcerting when the baby consistently leaves half the bottle. On no account try to make him take more. Some babies have smaller appetites than others. As long as he is well and happy, it does not matter in the least. It is often only a temporary phase, and he will soon take more as long as you do not try to make him take more than he wants.

If your child is taking much less than the usual amount from the bottle and his weight gain, in addition, is unsatisfactory, you should consult your doctor in order that he can make sure that the baby is well. It is often only a passing phase. Sometimes, in the case of the young baby, it is due to the baby falling asleep too soon during a feed. A gentle pinching of the toes may be sufficient to awaken him and get him to take more.

If you or your husband are of a small build, you should not be surprised if your child takes after you, and is also small, and therefore takes less food than big babies.

Often there is no apparent reason for the poor weight gain. As long as the baby is well and happy, and as long as the weight is increasing, there is no need to worry. You can thicken the feeds by adding a cereal, such as Farex, or other items mentioned in the section of weaning (Chapter 5).

When should weaning begin?

As in the case of the breast-fed baby, there is no rule as to when thickened feeds should be introduced.

If you wish to introduce thickened feeds when he is a month or two old you may do no harm. There is normally no particular advantage in so doing. If, however, he is a big baby, weighing over 10 lb, there is much to be said for introducing mixed feeds. We would certainly do so if he were taking 7 or 8 oz (196 or 224 ml) at a feed, because in that case he would probably be taking about two pints of milk in the 24 hours, and it is better not to exceed that. If he does not appear satisfied with a 7 or 8 oz feed, we would immediately give him some thickened feeds. We do advise you to watch your baby's weight, and to avoid an excessive weight gain as a result of the early introduction of cereals. Normally we would suggest that cereals would be introduced when he is about three months old. There is no rule about it. The danger of the premature introduction of cereals is that they may make him fat; when he is young, certain foods other than milk may possibly cause allergic symptoms, and it is just possible that they may cause indigestion because of a form of carbohydrate malabsorption.

Additional vitamins

Vitamin D has been added to dried milks and cereals, so that it is unnecessary to give additional vitamin D to artificially fed babies. Doctors think that in the past some babies have been given more vitamin D than they needed, and that harm can be done by so doing.

Green stools

Many mothers are worried when they see that the baby's stools are green. Provided that there is no diarrhoea, it is normal, and there is no point in trying to do anything about it.

5

Weaning

What foods can be given when the baby cannot chew?
The nature of the food which you give to the baby in the early days
of weaning depends primarily on the question of whether he can or
cannot chew. This is usually at 6 to 7 months of age. It does not
depend on the presence or absence of teeth. Before that babies have
firm hard gums, and can chew reasonable solid foods quite well
without teeth. Before the baby can chew one has to offer foods which
can be swallowed as they are. One therefore offers thick substances
without lumps in them — pre-cooked cereals, such as Farex
(warmed before being given), puréed fruit or vegetables, soup,
gravy, custard, jelly, fish, grated cheese, squashed banana, mashed
potato, carrot or turnip, lightly boiled egg, stewed apple (without
core), or minced meat. If you have a liquidizer or Mouli, there is no
need to buy puréed foods. It is cheaper and in some ways better to
prepare them yourself.

When travelling or in a hurry, tinned puréed fruit, vegetables or
soup can be used, but where possible fresh fruit and vegetables
should be given because of their greater vitamin content. Some of
the tinned soups or puréed meats have a high sodium (salt) content.
We advise you to beware of this. If you prepare your own puréed
foods with a liquidiser, we suggest that you should not add salt.
There is a possibility that there is a connection between salt intake
and raised blood pressure in later years.

There are several cereals from which to choose. Some mix more
easily than others. Farex is popular with babies and mixes easily with
cold or tepid milk. There is no need to add sugar to it, but if the
baby prefers it you can add a teaspoonful of sugar to a cupful of the
Farex mixture. There is no advantage in buying rusks. If the baby is
putting on too much weight, do not add sugar to feeds which you
liquidise yourself. Tinned puréed fruit may have a high sugar and
starch content.

Excessive use of starchy foods should be avoided, for they may
make the baby too fat. Cereals, therefore, should not be given for

more than one or two feeds in the day; mashed potato will only be given once in the day.

Foods to give when the baby can chew

When the baby can chew, a wide variety of foods becomes available. He can be given any of the following: a biscuit, thinly buttered toast, a crust, fish (taking care that there are no bones in it), finely cut up meat, bacon, raw apple or pear (without skin or core), a whole ripe banana, orange without pip or pith, chocolate, boiled egg, a piece of cheese, non-puréed vegetables, and many other foods. There is no need to keep consulting a book to find what he can or cannot have. If you use your common sense, and give him digestible foods which do not contain hard objects (such as large pips or stones in the case of fruit), which are readily masticated, and which are not greasy, you will not go far wrong. You should always see, however, that he has plenty of fresh fruit and vegetables, cheese and egg, meat and fish. These will do him much more good than starchy foods. Remember that babies differ in their tastes. Some prefer savouries, others prefer sweet or fruit juices.

Milk

Your baby will continue to have milk. It is better now that he should not have more than about a pint of cow's milk a day, for excess of milk will affect his appetite, and he will refuse other foods which are important to his growth. After about 6 months of age you can give cow's milk undiluted and without added sugar. It need not be boiled, as long as it is fresh and pasteurized. If it is not pasteurized it should certainly be boiled. If he is on the breast, the amount of milk which he takes will be automatically restricted by replacement with mixed feeds. You will also gradually replace breast milk by cow's milk. There is no point in continuing to use dried milk (except for convenience when travelling) after about 6 months of age.

You will note that apart from mentioning the maximum amount of milk which should be given, we have not discussed the quantities of food. You do not measure the amount of food you give after weaning has begun. You just give the child as much as he wants, as long as his weight gain is not excessive.

Foodstuffs to give after the first birthday

We do not propose to describe in detail the food which should be given to older children. We feel that all that is necessary is to mention some of the chief principles.

Firstly, money spent on food should be spent wisely. It is far better to spend money on meat, eggs, fish, milk, cheese, fruit and vegetables, than on cakes and sweets. You should try to give him meat or fish daily, an egg a day, and fruit several times a day.

We do not suggest that cakes, sweets and ice creams should not be bought at all. Children love them. What we do suggest is that if money is short, it is far better spent on foods which will help your child to grow up healthy and strong, than on substances which are merely pleasant, but which do him little good, and which may lead to dental decay. They can be given for occasional treats, but not as a regular thing at the cost of more important foodstuffs.

Although the foodstuffs mentioned are important for a child, you should never try to make him eat any of them, for if you do he will refuse them. The whole matter of food refusal is discussed in detail in the pages to follow.

Special diets are rarely necessary for children. A diet may have to be given for obesity, and there are certain rare diseases (such as coeliac disease) for which a special diet is necessary. Although, for instance, excess of fried foods should be avoided by all children, it is rarely necessary to limit fatty foods. We mention this, because numerous children are prevented from having fatty foods on account of so-called acidosis attacks (Chapter 26). This restriction will make no difference to the incidence.

Some children seem to have looseness of the stools if given certain fruits. Exclusion of the offending fruits may then become necessary. The reason for this is not clear, but the trouble usually clears up by the age of two or so.

How does one begin to wean the baby?

Babies are often conservative in their taste, and object strongly to a change from whatever they are having — breast or cow's milk. It is wise to begin, therefore, with a small amount of the new food, and gradually increase the amount each day until the whole feed is replaced. It is given with a spoon. You will be amused at the look of surprise on his face when he tastes it. He appears to be sampling it and making up his mind whether to take more. He may refuse to have any more after the first taste. In that case give him a drink of milk (if on the bottle) or put him to the breast, and then let him try the new food again when he is in a better temper after having the food to which he is accustomed. Do not on any account try to force him to take the new dish. Forcing of food in the weaning period is one of the commonest causes of food refusal and poor appetite. If you are unable by gentle persuasion to get him to take more, do not persist. Try again in a day or two. Never try to tempt him by putting the spoon into your own mouth first. That may introduce an infection into the baby from your teeth.

It is better if you can place the food in the middle of the tongue (half-way back) in the first two or three months for if it is placed on the tip he may push it out. As it is, quite a lot will come out again, and you will push it back with the spoon. It must not be lumpy, for he cannot chew until he is 6 or 7 months old and lumps may make him sick. It is important that the food should not be too hot, for that would hurt the baby, and once a baby has experienced discomfort from being given something too hot, he is not likely to forget it for a time, and he may firmly refuse any more food from the spoon.

It does not matter at which meal you first offer a new food. You should suit your own convenience. It may well be at your own dinner time. If you are breast feeding him, your aim will be gradually to increase the cereal or other food, at the same time reducing the time on the breast, until eventually the breast feed is stopped. The baby may prefer to have the cereal first, and then to finish with a short breast feed. He takes more and more of the cereal, until eventually he discards the breast feed or bottle altogether.

How should the baby be fed?

At first the new food is given by spoon. Cereals, fruit juice and milk can be given by a cup, certainly by about 6 months of age, and often sooner. In one large hospital in the United States, babies are fed from the cup in the newborn period and onwards. In England one usually begins cup feeding at about 5 or 6 months of age, because at that age the baby can get his lips round the rim and therefore drink without difficulty. You may find that he manages thickened feeds, such as cereal, easier than other liquids. Gradually the bottle is completely replaced by cup feeds. Spoon feeding continues for more solid foods.

The shape of the cup is of some importance. Some babies' cups are so rounded that the opposite rim gets in the way of the nose. The most suitable design is a cup with vertical sides, but sufficiently thick to avoid the danger of his breaking the rim with his teeth.

Any time from 5 months onwards, but maybe not till he is a year or so of age, the baby begins to show that he wants to learn to feed himself. This should be encouraged. He will begin by wanting to hold the bottle, cup or spoon. If a determined baby is prevented from doing so, he may be very annoyed. Some babies of 6 to 9 months of age would rather starve than be prevented from trying to feed themselves. They completely refuse food and scream when attempts are made to give it to them.

At first the baby is allowed to help to hold the spoon, and as soon as possible he is left to use it as well as he can. In the first place, he finds difficulty in filling the spoon. When he has mastered that he has to go through the stage of rotating the spoon just before it reaches the mouth, before eventually he can get the food into his mouth. He will probably get hold of the food in his hands and put it in his mouth that way. Let him, within reason. He must be encouraged to help to feed himself if he wants to, for he has to learn to be independent. If he does not want to feed himself, he should not be forced to do so. He will show the desire in due course. He will make a mess, but it is wrong to prevent him learning merely because of that. You should put a plastic sheet under his high chair to catch the droppings. He is protected by a plastic apron with sleeves. It often pays to take his shoes and socks off, for it is surprising how much custard collects in them. He should not be laughed at when he makes a mess. After about 9 months or so the baby begins to repeat performances which are laughed at. You will have to step in when he shows signs of inverting the dish on his head, but you should try to withhold your hand until then.

A heavy plate with a deep rim is suitable for him. We do not think that 'pushers' are of any use. A baby who learns to use one only has to learn not to use it when he gets older. An ordinary spoon is all that is required at first. A spoon with a curved handle is difficult for the baby to hold.

He has to learn to use a cup, but he will need help for quite a long time, for he is apt to let go as soon as he has drunk all that he wants.

Many babies are able to feed themselves entirely, managing a cup without help, by the time they are a year old. The average age for this is probably 15 to 18 months. Much depends on the child's independence, manipulative skill, and the opportunity which the mother gives him to learn.

By the age of about two the child can be given a knife and fork. As soon as he is able, near his third birthday, he graduates to an ordinary plate and an ordinary cup and saucer. Mothers tend to postpone these changes too long.

How long are full aseptic precautions necessary?

This is a difficult question. At some stage one has to decide that it is no longer necessary to boil every cup and spoon and other appliance used in connection with the baby's feeds. It is a matter of opinion as to when precautions can be relaxed. If milk is fresh and stored in a refrigerator, it would be reasonable to stop boiling (or heating) it when he is about six or seven months old.

One can say with certainty that at all times food should be handled with care, and the younger the child the greater should that care be, for young children are so susceptible to bowel infections. But it would seem reasonable to say that when a baby is 6 months old milk need no longer be boiled, if it is fresh and pasteurized. After the age of 6 months the cup and spoon need not be boiled before use, but they must always be clean. No food, nor anything which is used in its preparation, whether spoon, cup or anything else, should be left lying about, with dust or flies able to settle on it. This applies at any age. It is far better to be careful than careless.

How soon should the baby be fully weaned?

There is no need to lay down any rule about this. Some babies may be fully weaned in quite a short time — say, two months after first being given thickened feeds. Others are weaned slowly, either because the mother wants to do it slowly, or because the baby does not want to hurry the matter. It is usual for a baby to be weaned by about nine months, but if he still has a breast feed or bottle a little later; it does not matter. Every baby should be fully weaned by a year of age.

If you keep the child too long on strained foods, and so fail to give him solids when he is able to chew, you may find that he refuses to chew them when you offer them to him. You will then be faced with a difficult behaviour problem, for you cannot force him to chew. You will have to persuade him to chew by giving him nothing else but solids, so that he will have to chew or do without, but it will not be easy.

It is common to find that a baby has no objection to mixed feeds during the day, but for the last feed before he goes to bed he demands the breast or bottle. Eventually he may insist on sucking at the breast for a mere minute or two, before being given a cereal and then being placed in his cot. It is not always easy to persuade a baby to stop using the bottle. The process should be gradual. It is less likely to be difficult if he is fed from a cup at an early age, say 6 months, than if this is introduced later, for babies tend to become more and more conservative over their feeds. By the time his first birthday comes the bottle should be discarded. He may be annoyed about it, but he will not starve. This is not a rule which must be rigidly adhered to; you would not try forcibly to deprive the baby of the bottle if he were ill; but the longer you keep him on the bottle after this age the more difficult it will be to wean him off it. We have seen children of 4 years of age who still feed from a bottle. We read about a girl of 18 years of age who would never take milk except through a baby's bottle.

Sudden refusal of breast or bottle

It is common for a baby suddenly, and without any apparent reason, to refuse to have anything to do with the breast or bottle. No amount of persuasion will make him change his mind. Persuasion is unnecessary, for one simply feeds the baby from cup or spoon instead.

Food refusal in the weaning period

The extent of this problem depends on the age of the child, his personality, and the methods used to deal with it. The older the baby before weaning begins, the greater the likelihood that there will be difficulties, especially food refusal. Most babies become more and more determined as they grow older, and pass further into the phase of negativism, which all children go through. Personality is important, for some babies are more determined than others, and thus more likely to resist and to want to be independent. Placid babies usually present little difficulty in the weaning period. The brighter the child, the sooner he is likely to "get his parents onto a bit of string" — asserting his individuality, and discovering new ways of getting what he wants. The management of the child is important, for the more the mother tries to force the resistant child to take food, the more certain he is to resist.

There are certain factors which cause the baby to resist food. The baby who is thirsty may refuse a spoonful of dinner, but after a drink he is willing to eat anything on the plate. When the baby refuses food, give him a drink and try again.

He may refuse his dinner because he is tired or uncomfortable because of a wet nappie. It may be necessary to give him a nap before he is offered his dinner again, and in future to adjust the nap time so that he is not tired when his dinner is ready.

Babies as early as 5 months of age may have strong likes and dislikes. They may refuse one dish but enjoy another. One has seen babies who have experienced discomfort as a result of food being given too hot. They refuse anything like that food for a week or two after. The appearance of the food is important. A baby is more likely to take food of attractive colours, such as red jelly, than a nondescript mush, such as is so often offered to babies of this age. Babies also become accustomed to a particular dish or cup, and refuse food from other receptacles. Sometimes a baby will refuse his dinner if it is given from the usual dish, but take it readily if it is offered from another.

Temporary food refusal may be due to teething. When a painful tooth is coming through the baby may refuse solid food and want to go back to thickened feeds for a day or two.

Appetites vary from day to day, week to week and meal to meal. They fall off in hot weather. Do not be alarmed if your baby seems to eat less than usual for a few days. Most babies do this for unknown reasons. As long as the baby is well, it does not matter in the least. He will certainly be expected to take less if he has an infection, such as a cold.

Let us repeat again: Never force any child to take food against his will. It is always wrong to force food into his mouth, to hold his nose and put food in, or to hold his limbs and head and feed him. It is never necessary, and causes nothing but trouble, inevitably increasing his resistance. And do give him proper solids as soon as he is able to chew. But above all, use your common sense and do not be misled by anyone who attempts to lay down rigid rules of infant feeding.

Food refusal by the older child is discussed in Chapter 18.

6

The low birth weight or preterm baby

Though inevitably the preterm baby will be under the care of a doctor, we felt that we should mention some of the important points concerning the management of a preterm baby and the difficulties which have to be faced, in order that parents will have a better understanding of the problems concerned. In this chapter we include all low birth weight babies, that is babies weighing 5½ lb (2500 g) or less at birth, whether they were 'small for dates' or truly premature. In Britain the average weight of the baby born in the last 12 weeks of pregnancy is as follows:

Weeks of pregnancy	lbs	kg
28	2.9	1.3
30	3.6	1.6
32	4.2	1.9
34	5.2	2.4
36	6.4	2.9
38	6.9	3.1
40	7.5	3.4

The preterm baby's hold on life is a slender one, and the smaller he is the more slender is that hold. The centres in his brain which control his breathing and other vital functions are immature, so that he is liable to have irregular and shallow breathing and to have 'blue attacks', in which his breathing is so unsatisfactory that he becomes seriously blue for a minute or so at a time. He is liable to become chilled, having a subnormal temperature, or to become overheated, and so develop a high temperature. This is in part caused by lack of fat under the skin. He sucks badly, and is particularly liable to choke when feeding (going blue as a result), and to vomit. His stomach capacity is a small one, so that he can only take small quantities. His digestive system is easily upset, and unlike the full-term baby he can easily be given too much. He moves little, cries little, and sleeps nearly all day and night. He has a poor resistance to infection, poorer than that of a full-term baby. In many other ways he is immature, and so presents especial difficulties in management.

The smallest babies, those weighing less than 4 lb (1.81 kg) at birth, must be looked after in hospital, because of the special difficulties in feeding them. Above that weight they can usually be looked after in the home, especially if there is a special scheme for the home care of low birth weight babies. If the baby is born at home, and it is felt that he should be looked after in hospital, he must be kept warm during the move. Special heated baskets or other containers are usually brought by the ambulance for the purpose. Care must be taken not to overheat him, or to place an unprotected hot water bottle in such a position that it can burn him. He should not be bathed before he goes to hospital.

When he is born he is taken straight into a warm blanket and left undisturbed, except only that the midwife ensures that he can breathe, by sucking fluid out of his throat. He is not bathed until he is big and sturdy, and weighs 4½ lb (2.04 kg) or so. He is cleaned by olive oil on sterile cotton wool swabs, and the vernix, the greasy material on the skin, is left undisturbed.

The temperature of the room should be as near as possible to 70°F (21.1°C). His temperature should be taken three or four times every day. It should be kept at 97 to 98°F (36.1 to 36.7°C), and not allowed to drop below 97°F. He is protected from draughts by a screen round the cot. He wears only enough clothes to keep him warm, and that means very little, if the temperature of the room is maintained at the level mentioned. In hospital he is likely to be nursed without clothes. Napkins should be soft ones, preferably of the Harrington square type, rather than the rough Turkish towel variety.

He is left undisturbed in his cot or basket, except only when his napkin is changed or until it is time to feed him. After his feed he is placed on his abdomen and not left on his back, so that if he does bring some milk up he will not inhale it.

Visitors are not allowed, because of the risk that they will give him a cold or other infection. He is never handled for any purpose by his mother or anyone else without the hands being previously thoroughly washed, because of the risk of infecting him. On no account should anyone with a cold or any infection go anywhere near him. It is desirable psychologically for both the mother and child that the mother should handle her preterm baby as soon as possible after delivery — certainly in the first 2 or 3 days.

Feeding the premature baby
Unlike full-term babies, they cannot be fed on a self-demand schedule, because they may be too weak to make their needs known.

They must be fed on a rigid schedule. Preterm babies are far more liable to pick up infections than full-term babies. Special precautions must be taken to avoid carelessness in the preparation of his feeds.

We usually give the first feed within 12 hours of birth. The baby who weighs under 5 lb (2.28 kg) should not be moved from his cot for a feed, though he must be propped up, for it is difficult to swallow milk when one is lying down. The baby weighing 5 lb or more can usually be put to the breast, at least after two or three days. The reason why the small babies cannot be put to the breast is that they have difficulty in sucking, and if put to the breast either they would not obtain any milk, or they would quickly become exhausted with sucking and so not obtain sufficient milk. The smallest babies which have to be nursed in hospital, cannot even swallow. The baby weighing between 4 and 5 lb (1.81 to 2.27 kg) should be fed by a pipette, or by a bottle if he can suck well, or by the breast.

Before the baby is fed he should have his napkin changed. It is unwise to 'change' him after a feed, because it increases the risk of vomiting.

The best food to give to a low birth weight baby, except the smallest, is breast milk. In the case of the small baby who cannot be put to the breast, the milk is expressed into a basin which has been boiled, and given to the baby by a boiled pipette or bottle. If breast milk is not available, there is a choice of several foods, and there are differences of opinion as to which is best. Suitable foods are Cow and Gate Babymilk Plus, Cow and Gate V Formula, S.M.A., S.M.A. Gold Cap or Ostermilk Complete Formula; in all cases the feed is made up in the proportion of one measure to one fluid ounce of water.

Table 2 Approximate feeds for low birth weight babies (in total ounces or ml of milk* per 24 hours).
Modified from Crosse, V. Mary (1961) *The Premature Baby*. London: Churchill.

Birth weight	Day							
	2	4	6	8	10	14	21	28
4 lb (1814 g)	2 oz (56ml)	4 oz (112ml)	6 oz (168ml)	10 oz (280ml)	12 oz (336ml)	14 oz (392ml)	16 oz (448ml)	
5 lb (2268g)	2½ oz (70ml)	5 oz (140ml)	7½ oz (210ml)	10 oz (280ml)	12½ oz (350ml)	15 oz (420ml)	17½ oz (490ml)	20 oz (560ml)

*Breast milk undiluted, Cow and Gate Babymilk Plus or Premium or V Formula, S.M.A., S.M.A. Goldcap, Ostermilk Complete Formula.

The quantities sugggested are shown in Table 2. The quantities apply either to breast milk or to artificial foods.

These quantities are only approximate. The baby may take less or a little more, but he should not take much more. After the first fortnight the quantities are more rapidly increased, and the instructions in the section on 'artificial feeding' now apply.

Each feed should not take longer than 15 to 20 minutes. If feeds take longer, he should be fed by bottle for a day or two (with breast milk which has been expressed) and then tried again on the breast.

Small babies are fed frequently because of the small capacity of the stomach. If the baby cries for a feed in the night, he is given one.

The small baby should be weighed daily, but when he reaches 5½ lb (2.49 kg) the weighing should be twice per week, and then weekly. The baby who is under 5 lb (2.27 kg) at birth may not regain his birthweight until the third week. You should not try to hurry his weight gain. In general, it is safer for the 4 to 5 lb (1.81 to 2.27 kg) baby to gain not more than 4 to 5 oz (113 to 142 ml) per week in the first three weeks, for doctors have found that a more rapid gain of weight is liable to be followed by a fall in weight. A more rapid gain is safe in the 5 to 5½ lb (2.27 to 2.49 kg) child.

After the feed he should be laid on his abdomen, with the head of the cot raised, so that if he brings any milk up it will not be inhaled.

The low birth weight baby is given the clinic vitamin drops from the age of three or four weeks. In addition, it is wise to give him an iron medicine after about eight weeks, because otherwise he will become anaemic. This is prescribed by your doctor.

7

Twins

Historical

In many cultures twins have been objects of superstition and even fear. In many countries (including Greenland, Australia, Japan, North and South America) one or both twins were killed and the mother was thought to have been unfaithful, on the grounds that no man could father more than one at a time. Some Indian tribes thought that twins were transformed salmon and would not allow them to go near water in case they should revert to fish. It was thought in New Guinea that a woman might give birth to twins if she ate two bananas growing from a single head. The Hottentots had an unpleasant way of removing one of the father's testicles if he fathered twins, with the intention of preventing him repeating the performance. In other cultures twins were thought to have the power of controlling weather, fertility and survival in battle.

Famous twins included Jacob and Esau, Romulus and Remus, Castor and Pollux, Viola and Sebastian, Tweedledum and Tweedledee.

The largest live born twins totalled around 21 lb; an article in the *Lancet* of 1884 described stillborn twins weighing 17 lb 8 oz and 18 lb 0 oz, a total of 35 lb 8 oz.

A Moscow woman is said to have had 69 children in 27 pregnancies, including 4 sets of quadruplets, 7 sets of triplets and 16 sets of twins. A lady in Wurzburg, Germany, is said to have had 53 children of whom only 34 survived.

Mark Twain wrote "My twin and I got mixed up in the bath when we were only two weeks old and one was drowned, but we don't know which."

Incidence and causes of twinning

The incidence of twins in Britain is 1 in 86 births: that of triplets is 1 in 86^2 and that of quadruplets is 1 in 86^3. Each year approximately 10,000 pairs of twins are born, 95 sets of triplets and 3 sets of quadruplets. The incidence of twins in Nigeria is around 10 per cent of all births, as compared with 1.2 per cent in Britain and 0.3 per cent in China. The incidence of non-identical twins has declined in U.S.A., Canada and nine European countries since 1929, but has increased in Finland.

The incidence of identical twins is constant, 1 in 300 births, but the incidence of non-identical twins varies: factors responsible for the variations include genetics, the age, parity and social class of the mother, the season of conception, geographical factors and the administration of the 'fertility' drug (gonadotrophins). If a mother has non-identical twins, there is a three to ten times greater likelihood of her having twins again than there is for others, and there is a greater likelihood of twins amongst her relatives. The tendency to have twins is inherited through the mother. The incidence of non-identical twins rises with the age of the mother and the number of pregnancies which she has had. A woman of 35 to 40 is three times more likely to have twins (non-identical) than a woman under 20, and after the fifth birth a woman is five times more likely to have twins. It is said that twin conceptions are less likely in times of war, but more likely in the first three weeks of marriage. More twins are born in the lower classes, perhaps because the mothers have more pregnancies.

In Finnish Lapland there are more conceptions of non-identical twins in the summer, when there is light throughout the 24 hours, than in the winter, when it is dark day and night.

Identical or non-identical?

Identical twins (termed monozygos) are of the same sex, look alike, have the same hair colour, texture and whorls, the same eye colour, and similar nose, ears, lips and fingers. They are the result of fertilisation of a single ovum. Non-identical twins (also termed dizygos, binovular or fraternal) are unlike in appearance to a varying degree. The diagnosis cannot be reliably made on the appearance of the placenta; it is established by detailed study of the blood groups. Detailed inspection of palm prints is less satisfactory. Identical twins are more likely to be born by a younger mother, to be smaller at birth, to be born earlier than non-identical twins.

Other physical features

The average birth weight of twins is 2400 g (262 days' gestation) of triplets, 1800 g (247 days' gestation) and of quadruplets, 1400 g (237 days' gestation). In about half of twin deliveries, both twins are born head first, but in other twin deliveries one or both are delivered by breech. Occasionally one twin is born pale and anaemic, while the other is born plethoric: this is due to blood passing from one twin to the other before birth: both may have to be treated urgently — one by transfusion, the other by removal of blood. Jacob and Esau were probably examples of this 'twin-transfusion syndrome'.

Twin pregnancies are sometimes associated with hydramnios (excess amniotic fluid), toxaemia in pregnancy, prolapse of the cord or bleeding before delivery.

Subsequent progress

There is a somewhat higher incidence of congenital anomalies in twins, and a greater risk of cerebral palsy than in the case of single births. The reason for these findings is not clear. The smaller of twins usually remains smaller throughout childhood.

Twins, whether identical or not, tend to be later in learning to talk than singletons. The delay tends to be greater in middle class than in lower class families. Some have said that this is because the twins can understand each others' language and therefore do not bother to talk properly. We do not believe this. It is far more likely that the reason for late speech development lies in the fact that the mother of twins has less time to talk to twins and to read to them than the mother of a single baby: and it has been shown that if one of the twins dies in early infancy the surviving twin is not later than others in learning to talk. It would seem sensible for parents to make a special point of talking a lot, perhaps more than usual, to each of the twins. There is a slightly higher incidence of stuttering and reading difficulty in twins, and of left handedness in identical twins.

Differences do occur in the behaviour and mental development of twins, but these may be due to differences in the parental attitudes to the two children; for instance, if one twin is ill, the mother's attitude to him thereafter may be different from her attitude to the other child.

Twins are particularly likely to be jealous of each other, and the jealousy may be so severe that they may later have to go to different schools. There is good reason for a twin to be jealous of his co-twin if the latter is more clever, as often happens. Favouritism, as always, increases the risk of jealousy. Singleton brothers and sisters are liable to be jealous of twins — perhaps because of the interest and attention which they attract. Many twins dislike the interest and comments of others. One twin may be disturbed when the other is punished, or has to be admitted to hospital.

On no account should one twin be 'compared' with the other in his presence. This may happen when one twin is bigger than the other, so that the smaller one is regarded as 'delicate' or when one is more clever, or better looking, or kinder or better behaved. Comparisons inevitably cause jealousy and insecurity.

Twins tend to want to have everything the same for fear one might do better than the other. They are rivals for their parents' love. The mother is more than usually busy with having twins to look after, and so is likely to have less time for them than she would for single babies, and therefore she appears to show less love. One twin commonly becomes attached to more to one parent. They are so firmly attached to each other that they may show less affection to their parents.

It has been said that the first born of the twins is more likely to be a leader, to take responsibility, to be ambitious and aggressive: the second is said to be more gay, cheerful, stubborn and light-hearted; how much truth there is in this we do not know. Identical twins tend to be closer to each other than non-identical ones: it is said that they tend to be less gregarious and less aggressive than single children.

As for general intelligence, it used to be said that twins score on the average less well in IQ tests: but it has been shown that if one twin dies at birth or in the newborn period, the surviving twin scores as well as others — presumably because the parents of a single child have more time to devote to him than they have for twins, so that the single child gains from the extra attention which he receives.

Management

It is important that twins should be encouraged to develop their own individuality and they should not be treated (or dressed) exactly alike. Even identical twins have their own individuality and it should be encouraged. It is undesirable to give them both the same presents. If one twin has his own particular interests, they should be encouraged. They should not always go out together; one parent should at times take one out, and the other the opposite twin. They should have their own possessions, and different toys. It has been suggested that one should stress their differences rather than their similarities.

If one twin acquires an infectious disease, it would be a mistake to try to isolate him from the other twin. They should be encouraged to become independent of each other: if they do not, serious emotional problems may arise later when separation becomes necessary.

For many practical aspects of management, we recommend the book by Carola Zentner (published by David and Charles, Newton Abbott, 1975). She was a journalist who had two sets of twins.

Finally you can insure against having twins (with Lloyds) provided that you do it in the first three and a half months of pregnancy.

8

Crying

How soon does a baby cry?
There have been many reports of babies being heard to cry before
they were born — after rupture of the membranes.

Most healthy newborn babies cry the moment they are born. This
serves a useful purpose in ventilating the lungs. A famous psychologist suggested that the first cry is due to 'an overwhelming sense of
inferiority at thus suddenly being confronted by reality without ever
having had to deal with its problems'; and several psychologists have
said that the first cry represents the baby's desire to get back into the
nice warm place he has come from!

How does he cry?
The newborn baby does not usually shed tears: tears do not usually
appear till three or four weeks of age. In later months he may be
thought to be crying (at night), but it is found that he is not shedding
tears: he is just shouting for his mother, but that is likely to be
followed by true crying. When crying is allowed to continue for a
long time in the case of the older infant, he becomes distressed and
cannot stop even when picked up: he sobs, with sudden jerking
breaths, which gradually cease.

Mothers know that there are many different types of cry. The cry
of hunger is different from the high-pitched screams of pain, and the
cry of the tired child is different from the cry of hunger. Paediatricians in Finland and Sweden have used electronic devices to record
the cries of babies on a sort of graph (by sound spectrometry), and
have shown that the cries of hunger, pain, anger and frustration, and
the cries of babies with certain diseases, are all different and characteristic. In Sheffield we took tape recordings of 31 newborn babies,
and asked mothers to listen to the recordings in order to try to
recognise the crying of their own baby. Within 24 hours after birth
12 of 23 mothers, and by 48 hours of birth all mothers, correctly
picked out their own baby's crying. In five-bedded wards we found
that in the first three nights 15 of 26 mothers were awakened by the

crying only of their own baby, but after the third night 22 of 23 mothers were awakened only by their own child.

Why does he cry?

This is a question to which probably all parents would like to have the answer. They would often like still more to know how to stop him crying. There are some parents who do not even try to stop him crying. It is not always possible to say why a baby cries — any more than why many adults suddenly feel depressed, irritable and 'flat'. We cannot say why some babies cry and scream in the first few days after birth when put to breast (p. 45).

More obvious causes of crying include the following:

Hunger

Some adults experience discomfort or become bad tempered when they are hungry, and it may be that babies feel the same. Babies vary in their response to hunger: some yell for food as soon as they awaken, while others are more tolerant and are prepared to wait awhile. Some babies wait contentedly after feeding from one breast while their wind is being brought up, while others are furious if they are not immediately given the second breast. The older the baby, the longer he is likely to be willing to wait for food when hungry. Rigid feeding methods invite excessive crying.

Crying from hunger does not stop when the baby is picked up, or at least only stops for a minute or two. This is important, for one sees babies offered the breast every time they cry, when all they want is to be picked up and loved.

Wind

The causes of excessive wind — all dependent on the causes of air-swallowing — have been discussed in Chapters 3 and 4. It is easy to ascribe a baby's crying to wind when it is due to no such thing. We have seen scores of older babies whose screaming at night has been put down to 'terrible wind' or 'awful indigestion' when it was due to nothing more than the usual sleep problems described in Chapter 17. In fact older babies do not suffer from excessive wind. There is no such thing as a 'windy baby', but excessive wind is nearly always due to the feed taking too long — usually because the hole in the teat, in the case of a bottle fed baby, is too small, or, in the case of a breast fed baby, because he is continuing to suck after obtaining all the milk, and so he swallows air.

Evening colic

A common cause of crying in the first three months is the so-called three months' colic. It begins either in the Maternity Hospital or on return home. The baby, who is well behaved during the day, has severe attacks of screaming in the evening, usually between 6 and 10 p.m. This is particularly trying for the mother, who has been with the baby all day, and would like to have a little time to herself in the evening. The pain comes in attacks. He frowns, becomes red in the face, draws his legs up and screams with a high-pitched scream. The screaming may continue for ten minutes or so. It is not stopped by picking him up, or at least only momentarily. The attack goes off, only to be followed by another and another. He often seems to be tired and is just going off to sleep when another spasm of pain occurs. The attacks usually stop at about 10 p.m. It can often be observed that in an attack there is a lot of gurgling in the baby's abdomen. He often passes a lot of wind from the bowel, and the pain seems to be relieved when he passes wind below or has a motion. It may also be relieved by putting him on to his stomach.

In our experience many babies are said to have 'colic' when they have no such thing. The so-called evening colic is usually confined to the evening; if there is unexplained crying at other times of the day other causes should be looked for — the desire to be picked up, to see what is going on, wind from feeding errors, or other causes which we have discussed. Nevertheless, a few babies may experience attacks of pain at other times in the day or night. Occasionally the time of the beginning of the attacks seems to shift back gradually from 6 p.m. to an earlier hour. But in nine out of ten cases the attacks are in the evening. There are all degrees of severity. A baby with a severe form nearly drives the mother to distraction. In the mildest form the baby is nothing more than a little irritable in the evenings, and so presents no real problem.

Many mothers make the mistake of thinking that the baby is hungry. It is easy to see why they think so. His cries are not stopped by picking him up, and it seems that babies with colic get some relief by sucking. Not all babies will take the breast when having an attack, but most do, and they seem to stop crying for a time after it, but the attacks begin again in a quarter-of-an-hour or so. It is certainly not due to underfeeding, though underfeeding may make a baby cry, and if the weight gain is unsatisfactory you would naturally see that the baby gets more food. The weight gain of babies with colic is almost always satisfactory, and when one offers food additional to the breast milk the baby either refuses or continues to have colic just the same.

Some say that the colic is somehow connected with the father's homecoming. The early evening is a difficult time for the mother, who has to prepare an evening meal, get children off to bed, feed the baby and try to tidy up, apparently all at the same time. The father is blamed for a lot of things, but it seems hardly reasonable to blame him for the baby's colic. We see numerous cases of colic in babies whose fathers return home either later or earlier than 6 p.m., but still the colic occurs at the usual time. More often mothers are blamed for the baby's colic: they are accused of being nervy and tense and by some unspecified means this tenseness is relayed to the child. In our opinion this is nonsense: mothers of colicky babies are no different from any other mothers, but if their babies have severe colic, mothers are liable to become worried and tense as a result.

Many other mothers make the mistake of thinking that their milk or the artificial feed which they are giving is not suiting the baby. We have seen many babies taken off the breast and put on to the bottle on this account, only to find that the colic continued unabated. Breast milk always suits the baby, and it is always wrong to take a baby off the breast on the grounds that the milk 'is not suiting the baby' or is 'not strong enough'. We have already said that an extremely rare exception to this statement is lactose intolerance, in which the baby cannot tolerate the lactose in milk.

The attacks usually become milder as the baby gets older, and disappear by the age of about three months, and often sooner. Occasionally there may seem to be a slight recurrence of the colic at the age of about 6 months, when the baby is being given mixed feeds.

No one knows the cause of the attacks. They may be due to wind in the bowel. This is not due to any of the causes of wind in the stomach. The pain of colic, furthermore, is not relieved by bringing wind up.

Some mothers think that certain foods which they take may affect the baby through the breast milk. We have made a special study of this problem, and it is just possible that there may be something in it. We asked the mothers of 50 babies with colic whether they thought that any particular foodstuff taken by them upset the baby. Fourteen replied in the affirmative, blaming all manner of vegetables and fruit, but the interesting thing was that no two mothers blamed the same food — which suggests that it is unlikely that any food taken by them was really responsible. Nevertheless, when a baby has colic of the type mentioned, it is reasonable for the mother to try cutting out certain foodstuffs to see if it helps, and to note whether any particular food makes the baby worse. Some have thought that the 'colic' may be due to allergy to cow's milk — either taken by the baby, or taken by the breast-feeding mother. Others disagree with this.

If the colic is severe your doctor may give you some medicine for the baby (Merbentyl) in the evening. The important thing is for the mother to remember that this colic occurs in well, healthy babies who are thriving, that no one has ever found any disease to explain it, and that it gets better by about 3 months of age and sometimes sooner.

One problem which inevitably arises is the question of whether to pick him up when he cries or to leave him. We are sure that it is always wrong to leave any child crying because of pain. He should be picked up, even though he may develop a habit by expecting to be picked up in the evenings. When the mother thinks that the crying in the evenings has become a habit, because the nature of the cry is different, and it no longer comes in spasms and causes such piercing screams, then she can stop the habit by ignoring the crying.

Crying at the time of the mother's menstrual periods was discussed in Chapter 3.

Thirst

Constant crying by a well baby may be due to making the feeds too concentrated (Chapter 4), so that he takes too much sodium (salt). His crying is then ascribed to hunger, he is given more milk, and is made worse. The high salt content of certain tinned foods has been mentioned. The use of a 'water-softener' for water to be used for making up feeds may cause the same problem — that of giving the baby too much sodium.

Discomfort

We cannot always define the exact causes of a baby's apparent discomfort. Some cry when the light is put on, some when the light is put off, many when there is a loud noise, many when they are too hot, or too cold, have a wet nappy, an itching rash, some even when put into a bath. Most babies cry when the limbs or head are tightly held, and many cry when the clothes are removed or when their position is suddenly changed. It is normal and common for a baby to cry when passing urine or a stool (not necessarily a hard stool). Babies often object strongly to having the nose or ears cleaned.

Much crying is ascribed to teething (Chapter 10) when in fact there are other causes, such as the common sleep problems (Chapter 17).

The child's need for love and security

Every child's need for love will be described elsewhere (Chapter 13). Even the newborn baby cries to be picked up, and his crying stops as soon as he is taken into his mother's arms. When a baby is put back into his cot after a feed his screams may be merely an expression of disgust at being separated from the arms of his mother. Such crying will stop when he is picked up. Mothers often put this down to wind or to insufficiency of milk.

Many a baby lies as good as gold in a pram, or sits quietly in the arms of his grandmother until he catches sight of his mother, when he promptly shrieks for her. Those who do not understand babies are likely to say that the baby is 'naughty' or 'spoilt'. We disagree with this. It is normal and eminently desirable that a child should be strongly attached to his mother, who does almost everything for him, bathing him, feeding him when he is hungry, and attending to him when he is uncomfortable. Some time after 6 months he may cry when he sees his mother pick up another child — the first sign of jealousy.

Children go through phases of increased dependence on their parents. It is common for a 12-month-old baby to cry whenever the mother leaves the room in which he is playing. Most crying out at night is basically due to the child's love for his parents.

Many mothers fear that if they show love to their baby they will spoil him. There is no ground for this fear. It is the natural and normal thing to pick a baby up when he cries. We do not suggest that he should be picked up at the slightest whimper, or even every time he cries, but he should certainly be picked up if it is clear from the nature of his crying that he will continue if he is left. He may be crying merely because he is tired. Most babies at some stage cry just before they go to sleep. The mother should not feel that every time he cries she must pick him up. No harm will befall him if he is left to cry at times. She has her work to do, and cannot spend all her time holding the baby — and some babies seem to want to be held in most of their waking hours. We do suggest, however, that it is a bad thing to make a practice of leaving a baby crying for long periods for fear of spoiling him.

In some maternity hospitals babies are kept in the nursery, presumably so that when they cry they will not disturb the mother. We agree that when the mother is tired every effort should be made to allow her to rest. But when she is not tired, one must also think of the baby's needs. We think that it is wrong to leave any baby, even a newborn one, howling for a long period when all he wants is to be

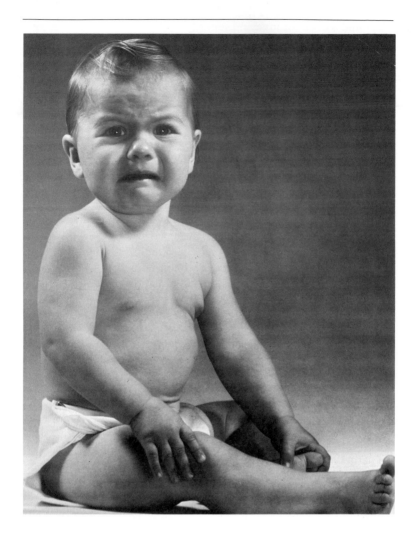

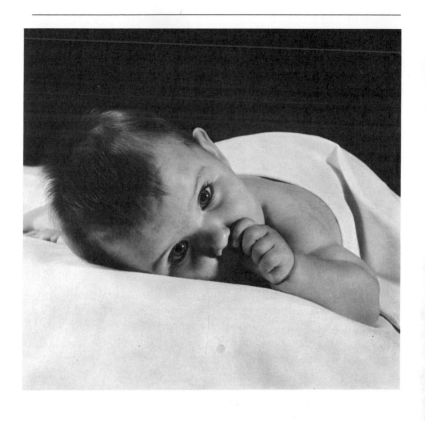

picked up and loved. We often feel surprised at the lack of concern shown by some mothers when the baby is howling hour after hour outside in the pram. They do not seem to hear. They do not seem to realize that their babies are human beings, with their own particular needs.

If a young baby is picked up when he wants it, and his needs are met as they arise, the mother will find that he will become less and less demanding as he grows older. We cannot agree with the many books which advocate that the baby should always be left to cry it out. They fail to consider the needs of the individual and differences in personality.

The child who is denied mother love when he asks for it is the child who grows up to be insecure, clinging to the mother's legs long after other children have learnt independence and more mature behaviour. Mothers who are most careful to avoid spoiling their children are often the possessors of children who are horribly spoiled and insecure.

It is easy to understand why many books recommend mothers not to pick their babies up when they cry. The idea is that by picking the baby up she will cause him to acquire a bad habit of frequent crying, knowing that by so doing he can get when he wants and that if she leaves him he will learn that crying is no use, for he will discover that no one pays any attention to him. There is an element of truth in it. Babies do learn habits rapidly. When a small child is ill, he learns bad habits. He is picked up when he cries, and he calls out in the evenings after the illness because he learnt while ill that if he did this his mother would come to see him. A child often behaves badly after the grandmother's visit, having become used to increased attention. In the same way if a baby is picked up at every whimper, he will soon learn to expect to be picked up the moment he asks for it. Once the mother realizes that he has got her on a piece of string, she can and must put her foot down and stop it. There is moderation in all things. Any mother who possesses a really determined baby knows that if she refuses to pick him up when he cries he will go on crying for hour after hour, and when a habit has been firmly established it may be difficult to break it. But not all such crying is due to habit and mismanagement. Unkind neighbours will ascribe the crying to faulty upbringing, while in fact the factor responsible is the baby's personality. If they had possessed a difficult baby with similar personality they would have been a little more sympathetic and understanding.

We feel that those who advise mothers not to pick children up when they cry, either have no children of their own, or else have had placid babies who cry little and demand little. It is a matter of common knowledge that some babies who are neglected by their mothers because of their fear of spoiling them, continue to cry excessively for week after week and month after month. It is equally obvious that babies whose mothers have picked them up within reason and loved them when they were crying, have grown up to be happy, well-behaved, loving children.

The younger the baby the more he should be picked up when he cries. Most babies so treated are less demanding as they grow older. But even the older baby should not be left to cry for long periods — except when an established habit is being broken (Chapter 17).

The mother should not be afraid of her natural instincts. She should use her common sense. If her baby wants love, she should give him love, and she will not do any harm. If she is ever in doubt as to whether he is crying because of some discomfort, such as that of teething, she should give him the benefit of the doubt and pick him up. If a habit is created, it can be broken by firmness.

The older child may cry because of insecurity, due to perfectionism, too much being expected of him in relation to his age, excessive discipline, too vigorous efforts to teach manners and to 'train him'. When the parents' effort to teach a child anything, whether table manners, politeness towards others, or clean habits, result in tears, it is high time that they reviewed their methods and relaxed. He will learn not by compulsion and discouragement, but by love, encouragement and good example.

Many tears are due to the parents' unwillingness to let the child play as he wants with his own toys.

Boredom
The age at which babies begin to cry because they are bored depends on the interest which they show in their surroundings, the amount of time they are awake, and their intelligence and personality. It is common for a 3 month-old baby to howl when left awake in a pram alone outside, and yet to lie perfectly happy and contented in the pram in the kitchen when he has company and can see some activity. At 5 months of age and onwards babies often cry when lying flat, but are happy when propped up so that they can see what is happening in the world around them. At this age a baby who is crying in his pram, even when propped up, may be perfectly content when propped up in his high chair, or when lying on a rug on the floor. The change of position seems to help. It is a common practice to leave a baby crying for hours on end in his pram outside the house, with nothing but a brick wall to see, when all that he wants is something

to do and to watch.

Any time after 3 months a baby will begin to hold rattles and other objects when they are placed in his hand, though he cannot go for objects and grasp them until 5 months or so, and he should be given suitable toys to play with. He will stop crying if picked up, but it is better to bring the baby into the kitchen and avoid picking him up, if all that is wanted is something for him to see, or a change in position.

Fatigue

Adults feel cross and irritable when tired, and the most trivial things upset them — things which they just take in their stride when they are feeling well. Babies and children are just the same, only they respond to fatigue in addition by crying. From the newborn period onwards babies cry when they are tired. The extent to which this happens depends largely on the child's personality. Some small children when tired fall asleep gradually and almost imperceptibly. Almost all babies in the first three months or more cannot help falling asleep after a good feed, but the older child can resist sleep and often does so for amazingly long periods, even though tired out. A tired, determined baby of six months or so may be most difficult to handle. He cries if put in his cot, he cries if picked up, he refuses a feed and cries. If left to cry, he may cry for two hours or so, until he is really exhausted and falls asleep. It is often necessary to rock this type of child to sleep. It is better to anticipate his fatigue rather than to wait till he is tired, for if he is put into his cot for a rest before he is overtired he takes it eagerly. This demands careful observation on the part of the mother, but with care she can prevent agonizing hours of crying by her baby. (For further discussion of sleep problems see Chapter 17.)

The ego and individuality

Anything which interferes with the child's growing need to be recognised as an individual is likely to cause crying and insecurity. Babies in the weaning period have their own likes and dislikes, and object strongly if the mother tries to make them take what they do not want. Food forcing, potty forcing and sleep forcing always cause resistance and rebellion and crying. Many older babies object violently if prevented from feeding themselves or in other ways practising their newly acquired skills. They object if they are inhibited from some pleasurable experience, such as playing with a particular toy — and still more if a brother or sister snatches the toy from them.

Most of the child's crying after the first birthday is due to a conflict with his growing sense of importance, his desire for attention and for independence, and his need for security and love and the development of self confidence. Whatever the cause, it is likely to be increased by fatigue, boredom or hunger. Perhaps even more than in the first year, the amount of crying is closely related to his personality — some children finding life, and particularly the learning of discipline, harder than others.

Many tears are due to not letting the child practise his new skills because of overprotection or other reasons. Many tears are due to discouragement and ridicule and anything which reduces the child's developing self-confidence and feeling of security. Fatigue and irritability in the parents is a potent cause of tears in the child, and a vicious circle is set up, the irritability of the parents leading to resistance in the child and therefore to more irritability in the parents.

Crying may be an attention-seeking device, or a means the child has discovered of getting his own way. Crying at the slightest knock is often due to excessive anxiety on the part of the parents when he has had a fall. If he discovers that by crying and screaming he can attract attention, it will continue. It will stop when it is ignored or if he is distracted, though when there has been a bad knock or injury, any humane parent would pick a child up to soothe him. When he falls and receives what is obviously a trivial knock, it is often wise to distract him, by pointing out to him something interesting or by showing him a toy. Crying after trivial knocks is often due to imitation of a brother, sister or friends. If a child discovers that by crying and wailing he can get his brother into trouble, he will do so.

Personality
An important underlying factor is personality. Some are happy, placid babies from the first day. Others lose no time in making it clear that if they disapprove of things they will not hesitate to say so, and they cry at the smallest thing. If a mother's first baby is a difficult character and her second child an easy one, the know-alls will say that the second child is a much better child because the mother has learnt how to manage children. There may be some truth in this, but usually the real explanation lies in the fact that the personality of the children is different. Personality differences are of great importance with regard to the teaching of discipline (Chapter 14).

Many babies, especially around 5 or 6 months, cry when strangers speak to them. Some babies cry when they see their mother, brother or sister cry. Many babies cry when spoken to sharply. A common cause of trouble is the baby's inability to reach a particular toy.

When the parents have taken a few days' break away from their older baby or toddler, a distressing thing is liable to occur on their return: the child, who had settled down completely in their absence, may for a short time (minutes or an hour) reject their parent and cry in distress. Mothers should know that this reaction is common, though difficult to explain.

Illness

When a previously well behaved child begins to cry one day without apparent reason, and behaves in an unusual way, it may be because he is ill. The usual causes of an acute illness are 'flu', middle ear infection (especially if he has a cold), or in the case of a girl, a urinary tract infection (see Chapter 26).

Unexplained crying

It would be foolish to suggest that one can always determine why a baby or child cries. When the common causes have been eliminated — hunger, thirst, discomfort, fatigue, boredom, the desire to be picked up and loved, or some cause of insecurity — there remain the differences in personality. Some children, like some adults, find life difficult and do not hesitate to announce the fact. They do not know quite what they want, and so they cry: but we dislike such labels as 'nervousness', 'naughtiness', 'temper', or 'spoilt'.

The cause of your child's bad behaviour may lie in your own fatigue and irritability. That, in turn, may be due to the fact that you are not getting out sufficiently in the afternoon or evening away from the children. It may be due to the fact that you are tired. If you do feel unduly tired, you should consult your doctor to make sure that you are not anaemic. If you are, a little iron or other medicine may work wonders in improving your own health, and in improving your tolerance of your children's noise and untidiness, dawdling and quarrelling: for you will have to try to tolerate those if you are going to have a happy, secure and loving child.

Children go through phases of good and bad behaviour, of crying without apparent cause, of being excessively resistant or unusually easy to manage. They have good days and bad days, good weeks and bad weeks. It is not always possible to discover why a child cries easily. If all the causes of insecurity mentioned above have been looked for and eliminated, one must fall back on the thought that some children are tougher and easier to manage than others. Some are going to excel in the arts, others on the rugger field, and no two are alike. Because a child cries easily when injured, or is unusually timid, you must not assume that you have failed, or that you are managing your child badly.

The use of a dummy or pacifier
We do not like dummies, though we know that they rarely do harm. We dislike them, firstly, because a dummy is no substitute for love or whatever else the baby needs when he cries. Secondly, one feels that dummies are potentially dangerous, in that they may introduce infection to the mouth, because they cannot be kept clean.

Only rarely does the persistent use of a dummy affect the position of the front teeth. But a dummy soaked in glycerine or other sweet substance, or one attached to a bottle containing a sweet substance (a 'Dinky' feeder), causes dreadful caries in the front teeth.

Dummies are used much more by the lower social classes than by others. It is most unlikely that one would see a middle or upper class child running about with a dummy in his mouth.

One of us saw a child with a dummy in his mouth having swimming lessons in the swimming baths: and we saw a child with a dummy descending a precipitous path 9000 feet up in the Alps.

We do not recommend dummies and can see no advantage in their use.

9

How will he grow?

Weight and height

When one thinks of the obvious fact that adults vary tremendously in their weight and height, it is surprising that so many doctors, nurses and mothers seem to think that there must be something wrong if an individual child weighs or measures less or more than what is termed the 'normal' for his age. You would hardly say that there is something wrong with a potato merely because it is larger or smaller than most other potatoes. Why should you with children?

What is the normal weight and height of children at various ages? It is impossible to say. A child may be pounds (or kilograms) below the average in weight, and inches (and even more centimetres) below the average in height, and yet be normal. You must realize that the 'average' is not the same as the 'normal'. Weight and height charts are based on figures obtained from a large number of children from varied social circumstances and with parents of varying body builds. 'Averages' are worked out from these, but only a few will conform exactly to these averages and practically none will conform to them all through their childhood. The average weight varies from country to country.

We do not mean to suggest that it is useless to weigh your child. In the first few weeks of life we consider that it is essential that the baby should be weighed at fairly frequent intervals, because a defective weight gain may be the only sign of underfeeding. Thereafter the child should be weighed much less frequently.

If you weigh your child too frequently, you will only cause yourself unnecessary anxiety, for most children have ups and downs, periods in which they gain weight rapidly and periods in which the weight gain slows or stops. Infections, such as a cold, will prevent the baby gaining weight. A child may eat less when teething, with the result that the weight gain is reduced. We have known many people who have made themselves seriously worried by weighing the baby too frequently, and they have wasted time by so doing. We know two people who weighed the baby before and after every feed for the first nine months, to ensure that the baby was not being underfed!

The baby will be weighed at birth. We suggest that he should then be weighed when a week old, and weekly thereafter for three months, then fortnightly till he is 6 months old, and thereafter monthly till he is a year old. After that regular weighing is not so important. It will be enough if he is weighed three-monthly till he is 2, and then six-monthly. There is no rule about this; it is only a guide.

The period in which the baby gains weight more rapidly than in any other is in the last month before he is born — if he is born at term. In that month he is likely to gain over 2 lb (907 g). The average weight at birth is 7½ lb (3402 g). A baby may weigh as little as 5 lb (2268 g) though not born before he is due, or as much as 14 lb (6350 g) though not born after he was due. Babies born after they are due are not usually bigger than those born at term.

In the first day or two after birth babies lose weight. The reason for this is not clear. The usual weight loss is about 5 to 10 per cent of the birth weight. In other words, if a 3000 g baby loses 10 per cent of his body weight on the first day, he will lose 300 g; he is likely to recover this by about the tenth day. Excessive weight loss, if the feeding is satisfactory, could be due to overclothing, with resulting fluid loss in perspiration or vomiting.

The weight gain varies from child to child. A weekly gain of 6 oz (170 g) a week is to be expected in the first three months. A weight gain of less than 6 oz (170 g) a week in the first three months is unsatisfactory, and is most likely to be due to underfeeding. If he has been underfed at first he may have a much bigger weight gain, when given what he needs, until he catches up to the average weight, when his weight gain and appetite fall off to the 'normal'. We have seen such babies gain as much as 20 oz (568 g) per week until they have caught up.

As he grows older the weight gain decreases. Between four and six months the average weight gain is about 5 oz (142 g) a week. From 6 to 9 months it is 3½ oz (113 g) a week, from 10 to 12 months 2½ oz (71 g) a week, and for the second year about 1½ oz (42 g) a week. Some gain more, some less.

It is important to remember that there are often considerable fluctuations in the weight gain, and for this reason too frequent weighings often cause worry.

You must not feel envious or worried because your neighbour's child is growing in weight and height faster than yours — as long as yours is well, happy and full of energy. There are big children and little children, and there is nothing to suggest that big children are in any way more healthy or better than little ones. If a child is below the average weight because of underfeeding or because of illness, proper steps must be taken to put things right. You must not assume that there is nothing wrong with him. But if a child, who is below the average weight for his age, is full of energy, runs about all day long without getting tired and is happy, it is most unlikely that there is anything wrong.

There are many factors which affect a child's weight and height. A child's build is likely to follow the family pattern. It is likely that small parents will have a small child. The smaller a child is at birth, the smaller he is likely to be in weight and height in later childhood, and the bigger he is at birth, the bigger he is likely to be later on. Of course, there are exceptions, but study of many hundreds of children has shown that this statement is true. In our experience the commonest finding when a child is well below the average weight and height, and is otherwise well, is simply the fact that he was a small baby at birth, or that he takes after one of his parents.

We frequently find that the baby of a small mother is of average birth weight, but the weight gain thereafter is less than that of babies of big mothers.

It is absurd to suggest that a baby *should* double his birth weight by a certain age and treble his birth weight by the age of one year. It would hardly be sensible to suggest that a baby weighing 2 lbs at birth should weigh 6 lbs at 12 months, or that a baby weighing 12 lbs at birth should weigh 36 lbs at the first birthday. (A seal usually trebles its birth weight within 18 days!)

In general children of a large family tend to be smaller than those of small families. There are many other factors which affect a child's weight and height apart from the obvious nutritional factor or malabsorption. Emotional deprivation, chronic infection, severe disease of the heart, chest, liver, kidney or pancreas all retard physical growth.

Some children have unusual 'rhythms' of growth. By this we mean that they may grow slowly for a time, at a rate less than the average, and so appear to be 'small children', and then have a rapid spurt of growth and catch up to others of their age. This spurt may happen anytime in childhood, but it is liable to happen at puberty. A child of large build is likely to reach puberty earlier, and the changes of puberty are completed sooner, so that growth stops earlier than it does in smaller children. Children of small build tend to reach puberty later and to continue growing longer, so that they may largely or fully catch up to their friends who were bigger than they were in childhood.

Tables 3 and 4 show the average weight and height of boys and girls at various ages in the first ten years.

Table 3 Average weight (in lb and kg) in relation to weight at birth

Age	Weight lb	kg	lb	kg	lb	kg
Bith	5	2.26	7	3.17	9	4.08
6 months	14½	6.58	16½	7.48	18½	8.39
1 year	20	9.07	21	9.52	23	10.43
2 years	24	10.89	26½	12.02	29	13.15
3 years	28½	12.93	31	14.06	33	14.97
4 years	34	15.42	36½	16.56	39½	17.92
5 years	38½	17.46	40½	18.37	43½	19.73
6 years	42	19.05	44½	20.18	48	21.78
7 years	46	20.86	48½	22.00	52	23.59
8 years	49½	22.45	55	24.95	57	25.86
9 years	55	24.95	60	27.22	65	29.48
10 years	58	26.31	65	29.49	69	31.30

Table 4 Average height (in inches and cm) in relation to weight at birth

Birth weight	5 lb	2.26 kg	7 lb	3.17 kg	9 lb	4.08 kg
Age Year	in	cm	in	Height cm	in	cm
2 years	32½	82.6	33½	85.1	34½	87.6
3 years	35½	90.2	36½	92.7	37½	95.2
4 years	38	96.5	39½	100.3	41	104.1
5 years	41	104.1	42½	108.0	43	109.2
6 years	43½	110.5	44½	113.0	45	114.3
7 years	46½	118.1	47	119.4	47½	120.6
8 years	47½	120.6	49	124.5	50	127.0
9 years	49½	125.7	51½	130.8	52	132.1
10 years	51½	130.8	52½	133.4	53½	136.0

The head

Just as there are variations in the weight and height of children, so there are variations in the size and shape of the child's head. Some children, taking after one of their parents, have a small head, and others have a big one.

The head size is closely related to the baby's size (especially weight). A small baby is likely to have a smaller head than a big baby, and a big baby a bigger head than a small baby.

The average head circumference of a baby of average birth weight is as follows:

Age	In	Cm
Birth	14	35
3 months	15.8	39.5
6 months	17.0	42.5
9 months	17.8	44.5
1 year	18.2	45.5

The shape of the head is often similar to that of one of their parents. It often happens that a baby's head becomes flattened on one side, and bulges out proportionately at the other side. This is merely due to his lying always on one side. It is useless to try to do anything for it, for he will probably object strongly to lying on the other side and if you leave him alone the shape of his head will right itself as he gets older — shortly after his first birthday. Other babies are born with a skull which is asymmetrical and which will remain so. These children develop normally in every other way, and no treatment will make any difference.

You will feel a gap between the bones of the skull in the midline at the top of the head (the anterior fontanelle). This gradually closes, and by the age of 12 to 18 months the gap cannot usually be felt. It varies, however, and may close much sooner than 12 months or later than 18 months in normal children. In many newborn babies the gap continues to the back of the head into another space, the posterior fontanelle, which closes after about 2 months.

You may be interested to know what sort of height your child is likely to reach. The following table, modified from an article by

Table 5 Height at various ages in relation to final height

Age (years)	Eventual height 5 ft (152 cm)				5 ft 6 in (168 cm)				6 ft (183 cm)			
	Height in earlier childhood											
	Boy		Girl		Boy		Girl		Boy		Girl	
	(in)	(cm)	(in)	(cm)	(in)	(cm)	(in)	(cm)	(in)	(cm)	(in)	(cm)
2	29	73.7	31	78.7	32	81.3	34	86.4	35	88.9	37	94.0
3	32	81.3	34	86.4	35	88.9	37	94.0	38	96.5	41	104.1
4	34	86.4	36	91.4	38	96.5	40	101.6	41	104.1	44	111.8
5	37	94.0	39	99.1	40	101.6	43	109.2	44	111.8	47	119.4
6	39	99.1	41	104.1	43	109.2	45	114.3	47	119.4	50	127.0
7	41	104.1	43	109.2	45	114.3	48	121.9	49	124.5	52	132.1
8	43	109.2	46	116.8	47	119.4	50	127.0	51	129.5	55	139.7

Professor J. M. Tanner, shows the usual height reached at different ages by children who are likely to be 5 feet, 5½ feet, or 6 feet, when they stop growing. It will be seen that as a rough guide, the adult height of a child is twice that of the height at the second birthday.

For example, a boy whose height at 5 years is 37 in, is likely to attain an eventual height of 5 feet.

10

The teeth and mouth

Eruption of teeth

The age at which the first tooth comes through varies tremendously. Some children, about one baby in every 1 000, are born with a tooth. We have seen a prematurely born child with five teeth at birth. Several famous people were born with teeth. They include Julius Caesar, King Louis XIV and King Richard III. The teeth are usually normal 'milk' teeth, which have merely erupted earlier than usual, and are usually the lower central ones. Sometimes the undersurface of the baby's tongue becomes sore as a result of irritation by the tooth. The chief trouble is that the tooth is often loose, because the root has not grown properly. If possible it should be left, for it will tighten up in the gum, and its removal may interfere with the position of the second set of teeth. At the other extreme the first tooth does not appear until after the first birthday — perhaps until 14 or 15 months. Thereafter dentition is normal, and the teeth are well formed.

The average age at which the first tooth appears is 6 months. The first teeth are usually the lower central incisors. The upper central incisors follow in about a month, and adjacent teeth (lateral incisors) about 1 or 2 months later. Most children have six teeth at the age of 1 year. Teeth next to the lower lateral incisors appear shortly after the first birthday, followed by upper and lower back teeth (molars). The first set of teeth is usually complete by about 2½. There are 20 teeth in the first set. The first tooth of the second or permanent set does not appear till about 5 or 6 years of age. There are wide variations in the age at which teeth appear, and there is no connection at all between the intelligence of a child and the age at which teeth erupt. As a milestone of development teething is useless. The age at which teeth appear often runs in the family.

There is misunderstanding about the symptoms and consequences of teething. There is still a widespread belief that teething causes bronchitis, a 'teething rash', diarrhoea, fever and convulsions. There is not the slightest evidence that that is true. Children are teething almost continuously from 6 months to 2 years or more, and most of them during that time acquire several infections, including bronchitis, rashes and bowel disturbances (diarrhoea). Mothers have perhaps naturally ascribed these to 'teething'. Convulsions are commoner in infancy and early childhood than at any other time in life, and it is easy to understand how a mother or other person, looking into the mouth of a child after a convulsion has occurred, would find that he was 'teething' and ascribe the convulsion to it. There is nothing more in the belief than that. *We have seen many tragedies due to fever, convulsions and other symptoms being put down to mere 'teething', and therefore treated lightly and not reported to the doctor, when in fact they were due to serious infections which could well have been cured if treated promptly.* Instead, the children died.

Teething does produce certain symptoms. It is only natural that it should be a painful process, for the erupting tooth has to push its way through bone and its sensitive lining (the periosteum), and rupture the latter before it shows itself. When a tooth is just about to split the periosteum, you will see that the gum is red and injected, and you may see little haemorrhages over the point where the tooth is pushing its way out. It is well known that some people feel pain more than others. Some feel bad toothache when they have only the smallest cavity in a tooth, while others have carious stumps which have never caused discomfort. Some babies seem to feel more dis-

comfort with teething than others. Some are little upset by the eruption of a new tooth. Others are irritable, cry a lot, and have a variety of symptoms as a result of the pain in the mouth.

Pain in the mouth causes it to water (salivate), and hence teething is associated with excessive salivation. All babies salivate and the salivation is obvious because their lips are not sufficiently co-ordinated to keep the saliva in the mouth. Some babies salivate more than others and 'drench' their clothes. Mothers naturally ascribe this to teething even though the baby is only 3 or 4 months old, and examination shows that no tooth is about to erupt. When a tooth is erupting, the amount of salivation increases. A natural consequence of pain in the gums is that the child rubs them. This is often the first sign that a tooth is erupting. One often notices that finger or thumb sucking increases when the tooth is appearing.

Painful gums may lead to food refusal, or to preference for softer foods in place of solids to which he has grown accustomed. We have seen troublesome food refusal in a child in whom four teeth were erupting at the same time. An obvious result of pain is irritability. The baby may cry more than usual when a gum is hurting him (Chapter 8).

The eruption of the back teeth (molars) may cause pain in the ears, so that ear trouble is suspected. Before you ascribe earache to teething, however, you should ask your doctor to examine the ears to make sure that there is no infection there. A peculiar result of teething is described in Chapter 19. This is refusal to sit on the potty during the days on which the gums are painful.

There is nothing much which can be done to relieve the symptoms of teething. In the past all manner of remedies have been tried. Doctors applied leeches to the face, blistered the gums with irritating substances, and rubbed the gums with hare's brain. In the middle ages it was customary to hang the tooth of a dog or wolf round the neck in order to drive away the pain. A Frenchman introduced the dangerous and altogether unnecessary practice of lancing the gum, and fatalities have resulted from this practice.

It is unnecessary to purchase and apply something to the gums, and there is possible danger in absorption of drugs through such an application. It is reasonable to give a child a sedative if he is suffering from severe pain. Chloral is the best medicine for the purpose, and your doctor may prescribe it if he agrees. You must not think that every disturbance of sleep is due to teething. These problems are discussed in Chapter 17. There is no need to give any medicine for the bowels because your child is teething. Neither is there any point in giving 'teething powders'; they are best avoided.

Care of the teeth

The care of the teeth should begin when they erupt. The teeth should be wiped once a day with a piece of lint and later with a soft toothbrush. When the child is 2, he can be taught to clean the teeth himself. He should always brush them before going to bed, and preferably after meals. As soon as he is old enough to understand, he should be taught the correct way of brushing the teeth. This consists of not brushing across the teeth, but brushing down away from the gums in the case of the upper teeth, and up in the case of the lower teeth. The inner surface and biting surface should also be brushed. He should not have any food (or sweets) after this bedtime tooth-brushing.

Dental Decay

Dental caries is essentially due to the action of organisms in fermenting carbohydrates — notably starch or sugar — mainly on the sheltered surfaces of the teeth, often with the help of dental plaques. Sugar damages the teeth when given as sweets, toffee, iced lollies and bottled fruit drinks. Syrupy medicines are known to damage teeth and should be avoided whenever possible. It is better not to give food between meals, except an apple, because of the debris it leaves between the teeth; apple helps to remove dental plaques only from the accessible surfaces.

Prevention begins before the child is born, for all the child's teeth, both the first and permanent set, are in place in the jaw before birth; hence the mother should take a good diet in pregnancy, with the necessary vitamins. Then when the child is 5 or 6 weeks old, vitamin drops are given — unless the baby is bottle fed, in which case vitamins have been added to the dried milk preparations.

It is a great mistake to start the sweet eating habit. Your child should be given a few sweets only on special occasions. If you constantly eat sweets yourself, you are setting a bad example. Apart from the damaging effect of sweets on teeth, they are costly — and the money is better spent on other things — and they are an important factor in causing obesity. Food between meals should be avoided as far as possible, because of the debris left between the teeth. The dummy dipped in syrup, or containing sweet fluid, has a disastrous effect in causing severe caries.

Another important factor, which can be prevented by proper treatment, is overcrowding of teeth. If teeth are overcrowded, and therefore too near to each other, debris is bound to collect between them and caries results. You should take your child to the dentist regularly from the age of 3 or 4, in order that he can keep them in good order, see that they are in a good position and correct matters if necessary. We all know how unbecoming prominent teeth are in an adult. This deformity can readily be prevented by proper treatment by your dentist. In the same way he can prevent overcrowding and so prevent much dental caries. It has been proved beyond doubt in many parts of the world that deficiency of fluoride in the water supply is associated with a high incidence of dental caries, and that fluoridation of the water decreases its incidence. It is possible that the addition of fluoride to toothpaste may help to preserve teeth.

You may feel it is unnecessary to treat dental decay in the first teeth, because the teeth will come out anyway if left. The reason why carious first teeth should be treated early is partly that a small cavity is filled quickly, so that the decay is checked, and partly that if decay is allowed to continue toothache is likely to occur, and if a filling has to be done then, it will be a big one, which may cause discomfort. The tooth may even have to be removed, and that may cause the second teeth to come through in undesirable positions. When a small child is having pain from toothache he is more difficult to manage when he visits the dentist.

You may think that it will be difficult for a dentist to examine and treat teeth in a 3 or 4 year-old. It is, but he is used to the problem and it is surprising how much a good dentist can achieve without the child objecting. It is important that he should do something when he first sees the child, even though it is not strictly necessary. He may pretend to brush them with his electrical brush — a painless procedure, which will not disturb the child. He should continue to do something, however trivial, at each visit, so that the child becomes used to him, and when a filling or extraction has to be done, he will be easy to manage. The importance of not suggesting fear by saying 'Don't be frightened' is discussed in Chapter 21.

Injury to teeth. When teeth are injured or broken, at whatever the age, you should consult your dentist on the same day, because proper treatment is important. If it is dislodged, try to see your dentist within an hour or two, so that he can preserve it if possible, by re-implanting it.

Alveolar frenum

Some babies have a fold of tissue under the upper lip, extending down to the margin of the gum; it resembles the fold of tissue under the tongue. It is called the 'Alveolar Frenum'. It does not usually do any harm, but it occasionally separates the front teeth. It would be wise to consult the dentist about this when the child is 3 or 4 years old.

Tongue and mouth

A uniformly white tongue is of no significance. Multiple small white areas on the tongue, inner side of the cheek and palate, resembling milk curds, are due to a fungus infection, Monilia (Candida) or thrush. If untreated the mouth becomes painful, and it is probable that the organism will pass down the alimentary tract and cause a thrush nappy rash. The infection is readily treated by your doctor with nystatin drops or miconazole; if there is a nappy rash it is treated by an ointment containing nystatin.

Multiple small blisters on the tongue (stomatitis) are due to a virus infection, and make the mouth sore. It is a self-curing condition (in about 10 days), and special treatment does not help. The child may take cold drinks, or drink through a straw, or manage ice cream, but feeding is painful otherwise.

A black tongue is harmless and non-infectious.

A patchy tongue with red patches and white surrounding areas, leaving a smooth surface, is likely to be a 'geographical tongue'. It is of no importance and treatment is not required.

11

How children develop

There can be few more fascinating pursuits than the observation of the dawn of understanding, of the way in which the baby learns to use his hands, to think, to walk and to become an independent being. You will find endless enjoyment in watching him, and in seeing the various stages of development unfolding. We can never understand how some mothers who apparently wanted to have children, and who have no particular financial problems which make it necessary for them to go out to work and no professional career which they want to maintain, are willing and anxious to hand over their baby to another person to bring up for them. They miss an immense amount of pleasure and of knowledge and understanding of their baby by so doing. To some of them a baby is just a reflex being, whose only actions are unconscious and involuntary, who makes a noise and soils his nappy, but otherwise just feeds and sleeps. But to the mother who brings her own baby up, who uses her eyes, and who has read just a little about how babies develop, the baby is a human being, with a definite personality, a being who loves and likes to be loved, who has a rapidly unfolding intelligence and understanding, who soon enjoys fun and play, who day by day learns new skills, or at least makes obvious steps forward in the process of learning them. If there has been a previous child or children, the development of the baby is no less fascinating, for then the mother notices, often from a day or two after delivery, the developing differences in personality from that of the other children, the way in which the baby learns some skills more quickly than his brother or sister, and some more slowly, and shows different interests.

A well-kept 'baby-book', describing the baby's developing skills, adds a lot of interest to the mother's observations. A simple exercise book is as good as anything for the purpose. You should put down the points of interest as they occur. If you wait for a week or two, until you can summon enough energy to write the book up, you will have forgotten all sorts of things which you noted and intended to record.

Our advice is that you should make the most of your baby. Enjoy him while he is yet a baby, for he will grow up rapidly, and you will soon be regretting that you no longer have a baby in the house.

In the section to follow we shall describe some of the principal aspects of development which you will observe in your baby, mentioning, in the first place, some important general principles. We felt that this section on normal development should be included here, because an understanding of development is so essential to intelligent management.

We suggest that readers who are particularly interested in this subject and who would like to read more about it would be interested in the book *The Development of the Infant and Young Child, Normal and Abnormal* (R. S. Illingworth (1983), 8th Edition).

Some principles of development

Firstly, do not make the mistake of thinking that development begins only when the baby is born. Development has been going on continuously from the time of conception.

Secondly, development after birth is continuous, even though it may not always be obvious to you. There are times when a baby seems to stop developing in a particular field, such as speech, for some weeks or even months. There is then a spurt of development, so that the child who one week is hardly able to say anything, 3 or 4 weeks later is able to say a great deal. These apparent lulls in development occur when another skill, such as sitting or walking, is being learnt. It almost seems that the baby is unable to learn two major skills at the same time.

Thirdly, the development of any skill depends on the nervous system being ready for it. Certain changes have to take place in the nerve cells of the brain and spinal cord before the relevant skills can develop. No amount of practice can make a child learn a skill, such as walking, before he is ready to learn it.

Because various animals, such as lambs, are born with a spinal cord in which the nerve cells have developed further before birth than those of human babies, those animals can walk and run almost immediately after birth, while human babies have a long way to go before the development of their brain and spinal cord makes walking possible.

Psychologists have carried out extensive studies of the newborn baby — by simple observation, or by sophisticated electronic or other mechanical devices. It has been shown that the newborn baby will turn his head slightly to follow a moving person. He looks at a proper picture of a face more than a picture in which the eyes, nose, mouth etc. are mixed up. He looks at a black mass on white paper longer than at three black dots. He turns his head to sound. He adjusts his position when an object approaches him, withdrawing from it. He can localise his mother's breast by the smell of milk: and he prefers his mother's smell to that of strangers. In the first few days he may imitate tongue protrusion. He shows more interest in the sound of speech than in other sounds. He distinguishes and prefers his mother's voice to that of strangers. Babies are born with a sense of smell and taste.

Fourthly, all children go through the same stages of development — except that some babies never creep — but the rate of development varies tremendously from child to child. In other words, although every child has to learn to sit before he can walk, the age at which children learn to sit and walk varies considerably. It is striking how frequently children are advanced in some skill and relatively backward in others. Some children are uniformly retarded or uniformly advanced, but they are the exception rather than the rule. One commonly sees a child who is unusually advanced, say in walking, and yet barely up to the average in other skills, or a child who is average or advanced in most skills, and yet backward, compared with others, in speech. These characteristics often run in families. In some families children are unusually early or late in developing certain skills, such as walking or talking, and there is a history of exactly the same thing on the mother's or father's side. Often there is no discoverable reason for these variations.

In the sections to follow, ages which we have given for the development of various skills are approximate only. Some normal children will learn these skills earlier and some later. The reasons for some of these variations will be described later. Some have already been mentioned. Do not think that your child is abnormal because he has not learnt various skills at the ages mentioned, for these are averages only, and do not apply to all normal children.

It is wrong to say that a child *should* pass a certain milestone, or reach a certain weight or height, by a certain age. All children are different.

The preterm baby
When a baby is born prematurely, he has not had as long to develop before birth as a full-term baby. If he is born very prematurely, he may not be able to suck or swallow, and as a result he has to be fed by a tube into his stomach (in hospital). He sleeps almost the whole day and night — much more than a full-term baby does. He shows no interest at all in his surroundings — and it will be some weeks

before he does so. He shows certain primitive reflexes, which will be described in the next section. As he grows older, you must make allowances for his premature delivery, and not expect him to achieve various skills as soon after birth as a full-term baby. For instance, if he were born two months prematurely, he has missed two months development *in utero*; 4 months after birth he should be regarded as corresponding to a 2 month-old baby. Allowance must be made for prematurity when studying his development. It does not mean that he is in any way backward. There is no question of his 'catching up' in that there is nothing to catch up: obviously when he is older the 2 months difference is irrelevant: when he is 10-years-old the 2 months difference cannot matter. Mothers (and doctors) get confused over this matter. It must be obvious, however, that if a baby is born three months prematurely, he must not be expected to smile at his mother at 5 or 6 weeks, as a full term baby does, but at 5 or 6 weeks + 3 months: but it does not mean that he is 'backward'. Mothers who forget this are likely to be anxious about their child's development, as compared with others they know. It does not mean that he is any less intelligent. It is just that one must allow for the development which he missed before birth.

The full-term baby at birth

The newborn baby exhibits various 'reflexes' by which we mean that in response to certain stimuli he carries out certain movements involuntarily — just as your leg jerks forward when your knee is tapped immediately below the knee-cap. When you slip your finger into the palm of his hand, his hand closes on it, grasping it firmly ('the grasp reflex'). When you hold him in the standing position, and his foot touches a firm surface, he is likely to set off walking slowly and steadily forward ('the walking reflex'). He will 'walk' like this for the first few weeks of his life if you gently push his head back by a finger under his jaw. When you startle him or abruptly move him, you will see his arms suddenly draw away from the side of his body. You will often see him lying with his head turned towards one side and his arm straight out on the same side. If you touch his jaw, he will start mouthing for food. If you bring his face up against your chest, or against your hand or touch the face around the mouth in the newborn period, he will start 'rooting' for milk. All these reflexes disappears as he grows older. It will be difficult to see the walking reflex, for instance, after he is about three weeks old, unless his head is pushed back as described. We do not know the function of most of these reflexes.

Many of these reflexes, like the grasp reflex, disappear within five or six weeks of birth: we think that they disappear earlier in the more mature and the more 'intelligent' baby.

You will see that if you place him on his back, he will turn his head to one side. If you place him on his stomach, he will turn his head to one side and lie with his knees drawn up under his abdomen, with the buttocks high off the ground. He cannot lift his chin off the table or couch. If you hold him with your hand under his stomach, his head drops forward. When you hold him in the sitting position, he rolls up in a ball, and his head falls forward, for he lacks the strength in the muscles. He lies with his hands largely closed. He yawns, hiccoughs, sneezes and stretches. He will almost certainly suck his thumb or fingers. He can certainly cry, as you will soon discover. He sleeps most of the day, and we hope most of the night — though he does not sleep as long as the preterm baby does.

Birth to 3 months

You will be surprised how soon you notice changes in his behaviour. He watches you as you talk to him, as long as he is not crying. He will begin to open and close his mouth as he watches, and his head may bob backwards and forwards. It is not usually until about 4 to 6 weeks of age that he smiles as you speak to him — but his intent regard of earlier days was obviously the forerunner of the smile. When we say that he smiles at you, we are not referring to facial movements in his sleep, or when you tickle his face: we mean that he smiles when he watches you as you talk to him. Many mothers have the extraordinary idea that the early smile is due to wind. We cannot understand why it should be thought that babies smile when they have pain. Two or three weeks after he has begun to smile he will begin to 'vocalize' — to make little noises with pleasure when he smiles at you. At first you will only see an occasional smile, but by the age of 3 months he will be a ready smiler — and a talker, too, for he will coo and talk to you a lot — and he will probably lie and talk to the ceiling. He not only smiles and coos, but he squeals with pleasure. Before four or five months of age he does not usually smile when tickled, but at about two months of age he squirms when tickled in the usual places.

The baby shows other signs of developing understanding. You may notice, after a time, that he quiets not only when you put him in the bath, but when he sees it, and not only when you feed him, but when he sees that you are about to do so. He quiets when you pick him up. Whereas in the newborn period his eyes seemed to roam all over the room without looking at anything in particular, you will soon find that large objects, such as the window, begin to catch his eye, and he looks intently at them. By about 6 to 8 weeks of age he clearly follows moving persons with his eyes. At about 3 months he may show a lot of interest in a strange room to which he is not accustomed. At about this age he will turn his head towards the direction of approaching footsteps or other sounds.

He shows his developing maturity in many other ways. He sleeps less during the day as he grows older, and he falls to sleep less readily during a feed. By the age of about 3 months he may remain wide awake and show pleasure when he has finished a feed. He chokes less when sucking, he possets less, he sneezes less, and he hiccoughs less after he has been fed. As he grows older you will no longer see his jaws tremble. By the age of about 10 weeks he sleeps through the night without waking for a feed, and his daytime feeds are less frequent and more regular.

During the first 3 months he develops a lot of strength and control in the neck and spine muscles, preparing him for sitting and walking. When he is held in the sitting position, he becomes able, more and more, to lift his head up. At first he lifts it up momentarily and cannot maintain the position. By 3 months he can hold it up almost indefinitely. When he is lying on his stomach he can just lift his chin momentarily off the couch when he is 3 or 4 weeks old, but by the time he is 3 months of age he can hold his chin off the couch for a long time, and not only his chin but his shoulders. When he is pulled up into the sitting position from lying on his back, his head lags behind less and less.

Whereas the hands of the newborn baby are for the most part kept closed, the hands of the 3 month-old baby are open — as if he is getting ready for grasping objects. At about 3 months of age he will hold a rattle if it is placed in his hand, though he cannot pick it up himself. By the age of 3 months, however, he is beginning to show the desire to grasp objects placed in front of him — but is not yet old enough to get hold of them.

Three to 6 months
Further rapid strides are made in various fields of development between the age of 3 and 6 months. The baby is now awake for a much greater part of the day than he was in the first 3 months. He plays after a feed, instead of falling asleep like the younger baby. He shows intense interest in his surroundings, and is a more happy sociable person.

At 4 months of age he laughs aloud. He smiles without being spoken to. He smiles when he is pulled into the sitting position — but may cry when he is laid down again, for he enjoys being propped

Prone. 44 weeks — creep.

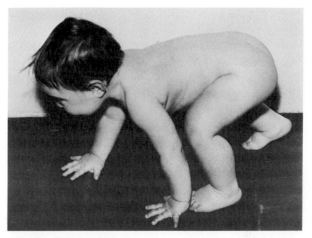

25 weeks. Walking like a bear.

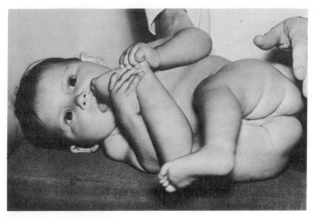

20 weeks. Feet to mouth.

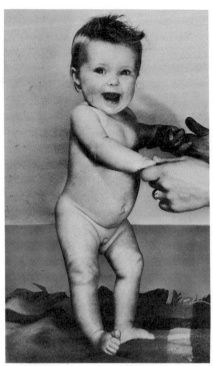

24 weeks. Bearing almost all weight.

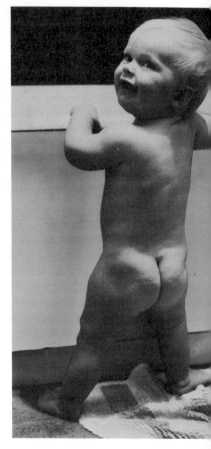

48 weeks. Can stand holding on to furniture and can walk holding on to it . ('Cruises'.)

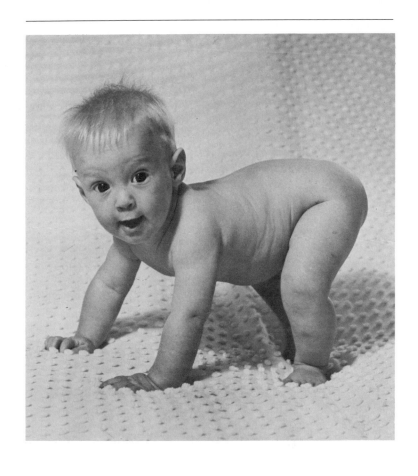

up. He kicks and laughs in the bath. He is particularly 'talkative' at this age, cooing for long periods when talked to. In fact he 'talks' more at this age than he does at 6 to 9 months. Between the age of 3 and 4 months he begins to turn his head when he hears a sound — an important sign that he can hear. He shows more interest in strange rooms, and he is interested in small children. He pants with excitement when he sees a brightly coloured toy or his bottle, both arms moving and the legs kicking, as he makes obvious efforts to reach it. If a rattle is placed in his hand, he shakes it vigorously, but he is unlikely to be able to reach for an object and grasp it until he is about 5 months old. He cries less, but he may cry when his mother leaves the room. He may indicate his developing memory by crying when he is brought near to his cot, to be placed there for a nap. When he awakens he awakens to play, and does not immediately cry for food like the younger baby, for he is able to wait longer when he is hungry, and he is less upset by a wet nappy. You will notice at this age that he will lie on his back, with his head in the mid-position, not turned to one side, and looks at his fingers and hands, playing with his fingers. The hands come together now, and he clutches at his dress, maybe pulling it over his face. When placed on his stomach, he holds his head and chest well off the floor, bearing his weight on his forearms. If you hold him in the standing position, you will find that he will bear quite a lot of weight on his legs.

In the next 2 months (age 5 to 6 months) he makes rapid progress in learning to sit, in preparing for walking, and in the use of his hands. At 5 to 6 months he likes to be propped up in his high chair, and it is a help to feed him in it. At first he becomes tired after a quarter of an hour or so in this position, but by the age of 6 months he may tolerate and enjoy an hour at a stretch. By 6 months he can bear almost the whole of his weight on his legs in the standing position, and he bounces with delight when so held. Many mothers fear that if they allow their baby to bear weight he will become bowlegged or knock-kneed or develop rickets. They fear that if they allow him to sit he will become weak in the back. There is not the slightest truth in these fears. A mother who keeps her baby off his legs weakens the baby's legs and back. At 5 months of age he can hold his head up steadily in the sitting position, and at 5 or 6 months he can lift it off the floor when lying on his back, and he may hold his hands out, asking to be pulled up. At about 6 months he can sit with his hands forward for support. At about 5 months of age he begins to roll from his stomach to his back, and about a month later from his back to his stomach. He is now 'mobile' for the first time, and may progress quite a distance by rolling. He may also learn to progress on his back by arching it and letting himself go again, repeating the process over and over again. When placed on his stomach he can bear his whole weight on his hands, and at 6 months he can bear it on one hand, reaching for a toy with the other.

Whereas at 4 months he was unable to reach for an object and get it, at five months he can just achieve this. He goes for it with both hands, overshoots the mark, misjudging distance badly at first, but eventually succeeding. This is a great step forward, for now he can play with all sorts of toys. A whole new world has opened for him. At first he can only grasp large objects, and it is not until about 9 or 10 months that he can bring his thumb and forefinger together to pick up a small object of the size of a pea. You will notice that at about 6 to 7 months he will begin to go for a toy with one hand instead of two, and he will begin to pass a toy from one hand into the other. When lying on his back he can play with his toes, and he may take them to his mouth. He loves to splash in the bath. He takes great pleasure in crumpling paper. He holds his bottle and may try to hold the spoon when he is being fed. He begins to take everything which he can get hold of to the mouth. He characteristically bangs toys on the table or his high chair. When he is about 6 months old you may notice that when he drops a toy he looks to see where it has fallen.

He shows his developing understanding in many ways. At 5 months he smiles when he sees himself in the mirror, and a month later he not only smiles but coos with pleasure as well. A little later he reaches forward to pat his image. At 5 to 6 months he shows definite likes and dislikes at meal times, and may firmly refuse dishes which he does not like. He may learn to 'imitate', when his mother puts her tongue out, or 'blows raspberries', but he may do this spontaneously. He begins to enjoy the hide and seek game when his head is covered with a cloth, squealing with delight when it is removed. He may begin to show 'coyness' in the presence of strangers, or even to be afraid of them. At about six months of age he begins to respond to his name. He tries to make people look at him by coughing or other noises. If he has had enough to eat he will turn his head away and keep his mouth tightly closed. He does the same when his nose is being cleaned. He may begin now to show independence or personality by refusing to take food if he is not allowed to help to hold the spoon, but this sort of behaviour is more likely when he is nearer his first birthday. At about 6 months most babies learn to chew — an important milestone, for it signifies that the baby is now ready to take solids. He cries much less. When he does cry he makes a noise like Mmm, Mm, Mm. Whereas he learnt to cry long before he could laugh or even smile, he now cries little, tolerating hunger or a wet nappie for quite a long time.

Six to 9 months

Most babies can sit almost without support in a pram at the age of 6 months, but few can sit without support on the floor until about 7 months, and then only for a few seconds. It is not till about 9 months that a baby can sit securely for prolonged periods, and even then he is apt to overbalance if he tries to reach something behind him, though he can go forward for an object, into the creep position if necessary, and return to the sitting position. At 9 months he can pull himself up into the sitting position.

At about 8 to 9 months he may begin to crawl, pulling himself forward with his hands, though many babies go through a stage of going backwards before they learn to go forwards. About a month later he creeps — with his stomach off the floor, on his hands and knees.

At about eight months he can stand holding on to the play-pen, but he cannot let himself down for another two months, and may scream for help if he is afraid of a bump. At 9 months he can pull himself up into the standing position, after repeated efforts in which his feet seem to get in the way. He still finds it difficult to let himself down, and so cannot pick objects up from the floor when standing in the play-pen.

During this period he makes important strides with his hands, learning to pick up much smaller objects. When he is 9 to 10 months of age he is able to bring his thumb and index finger together and can pick up an object as small as a currant or a thin piece of string. You will notice that he begins to point — and to go for objects with his index finger. He loves to play with paper, and handles everything within reach. From the age of 6 months, when he learnt to chew, he is able to feed himself with a biscuit or crust, for he is able to grasp it and pick it up if he drops it. He is apt to blow bubbles in milk which he is drinking from a cup, and to finger food on his plate.

He shows his developing understanding by his excitement when he sees food being prepared, by his determination to reach a toy when it is out of reach, by imitating sounds, and by his response to 'No' (at about nine months). He learns to look round corners, to bend over to one side or to hold his head higher in order to see someone who is talking to him. He begins to show affection — by patting his mother's face, clasping her neck, or bringing his face up to it. Not only does he cough or make a noise to draw someone's attention, but he may pull at her dress as well. At nine months he may begin to respond to such sentences as 'Where is mummy?' He may begin to play patacake and to wave bye bye — though some do not do this till they are nearly a year old. He may be afraid of strangers, particularly when he is on the floor and they seem to tower over him.

His speech, like all other skills, is developing during this period. You may not have realized that all the different sounds he makes from the age of 8 weeks or so are steps towards speech. Babies have to learn to make different sorts of sounds before they speak. At about 7 to 8 months, for instance, babies begin to make sounds like da, ba, ma, and a month later they combine them, saying dada, baba, mama, but without any particular meaning. At about 9 months a baby may imitate quite a few sounds made by his parents.

Nine months is a delightful age. Make the most of your baby then, for he will never be as good again in all his life! He is a happy sociable person, admittedly a little shy, but he is easy to manage, cries little, and has not yet seriously begun to enter the phase of resistance and negativism which will so try your patience when he is a few months older. He is only just beginning to creep — and has not seriously begun to get into trouble. Furthermore, sleep disturbances, so common in later months, are not usually serious at his age.

Nine months to a year
During this period he becomes actively mobile. He creeps with greater ease and speed, and by the age of a year he may creep on all fours — on hands and feet, instead of hands and knees. At about ten months he begins to lift one foot off the ground as he stands at the play-pen, and in another month he walks holding on to the play-pen or other furniture. He walks with two hands held at 10 months, and one hand held at a year. A few babies walk without support before this age, but that is exceptional. Many babies learn a strange method of progression on one buttock and the opposite hand. Some call this 'shuffling' or 'hitching'. He is so active in his pram that special precautions have to be taken to see that he is safe in it.

An important milestone of development is the ability to let objects go from the hand. While a baby learns to grasp objects at about 5 months, he cannot deliberately let them go till about ten months. Babies go through a characteristic stage of holding an object out to the mother or father, and placing it in the hand, but not letting it go. Once they learn to 'release' objects they soon discover the delightful game of dropping things over the edge of the high chair — particularly if there is a kind person to pick them up again. They take much pleasure in this, as in other new skills. They love to put things in and out of baskets or boxes, and to hand one object after another to the

parent. At 11 months the baby may deliberately roll a ball towards his mother in play. He likes an audience, and repeats anything which people laugh at — and he joins in the laughter. He enjoys games and now covers his own face in the peep-bo game. He likes to put toys on his head and laughs as he does it.

Babies are liable to go through a shy phase at 12 months. Any time after 9 months they may show the first signs of jealousy — when the mother picks up another child. You may be impressed by the obvious signs of his developing memory. If you watch him carefully, you may find that at a year he can remember things which happened at least 2 or 3 weeks before.

Babies who are given a chance to feed themselves, if they show signs of wanting to do so, make big strides between 9 and 12 months of age, and many babies can feed themselves entirely, with only a little help with a cup (and not always that), by the time they are a year old. You will notice that after 9 months of age your baby begins to slobber less. The amount of slobbering varies a lot from child to child. It is likely to increase when each new tooth is appearing. Most babies have quite good control of saliva by the age of a year, tending to slobber thereafter only when they are watching something of particular interest. You will notice that he is taking fewer and fewer objects to his mouth. Whereas the 6 to 7 month child takes almost everything to the mouth, the year-old child takes little to it. Babies

vary in this respect, some continuing longer than others.

Between the age of 9 and 12 months the development of speech is becoming more obvious. You will notice that your baby learns the meaning of words long before he can say them. Then he says part of a word obviously with meaning — e.g., g for dog. By the age of a year many babies can say two or three words with meaning (e.g. dada, mummy, girl, teddy), but others cannot do this till later. He shows his understanding in other ways. One of these is in helping to dress. The year-old baby is likely to hold a hand out for a sleeve or a foot out for a shoe. His increasing maturity is shown by his lessened sleep. Most babies at a year of age have only one nap during the day.

We have not discussed bladder control, for it is described in Chapter 19. We mention there the fact that resistance to the potty commonly develops round about a year of age. Babies at this age often show an interest in the stool which they passed.

A year to 18 months
Most children learn to walk without support between thirteen and fifteen months of age. The variations in the age at which children learn to walk are discussed in Chapter 12. You will notice tht when your child begins to walk his feet go forward in different directions, his steps are of varying lengths, and he walks with his feet far apart. If he looks up he falls down. After he has first taken off alone, he has a lot to learn. He is unsteady at first and may collapse suddenly on to the floor. He cannot stop and start easily, turn corners or run. He

cannot throw a ball without falling. He tends to hold his arms up in the air as he walks. At about 15 months he begins to creep upstairs. He can pull himself up into the standing position. Though he has learnt to walk, he is apt to revert to creeping at intervals, especially when he is in a hurry. By the time he is 18 months old, he is much more stable on his feet, but he still cannot run and turn corners. He can carry a doll as he is walking, and he can seat himself in a chair. He loves to pull or push a toy. He can walk upstairs if his hand is held. He can throw a ball without falling. He still walks with a broad base — with his feet widely separated.

His recently acquired mobility, together with his ever-increasing curiosity, gets him into endless trouble. He investigates the coal bucket and the wastepaper basket, and finds them fascinating, for they give him endless opportunity to practise his casting game — putting objects in and out of containers and throwing them on to the floor. The open bookcase is a magnet, and gives him similar opportunities. A lamp flex, a newspaper, an envelope left lying in an accessible place, an overhanging table cover, will all be investigated by him. He is into everything, and always on the go. The play-pen is unlikely to contain him. Either he screams with fury when placed in it, or he walks it round the room and even discovers how to get it through an open door. He may refuse to sit in a pram even when he is being taken to the shops, preferring to walk, though this depends largely on his personality.

Though he continues to progress in the use of his hands, he is unable to place objects accurately, and at 15 months he is unlikely to make a tower of more than two small cubes, and even at 18 months he can only put three cubes on top of each other. He begins to scribble with a pencil. He repeatedly pulls his shoes and socks off, and will not keep his gloves on in cold weather. By the age of 15 months he will probably manage to feed himself fully if he has been given a chance, and as long as large pieces of food are cut up for him, though many children still rotate the spoon at this age just before it reaches the mouth, and tilt the cup too far when they are about to drink, let it go when they have finished, or put it down on the table so hastily that the contents spill. He is still likely to pick up with his fingers bits of food which he has dropped. By 18 months a normal child should be able to feed himself without any help. He likes books, but he can only turn two or three pages at a time.

His understanding of words has progressed so much that by 15 to 18 months he will go on simple errands — to fetch a pair of slippers or a toy, and to place a toy or book on a chair or on a table, for he is beginning to learn where things are kept. By 18 months he will point to simple objects in books when asked, though he may be unable to say the word in question. He will point to three or four parts of the body on request. He begins to copy his mother in her everyday tasks, such as sweeping the floor, dusting or washing up. He likes the rhythm of music and may move his body to the tune. He loves his teddy or other doll, though he carries it by one leg or drops it on the floor.

His speech may progress rapidly in this period, so that he learns countless words: or else he may seem to make little if any progress, even though it is obvious that his understanding of words is making great strides. He is likely to use 'jargon' — a language of his own which no one but his parents can understand.

During the period he first begins to learn clean habits — telling his mother when he has wet his pants, and later when he is about to do so. By 18 months many children are dry by day if given the potty frequently: but few are dry by night.

Another characteristic feature of this age period is negativism — the child's seemingly constant wish to do the opposite of what he is asked to do. Bound up with this is his desire for fuss and attention. This negativism, together with his inability to understand anything but the simplest of requests, makes it a difficult age. The period from a year to about 2½ can be very troublesome in a determined child.

Eighteen months to 2 years
The child becomes more stable on his feet, so that by about 2 years he can run. He can walk backwards, and walk up and down stairs

alone, placing both feet on each step. He can kick a ball without falling and pick up an object from the floor while standing.

At about his second birthday he begins to turn door knobs and to unscrew lids of jars. He can make a tower of about six small cubes and turn pages of a book singly. He can put on simple clothes, such as socks, pants and a cardigan, though he is likely to put both legs through one hole in the pants, to put the sock on in such a way that the heel is on the front of the foot, and to put shoes on the wrong feet. He can wash and dry his hands. He knows where many common objects are kept, and helps to set the table. He spends a lot of time imitating his mother's every-day tasks. Doll play is now more elaborate, and he places the doll in the crib and wraps it up. He delights in tearing paper, in banging and in making a noise. He is an aggressive person, hitting others and snatching toys from them. He will not play with others, but watches them or plays on his own. He begins to learn the meaning of property, and has definite ideas of what is his, refusing to let anyone else share it.

Shortly before his second birthday he begins to put two or three words together — an important milestone of development. Children at this stage go through a phase of repeating words said to them. By his second birthday he begins to use the words I, me, you correctly.

At about his second birthday he begins to develop fixed ideas about how things should be done and where they should be placed. He develops the so-called sleep ritual (Chapter 18). In the bathroom he may be furious if the sponge, soap or toy is not placed in the usual position. This does not mean that he is in any way tidy himself.

He has full control of the bowels, and only rarely has an accident in the daytime and wets himself. He is likely to be dry at night if he is lifted out late in the evening.

Two and a half

By this age he has learnt to do many more things with his hands. He can build a tower of eight cubes. He can undress almost completely, as long as buttons are undone for him. He can get simple clothes on, though the coat is apt to be twisted, and clothes will be back to front. He holds his pencil, and may imitate simple strokes. He can thread beads and loves to build with pieces of wood of different shapes.

He learns to jumps with both feet, and to walk on tiptoe. He may try to stand on one leg, but he cannot.

His speech improves enormously, though he mispronounces words, and is likely to substitute one letter for another. Lisping is particularly common at this stage. It results from protrusion of the tongue between the teeth as he tries to pronounce the letter 'S'. He talks incessantly, and keeps up a running commentary all the time he is playing.

He is much more imaginative than the younger child. He picks imaginary fruit off pictures in magazines, and may keep an imaginary friend behind the sofa.

He may begin to notice anatomical differences in the sexes at about 2½. His colour sense begins at about this age. He is liable to show a definite preference for either his mother or his father. He still has 'rituals', disliking changes. He may fuss a lot when new clothes are tried on. He loves to be told stories and often demands the same one day after another. He is furious if the wrong word is used or if a line is omitted. He will not play with other children. He likes their company, but plays on his own. At about 2½ he is likely to be cross when awakened from his nap. He rarely wets himself during the day or night, and now attends to his own toilet, climbing on to the lavatory seat by himself.

Three years

This is a delightful age. The peak of negativism has passed. There will certainly be resistance; but the 3 year-old is usually an understanding child, who is co-operative if wisely managed, and anxious to please. He continues to get into trouble, but has learnt a lot from wise discipline, and meddles less in things which he should not touch. He will now join in play with other children, instead of playing apart from them.

He can stand on one foot for a few seconds, can run fast and steadily, but cannot skip. He goes upstairs with only one foot per step, but puts both feet on each step when coming down. He jumps off the bottom step. He is so secure on his feet that he can be relied upon, within reason, to get cups and saucers from the cupboard and set the table. He can ride a tricycle.

If he has been given a chance to practise, he can almost completely dress and undress himself, though he still puts clothes on back to front, still gets shoes on the wrong feet, and still needs help with buttons behind.

He 'pots' the doll, feeds it, dresses it and undresses it, and really uses his imagination in play. His conversation with his teddy bear is fascinating to hear.

He continues to speak incessantly throughout the day, and is now constantly asking questions. He wants to know where babies come from, he wants to know the name of objects which he sees and the meaning of words. He may count up to 10 and be able to count 3 or 4 objects. He knows numerous nursery rhymes, if he has been given the chance to hear them. He loves to have stories read or told to him, and he likes to hear about his own infancy, and the shocking things which he did. His memory goes back to events many months ago.

He is likely to have discarded his midday nap. He is less irritable when awakened, and most of his 'rituals' and dislike of change have disappeared.

He may show considerable interest in the genitals of his own and opposite sex.

Four years

Though the 3 year-old is a delightful child, the 4 year-old is more mature and 'reliable'. The 3 year-old is still a baby when he is tired or bored, and still dependent, though less so than a 2 year-old. The 4 year-old can be relied on a great deal more to behave well — though one can never predict what he will say or ask. He is typically a boaster and a fabricator. He boasts of his knowledge, and is firmly convinced that he knows everything. He boasts of what he can do with his hands, and of tricks he can do with his legs. He tells 'tall stories', of creatures he has seen in the garden, and makes up the most unlikely stories to explain mishaps, such as breakages. These should not be regarded as lies, for the 4 year-old has little idea, if any, of truth and untruth. He fabricates words, and wears his mother out by constantly repeating them, laughing as he does. He really thinks that he is a humorist. He likes to have an appreciative audience. He loves to play with other children, and enjoys a party. His play is highly imaginative, and he makes trains, boats, cars, hospitals and houses out of the most unlikely objects.

He can dress and undress himself with only an occasional mistake, and he is likely to be able to tie shoe laces. He can manage buttons, except at the back. He can wash himself in the bath and dry himself, though supervision is necessary.

He learns to skip, and can stand on one leg for several seconds. He can learn elementary dancing. When going down stairs he only puts one foot on each step.

His interest in the genitals of the opposite sex is less, if he has been given a chance to see them, but he is interested in lavatories and potties, and talks openly about them, passing water and having a motion. He continues to talk incessantly, to question continually, to be always on the go, and to revel in noise.

The development of speech

Babies learn to communicate with their mothers long before they can speak: and older babies learn the meaning of numerous words long before they can articulate them.

A baby communicates by crying, watching his mother as she talks to him, opening and closing his mouth, bobbing his head up and down, and then beginning to smile — at an average of four to six weeks — and later to vocalise and laugh. He communicates by showing affection, putting his arms round his mother's neck, clinging to her, kissing, with a massive movement of arms and legs when the parent approaches, frowning, crying, pushing his mother's hand away, and by about six months by pulling at her sleeve or coughing to attract attention. The age at which these non-verbal methods of communication develop depends not only on his innate intellectual potential, but on his parents' responsiveness, love for him, tone of voice, facial expression and the time they devote to talking to him and playing with him.

Every child goes through the same stages in speech development, beginning to make vowel sounds in response to the mother a week or two after he has begun to smile at her. Then in a few weeks consonants emerge. At about four months he says 'ah goo' and razzes ('blowing raspberries'). At about six months he adds syllables — ma, da, ka, der, and in another month combines them to vocalise mumum, dadada. Up to about nine or ten months even deaf babies pass through these stages, but then the factor of imitation enters, and the deaf child cannot then progress without the employment of special methods. At 12 months jargon begins — a variety of sounds with an occasional intelligible word; the jargon is meaningful to the baby, but not to the mother. By the age of 12 months the average baby says two or three words with meaning, and by 21 to 24 months spontaneously (not by imitation) combines words to make short sentences.

Is he left- or right-handed?

You may not know until your child is three or four years old. You are likely to notice preference for one hand when he is 6 to 12 months old, but sometimes one finds that the child prefers one hand at one time and the other hand a few months later. Eventually it becomes clear that he is definitely either left- or right-handed.

When a child after the age of a year uses both hands equally easily and frequently, it sometimes happens that speech is late in developing, but you cannot do anything about it and should not try.

Handedness is thought to be partly genetic and partly the product of environment — of management, imitation and the culture in which the child is born. Left-handedness is more common amongst mentally retarded persons: the incidence of left-handedness in ordinary schools is about 5 per cent, as compared with 12 per cent in special schools. Left-handedness is not just the opposite of right-handedness: few 'left-handed' children are entirely left-handed: they are mostly mixed right and left-handed, predominatly left.

The relationship between delayed speech, delayed reading and left-handedness is extremely obscure. It is used to be said that if a left-handed child is forced to use his right hand, it will cause stuttering, but we now know that to be untrue: but emotional disturbance resulting from unkind and unpleasant methods used to make him use the right hand may cause emotional disturbance and therefore, amongst other behaviour problems, stuttering.

How can you tell if your baby is developing normally?

Before describing development in average babies, we emphasized that when we mentioned the ages at which various skills were learned, we meant not that a child who acquires these skills at a later age was necessarily abnormal, but that these were the average ages at which the particular skills were learned. It followed that most babies would learn these skills either sooner or later than the average, just as most men and women weigh more or less than the average weight for their particular age. Very few, if any children, wil learn all the skills mentioned at exactly the ages given.

It is important to note that no child is backward mentally, or has a low intelligence, because he is later than the average in one or two fields of development, such as walking or talking. A mentally backward child is late in all fields of development, except occasionally in sitting and walking. There are numerous factors which affect the age at which various skills are learned and we will discuss these in some detail in Chapter 12. Naturally, if your child is very late in learning any particular skill, it would be reasonable for you to discuss the matter with your doctor. If he is late in talking, or late in talking clearly, you must have his hearing checked.

The most important early indication that your child is developing normally is the smiling at about 6 to 8 weeks of age if he was full term, and his interest in surroundings, the way in which he follows moving persons with his eyes, and his general alertness when awake. These features are late in developing in backward children.

Just as backwardness in certain skills such as sitting, walking or talking does not suggest that the baby has a low level of intelligence, unusual advancement or isolated skills (except in speech) does not mean that he is of superior intelligence. It would be wrong to suggest that he is going to be a brilliant child because he is able to walk without help at 9 months.

We feel that it is important to emphasize the lack of significance in these normal variations, because we know how mothers are worried and envious when a neighbour's or friend's child learns skills sooner than her own baby. Unkind people may suggest that there is something wrong with a child who is later than another in learning to walk or talk. Some children are slow starters. They are a little later than the average in most fields of development, and then make a spurt forward and do extremely well in later life. In any case, success in life does not depend just on intelligence. It depends on personality and opportunity, amongst other things, and you should not feel that because your neighbour's child appears to be more intelligent than yours, he will be a better, nicer or more successful person that yours when he grows up.

12

Variations in development

In this chapter we propose to discuss the variations in the age at which skills are learned, and the factors concerned.

In all figures we refer to fulll-term babies: if the baby is born prematurely, due allowance must be made (Chapter 11).

All babies are different; very few indeed are exactly average in all aspects of development. Some are later or earlier than others in the various fields of development, though the overall level of intelligence is the same. Familial factors are of great importance: in some families late or early sitting, walking, talking or control of the bladder is a feature. Some developmental skills are greatly affected by the mother's management. For instance, if she keeps the baby off his legs, he is likely to be retarded in walking; if she does not talk to the baby, he is likely to be late in the development of speech; if she smacks the child for not using the potty, or neglects to help him when he wants to void, he will be late in bladder control. Emotional deprivation has a profound effect in retarding development. The baby's personality is a factor: the really determined awkward character is particularly likely to rebel against food forcing or potty forcing or sleep forcing, and do the opposite of what is required. The child's intelligence has a great effect on the age at which skills are acquired, particularly speech. Finally, organic disease such as cerebral palsy or deafness greatly affects several fields of development.

The danger of so-called assessment is that these normal variations are not understood, and the mother is then subjected to unnecessary worry. For instance, the mentally subnormal child is late in *all* aspects of development except very occasionally walking, and it would be seriously wrong to suggest that backwardness in any one or two fields of development, like walking or talking, means that the baby is mentally retarded; some babies are slow starters, late in most or all fields at first, and then catching up to the average or above average. Mothers are liable to be unnecessarily worried by those who assess babies without fully understanding what they are doing.

Smiling

The youngest age at which we have seen a child smile in response to the mother's overtures is 3 or 4 days. The majority of normal babies learn to smile before they are 8 weeks of age — provided that they were born at term.

We do not know whether unusually early smilers will grow up to be unusually happy children. We suspect that that is the case.

Grasping objects

Deliberate grasping, by which we mean going for an object and getting it without it being put into the hand, may begin as soon as 4 months, or as late as 6 months.

Children with stiffness of muscles due to cerebral palsy, and those with mental retardation, are older than 6 months when they begin to reach out and get hold of objects.

Sitting

We have seen normal babies who were able to sit without support at 5 months, while others have not been able to sit without support for a few seconds till 8 to 9 months. The age is often a familial feature.

Babies are delayed in learning to sit if their mothers keep them lying down at an age when they enjoy being propped up — from a month or two onwards. A baby who has been brought up in an institution is likely to be late in learning to sit, because he has not been given the opportunity to sit propped up. Any prolonged illness which has kept a baby lying down will delay the age at which he learns to sit. Weakness and flabbiness of the muscles due to rickets or other conditions will delay sitting. Mental retardation, or mechanical difficulty such as cerebral palsy, delays sitting.

It often happens that children who learn to sit early also creep and walk early. There is often no discoverable reason for lateness in learning to sit.

Creeping

By 'crawling' we mean that the child lies flat on his abdomen and pulls himself forward. By 'creeping' we mean that the child is on hands and knees, and uses all four limbs to move forward. Children learn to creep about a month after beginning to crawl.

Not all children learn to crawl and creep. We do not know the factors responsible for this. It does not matter in the least, and it certainly does not retard walking. One factor, which does not apply to all babies, may be the fact that they are never placed on their stomach and so do not learn the appropriate movements.

We have seen an exceptional child of merely average intelligence creeping at 6 months of age, but the ability to creep is rare before 8 months. Creeping usually does not begin till about 10 months.

There is a fairly close connection between the age of creeping and the age of sitting and walking, but there are exceptions. The causes of lateness in creeping are similar to those of lateness in sitting.

Walking

The earliest age at which we have seen a child walk without help is 8 months. The latest age at which we have seen a normal child learn to walk was 4 years. Lateness in walking is extremely common and a frequent cause of anxiety. It may be due to one of many possible factors. Firstly, the age at which children learn to walk often runs in the family. In some families children learn to walk particularly early, and in others unusually late. It is interesting that such children are not usually advanced or retarded in other fields of development — except in skills allied to walking, such as sitting and creeping.

Secondly, lateness in walking may be due to mere lack of confidence. Some babies do not care in the least if they have frequent falls when learning to walk. Others care a great deal, and may refuse to try again for a few weeks after a bad spill. Slippery shoes make it difficult for a child to learn to walk, and it is for that reason that we advise that all shoes for toddlers and young children should have non-skid soles.

Some babies demand nominal support in the form of one of the mother's fingers for quite a long time before sufficient courage is mustered to take off without support. We have known a child demand one hand or finger for support for five months before eventually he decided to walk alone. We knew one child who for a time would walk alone on Sundays only — when his father was with him. Reins may help at this stage, by giving a minimum of support, but sufficient to give the child confidence. Even with reins a child may take weeks to summon up enough courage to walk alone. When a child has been delayed in walking alone, and does take off, his gait is more mature and steady than that of an average child who has passed through the stage of walking with one hand held in 3 or 4 weeks. In other words one can see from the way in which he walks that he could have walked much sooner if he had been willing. It is no use trying to force a cautious child to walk alone before he wants to do. Falls will only increase his fear and determination to demand support.

A third cause of lateness in walking is excessive fondness of hitching or shuffling — that strange method of progression on hand and buttock. The trouble about the latter method of progression is that it does not help the child to walk, being a different sort of movement.

A fourth cause of lateness in walking is the mother's failure to give the child a chance to learn. Some mothers keep their babies outside in the pram all through the day, however much they cry, at an age at which they want to practise pulling themselves up to the standing position, or walking while holding on to furniture. Others fear that if they allow the baby to bear weight on his legs he will develop rickets, knock-knee or bow legs. There is not the slightest foundation for those beliefs. He should be helped and encouraged to bear weight on his legs, for failure to give him the chance will do nothing more than weaken him.

A fifth cause of lateness in walking is weakness and flabbiness of muscles, due to rickets or other conditions. Any serious or prolonged illness which has kept a child off his feet will delay walking. Babies brought up in an institution are later than others in learning to walk — because they have not had the chance to learn. Stiffness of muscles, such as occurs in cerebral palsy, will seriously delay walking. A rare cause in a boy is muscular dystrophy.

If your child is unusually late in walking, and it is not an obvious familial feature, we suggest that you ask your doctor to check that there is no good cause for it. Lateness in walking is not due to obesity or to congenital dislocation of the hip.

Mentally retarded children are usually late in walking, as in other skills. Let us repeat, however, that lateness in walking, or in any other single skill, when the child is normal in other respects, has no bearing on his intelligence. It does not mean that he is mentally retarded. You can take it for certain that if your child is later than the average in walking, and yet is speaking normally, he is of normal mentality.

Finally, it must be admitted that in many cases it is impossible to find a reason for lateness in walking.

Speech

The variations in the age at which speech develops are very great — more than in any other field of development — and they occasion much anxiety in parents. Speech tends to be learnt earlier in girls than boys.

The earliest age at which babies say words with meaning is about 9 months. There are several stories, however, about prodigies who were said to speak long before that age. It is said that Thomas

Carlyle went to a party at the age of 10 months, by which age he had not been heard to say a word. He surprised everyone, when he heard another baby crying, by exclaiming suddenly, 'What ails thee, Jock?', and from that time onwards he spoke in sentences. We have heard a child speaking in sentences before he was a year old.

Although we have said that the average baby says two or three words with meaning before he is a year old, many normal babies do not say their first word until after the first birthday. Although the average child begins to put two or three words together shortly before his second birthday, many normal children begin to do this much later. You need not have the slightest anxiety about your child being mentally retarded because he is late in speaking, provided that he is average in other respects, and particularly if he understands the meaning of words. Hence it helps a child's speech if you go out of your way to name common objects for him. When you are dressing him, for instance, it is easy to name his shoe, socks and parts of the body. The understanding of words far outstrips the ability to say them. We have seen a child of high intelligence who was unable to say more than three or four words at the age of 15 months, which is well below the average, but who was able on request to point out more than 200 common objects in a picture book when asked 'Where is the dog ... cup?', etc. When your child is later than the average in speaking, you should observe how many words he can understand. The understanding of words is far more important for estimating his intelligence than articulation.

A child may begin to speak at the usual time and after learning to say perhaps 10 words, make no further progress for 5 or 6 months, or even lose the ability to say some words, then suddenly, and for no apparent reason, he begins to speak a great deal and in a short time makes up all the leeway. These lulls and spurts in the development of speech are common. During these lulls he is constantly learning the meaning of new words. It is his articulation which does not progress.

Unusual earliness or lateness in the development of speech commonly runs in the family. One often finds that the mother or father of a child who is late in learning to speak was equally late.

Unusual earliness in the acquisition of speech is usually, but not always, associated with a higher than average degree of intelligence. Lateness in speech, even when marked, by no means excludes superior intelligence. Mentally retarded children are always late in speaking.

Lateness in learning to speak may be due to lack of opportunity to learn. Children who are brought up in an institution from early infancy are nearly always later than the average in learning to talk. A child who is left out in the pram all day, with no one to talk to, is not able to learn to talk as soon as other children. Twins tend to be later than others in learning to talk, probably because the mother of twins has less time to talk to two and to read to two than she would have for a single baby. Contrary to popular belief, children learn speech more from their parents than from their brothers and sisters. On the average, the first born speaks earlier than subsequent children. Speech is not delayed by bilingualism.

Lateness in speaking is occasionally associated with delay in the establishment of the dominance of one hand (so that he is not definitely either right or left-handed). This rights itself in time without treatment.

An important cause of lateness in talking is deafness. The child who is deaf is unable to learn to talk without special methods. Early signs of deafness include a general failure to respond to sound (after about 3 months of age), and screaming attacks when he is unable to make his wants known. A special form of deafness delays the acquisition of speech and is particularly difficult to diagnose, and in fact only an expert can diagnose it, by means of special methods. This is high-tone deafness, in which the child can hear many sounds, such as the shutting of a door, but not others. Such deafness is unlikely to be recognized by parents, but it should be looked for when a child is unable to speak by the age, say, of 2 or 3 years. It should be emphasized that there is no question of deafness when a child is able to say a few words distinctly, but says less than the average child, or is merely later than the average in joining two or three words to make a sentence. Complete deafness can only be suspected if there is a complete absence of words at the usual age, especially if the child has developed normally in other ways, and partial deafness can only be suspected if there is delay in beginning to speak and the words which are uttered are badly formed owing to the substitution of letters — especially for the letters G. L. and R — a substitution more marked than the common lisping and 'baby talk' heard in most children. We repeat that it is only the expert and specialist who can diagnose partial deafness in a small child. Early treatment and speech training is essential for deaf children. It should begin as soon as the deafness is diagnosed — preferably not later than the first birthday.

Delay in learning to speak may be due to cerebral palsy, but that would be readily diagnosed by stiffness in the limbs and delay in walking.

Finally, lateness in the development of speech often occurs without any discoverable reason.

Tongue tie is *not* a cause of lateness in the acquisition of speech. Experts think that it rarely if ever causes indistinctness of speech. Some think that it may cause the letter B to be used instead of the letters D, L, N and T. If the child can protrude his tongue in the usual way and touch the roof of the mouth with it, tongue tie need not be considered.

A child who is late in learning to talk and who can hear normally cannot be helped by a speech therapist. Help can only be given when speech has been learnt, but is defective.

Do not make the mistake of thinking that he is not talking merely because he is 'lazy'. Neither is his lateness in speech at all likely to be due to jealousy. He does not speak because he cannot speak. If you try to make him speak by refusing to do what he is trying to tell you by gesticulation and other means, he will feel badly thwarted, and you will cause a severe emotional disturbance. Nothing but harm will come of it. Just be patient. He will talk as soon as he is ready to do so.

Stuttering and indistinctness of speech

All children who are learning to speak repeat themselves and repeat the beginning of words, especially when they are excited. Unfortunately parents often think that this is stuttering and take steps to stop it. They tell the child to speak slowly and distinctly, to take a big breath before speaking, and to repeat words, or they try to help him to say different words. This draws the child's attention to his difficulty and may lead to genuine stuttering. It is far better for the parent to take no notice of what he thinks is early stuttering at the age of 2 to 4, for any attempts to stop it will only make it worse. True stuttering is more common in boys than girls.

If there is anything but the most trivial degree of stuttering when the child is 4 or older, it is desirable to have it treated by a competent speech therapist. This and other defects should be treated before the child goes to school, so that he will avoid ridicule and teasing. Stuttering is treated by so-called 'timed syllabic speech' in which the child is taught to speak slowly with every syllable pronounced equidistantly from the next.

A certain amount of substitution of letters in words is almost universal when children are learning to speak. Of those the commonest is the lisp, in which 'th' is substituted for 's', because of protrusion of the tongue between the teeth. It usually cures itself without treatment. Other letters are often mispronounced, but no treatment is needed unless they persist until after the fourth birthday. If the defects persist beyond that time in anything but the most trivial degree, they should be treated by a speech therapist, so that speech will be normal by the time school is started. The more numerous the substitutions, the less likely it is to clear up spontaneously. If speech is delayed or in any way unusually indistinct for the age, the hearing should be checked by an expert, in case there is a hearing difficulty (e.g. for high tones).

When a child is learning to speak, temporary deterioration of speech sometimes follows infections of the nose and throat. Nasal speech may be due to adenoids.

Other fields of development

The age at which children learn to feed and dress themselves depends not only on their skill with their hands, but the opportunities given to them to learn, and their determination and independence. If children are not given a chance to learn to feed themselves, because of the mess which they make, or to dress themselves, because of the time they take, they will inevitably be delayed in learning those skills. The personality of the child is important, for some children are content to have everything done for them, and so are likely to learn independence later than others, while others are so determined to be independent that the mother can hardly avoid allowing them to do things for themselves.

There are great variations in the age at which children learn to be clean and dry. The factors involved are discussed in Chapter 19.

I.Q. range

I.Q. tests have numerous limitations, but we felt that readers would be interested to know the overall range of intelligence test scores.

I.Q. score	Percentage	I.Q. score	Higher ranges 1 in
150 or +	0.1	Over 180	1 million
130 – 149	1.0	Over 170	100,000
120 – 129	5.0	160	10,000
110 – 119	14.0	150	1,000
100 – 109	30.0	140	170
90 – 99	30.0	136	100
80 – 89	14	125	17
70 – 79	5		
Below 70	1.0		

For other aspects of intellectual achievement, in average, advanced or retarded children see Chapter 33.

13

The background of behaviour

We believe that it helps parents to have some understanding of the factors which affect a child's behaviour. Behaviour is a highly complex result of the interaction of factors in the parents, friends, teachers and neighbourhood with the child's personality, intelligence and developing mind. A child's personality and intelligence, like those of the parents, are partly inherited and partly the product of the environment. Relevant factors in the parents, apart from their inherited personality and intelligence, include their age and health, the sort of childhood which they had, the number of years of marriage before the baby was conceived, the size of the family, the spacing of births and their desire for a child or child of a particular sex.

The difficulties of child management
If child management were easy, and it were possible to describe in a few words the answer to every problem which arises, there would be little disagreement amongst doctors and others. As it is, human nature is very complex, and children and their parents vary tremendously in personality and intelligence, so that it is inevitable that there will be wide differences of opinion on child management. These differences in personality and intelligence are probably the chief source of confusion. Parents, particularly if they are doctors, are liable to read altogether too much into their experience with their own child or children, thinking that because a particular line of treatment or management worked in their child, it will work equally well in all others. They forget that children are individuals, and that what will work with one child will often not work with another. This is especially likely to occur if a parent has had a placid, easy going sort of child, who responds to strict and rigid methods without a murmur. He does not realize that the same methods applied to more determined, obstinate children will cause nothing but trouble and the most severe behaviour problems.

Children differ

Your child will not be the same as your neighbour's. If you have two children, it is unlikely that the second will be the same as the first — and you may well discover differences in the first week of his life — in the way he behaves on the breast, in the way he insists that he be given a feed as soon as he wakes up, or in the energy which he puts into kicking and other movements. Some babies are easy to feed from the first day, and give no trouble. Others are cross and irritable when put to the breast, screaming and kicking, biting the nipple, and making themselves thoroughly awkward. Some are placid, easy-going babies who put up with anything. They do not care whether you feed them three-hourly or four-hourly. They do not mind being kept waiting. They make little fuss when the nappy is wet. They do not object when you 'burp' them after they have taken milk from one breast and before being put on the second. In the weaning period they present no difficulties. They show little desire to feed themselves. They sleep for long periods and have no objection to the afternoon nap when they are three years old or more. Other babies have decided views. They will not wait one minute for food. They emit piercing yells as soon as the nappy is wet. They think that they are being starved if they are not put straight on to the second breast after sucking from the first. At five or six months they know just what they like and still more what they do not — and what they do not like, not even a determined mother can make them take. They would rather starve than be prevented from holding the spoon with which they are being fed. They will not eat anything if they are tired or if they are kept waiting for it. Some babies, if there is a momentary pause in their feeding, will refuse the rest, at least for a few minutes. Some will refuse food if it is given by one person, but accept it gladly from another. They sleep little and yet are bouncing with energy. As for the afternoon nap, it is finished by the second birthday.

Some are sociable. They smile early and smile easily. Others are serious souls who think that life is no laughing matter. Some prefer toys to being cuddled, others cuddling to toys. One is universally called a 'good' child, a child whose babyhood the mother finds a sheer joy. Another is a 'bad' child, who the mother feels cannot grow up too soon. Some in the resistant phase (1 to 3 years), are the essence of perversity. Others are just mildly awkward. Some, when tired, just lapse into sleep. Others, when tired, are really impossible; they are irritable and aggressive and 'fight' sleep. Some at two years will make an issue of the most trivial variation in their routine. Some are shy. Others talk to anyone. Some are more sensitive, independent and imaginative than others. Some are daydreamers. Some refuse to be pushed in a pram at 18 months of age. Others refuse to walk at that age, except when they are free to walk where they want, and they demand to be pushed in the pram. Some are leaders, others are always led. They are all different.

A mother whose first child is placid and easy to manage is particularly liable to get into difficulty when her second child is the exact opposite — determined, active and thoroughly perverse. She has found that rigid methods, as advocated in many books, worked well with her first child and does not know what has gone wrong when they completely fail to work with her second one.

You should not have a feeling of failure because your child is difficult and cries a lot. Do not be put off by unkind or implied criticism from mothers who had easy babies themselves. Some babies are difficult to manage, however wise the management. Whatever his personality, accept him for what he is.

Your child has behaviour problems, or will have

All children do. Do not think for one moment that because your child has his problems — is bad tempered, cries a lot, is shy, refuses his food or screams at night — that he is 'nervous', maladjusted, or anything else but a normal child, or, alternatively, that you have failed. All children have behaviour problems, like all parents and all teachers.

It is difficult for a child to learn that he cannot have all his own way, and problems inevitably arise. Do not feel that there is anything wrong with your child because he has these problems. Nearly all children have unaccountable phases of difficult behaviour, phases of aggressiveness, timidity, shyness, excessive weeping, sleep disturbance or disobedience, without any apparent error or change in management or environment. These phases cause a lot of anxiety, but properly managed they are only short lasting.

Some children, like some adults, find life more difficult than others. The placid child often presents few problems, but the active child, particularly if he has a vivid imagination, may be difficult to handle. He will be much more interesting, in many ways, than a placid one.

You will make mistakes

You will make mistakes. All parents do, but fortunately children are very forgiving — until they get older. It is not occasional mistakes which do harm to the child but the long continued harmful attitudes, the constant fear of spoiling, the excess of discipline or the lack of it over years which does the harm. Some of the problems which you will be up against will tax your ingenuity to the utmost, and the solution to some of them can only come through trial and error. It is no use thinking that there is a simple solution to every problem, or that any book will tell you exactly what to do in a given set of circumstances, but we hope that this book will help you to understand enough about the workings of the child's mind, and about the way in which the child develops, to think out a simple, practical way of dealing with the problems in your child. When in doubt use your common sense, but you do need the basic knowledge of how the child's mind works, and how children differ in their personalities and needs, and therefore in their management.

If we had to begin again, we would avoid many mistakes which we made — but make many new ones instead.

Basic needs

The child's personality is moulded by satisfaction or otherwise of his basic needs — for love and security, firm loving discipline, the gradual acquisition of independence, the example in the home, the freedom to develop his individuality and interests, satisfactory health and nutrition, and a sensible attitude to sex.

Love

Whenever one tactfully suggests to a mother that what her problem child needs more than anything is love, the invariable reply is 'He certainly gets that. We have always given him everything that he wants, everything that money can buy.' But love is much more than that. In thousands of poor homes there is little money with which to buy anything for the children, but there is an abundance of love. Love does not consist of giving a child everything that money can buy, everything that he asks for. In fact, an essential part of every child's training is to learn that he cannot have everything that he wants. He has to learn to accept a 'No'. He needs something that money cannot buy — his mother's love and companionship, sympathy and understanding.

Rousseau in his book Emile (1762) wrote 'Do you know the surest way to make your child miserable? Let him have everything he wants; for as his wants increase in proportion to the ease with which they are satisfied, you will be compelled, sooner or later, to refuse his demands, and this unlooked-for refusal will hurt him more than the lack of what he wants. The child, who has only to ask and have, thinks himself the master of the Universe: he considers all men are his slaves: and when you are at last compelled to refuse, he takes your refusal as an act of rebellion, for he thinks he has only to command. All the reasons you give him are so many pretences in his eyes; they seem to him only unkindness; the sense of injustice embitters his disposition. He hates everyone. Your child must not get what he wants, but what he needs.'

Love is one of the chief basic needs of every child. The one-day-old infant often stops crying when he is picked up by his mother. As he grows older he becomes more insistent that he should be picked up and loved. He is particularly demanding when he feels poorly, tired or afraid, or has pain from an erupting tooth. From nine months or so onwards he may feel disturbed and jealous when he sees his mother pick up another child and show him her love. Between the age of one and three years he characteristically goes through a phase of increased dependence on his mother. All through his childhood and beyond he needs above all things, love. A good loving mother or father has more actual physical contact with the small child than a less good parent. The good mother and father pick up the baby or small child more, cuddle him, hold him on the knee, give a squeeze of affection, just pat the head, all apparently trivial acts of love which help the child and strengthen the bond between child and parent.

Unfortunately many mothers are afraid that if they show love to their baby they may spoil him. But if he is picked up within reason when he cries, he is not spoiled. Some mothers pick a child up to love him only after a feed, but children, like adults, want to be loved all the time. A baby is spoiled by the mother who will not leave him alone when he is lying content, who constantly picks him up when he is not crying, who will never let him play as he wants without joining in or interfering with it, who is over-anxious, repeatedly going in to see him at night to see if he still breathing, who is always worrying about his bowels and 'habit training', or about the amount he sleeps and eats, who will not let him grow up and learn independence, giving him what a psychologist called 'smother love' instead of 'mother love', and who prevents him going out of doors if it is cold, because he is 'delicate', or may 'get his feet wet'. A child is spoiled more than anything by lack of discipline and by over-indulgence.

Love consists of a lot more than picking a baby up when he cries. It involves, firstly, giving him time, attention and companionship. Some mothers resent the loss of freedom when a child is born, leaving him for the greater part of the day in charge of a 'help', who may well leave him outside in the pram crying for hours on end for love and the company of others. Some are so occupied with charity

and church work that they neglect their children, leaving no time for them. Some mothers hand the baby over to a nanny to bring up — and then feel surprised when he grows up to love the nanny more than them. The problem of the mother at work is discussed on page 166.

It is undesirable to leave the child, in his first three years or so, for prolonged periods. It does no harm to leave him for occasional days or periods of, say, two or three days, and it is most desirable for the mother to have breaks without her children, and good for them to become accustomed to being without her for short periods, with the certain knowledge that she will soon return. When she is away she will realize how much she has missed them — and how good they really are. It is a different matter when she is away from her children day after day for months and years. Not only do such children lose the loving companionship of their mother, and become liable to develop various forms of insecurity as a result, but they receive a large part of their early training from people such as 'helps', who by their personality and example may be unsuitable for the purpose.

The woman who has excessive house pride, particularly if she has had to wait a long time for her first child, and has become accustomed to having everything in the house spotlessly clean and tidy, may find that she cannot give time to her child. Even one child in his first few years takes an incredible amount of time. The choice is obvious. Either she has to give less time to her home or insufficient time to her child.

Parents should try to make time to give their child love and companionship and to join in his play. This does not mean that a child should never be left to play alone. He should. It does mean that every child should look forward to some part of the day when his parents can join in his play, read to him or play out of doors with him. It means that time should be devoted to organizing 'treats' for him — occasional parties, having his friends in, taking him on excursions (e.g. to the railway station).

True love consists of much more. It consists of sympathy, understanding, tolerance and patience; of accepting a child for what he is, and not expecting too much of him; and of making him certain at all times that he is wanted and loved. It involves firm, loving discipline in place of angry scolding and punishment. It is shown not necessarily by what is said, but by the smile, the facial expression and the tone of voice. It involves the avoidance of sources of friction, such as constant hurrying and impatience. It means the absolute avoidance of unkind criticism and of ridicule; of comparing him, when he has failed in some way, with his brother or sister or friend; of talking about his shortcomings in his presence, to his father on his return from work, and still more to visitors. He should be told and told often that he is loved. This is easy when he is behaving well, but not so easy when he is being 'naughty', crying at everything perhaps because he is tired, or being resistant and negative. He should be certain of his parents' love at all times. It is hard on a child when his father is cross and irritable with him on his return from work and takes it out of him because he has had a worrying time at the office. It is always wrong and evil to use such words as "Mummy won't love you if you do that.' The mother may not mean what she says, but the child may believe her. Children (like adults) need love above all at times when they are least lovable. The two year old who screams and cries on being awakened from his nap, or who is cross and bad tempered and wants to do the opposite of everything that is asked of him, needs not scolding and punishment, but love. It is difficult for a child to be certain of his parents' love when they are constantly scolding him and always pouncing on him, particularly when both parents rebuke him for everything which he does wrong.

Unfortunately bad behaviour leads to anger in the parents. It is easy enough for a mother to love her child when he is showing affection for her, but when he is rebellious, and seems to spurn her in favour of his father, it is not so easy.

It frequently happens that more is expected of a child, in the way of manners and good behaviour, than is reasonable for one of his age and level of understanding. Misguided efforts to 'teach him' manners and good behaviour lead to constant friction. Such a child can hardly fail to feel that his parents are always against him. Everything which he does is wrong. Each day in some houses is one long day of remonstrances and constant disapproval, exhausting equally to the child and his parents. No child is spoiled by being loved. He *is* spoiled by the lack of it.

Lasting love between child and parent as the child grows up is built up by hundreds of kindnesses, hundreds of occasions when tolerance and understanding have been shown. Children are likely to grow apart from their parents in later years if the home has been an unhappy place, with constant criticism, favouritism, bickering, scoldings and disparagement. Remember what Oscar Wilde said: 'Children begin by loving their parents: as they grow older, they judge them: sometimes they forgive them.' It is a pity if an adolescent feels like G. K. Chesterton did, that the only person who understood him in his early years was his tailor, who knew to measure him afresh each time they met!

Some parents are determined that their children will be perfect. As the children grow up and prove to have imperfections like everyone else, they show their disapproval of their children in no uncertain way. In adolescence such children feel insecure, unwanted, and grow apart from their parents.

Pride in your child

Do not be afraid of being proud of your child. Everyone will expect you to regard him as the most beautiful baby that was ever born. You will be expected, when he is older, to regard him as phenomenally clever. You will be expected to talk endlessly about his tricks, and to show your photograph album to visitors. That is normal. We believe to be abnormal those parents who never seem to show the slightest interest or pride in their children, and who never talk about them.

Favouritism

Favouritism has a disastrous effect, for the unfavoured child inevitably feels that he is not loved. It is extremely common. It is always stoutly denied by parents, because they are unaware that they are guilty of it, though it is obvious to everyone else, including the child.

Favouritism arises from a variety of causes. When there has been a succession of boys and at last a girl is born, that girl is apt to be the 'favourite'. The girl is apt to be the father's favourite, and the boy the mother's. It then often happens that the third child is no-one's favourite and feels unloved. When a child is born many years after the previous one, particularly if he was much wanted, he may be a

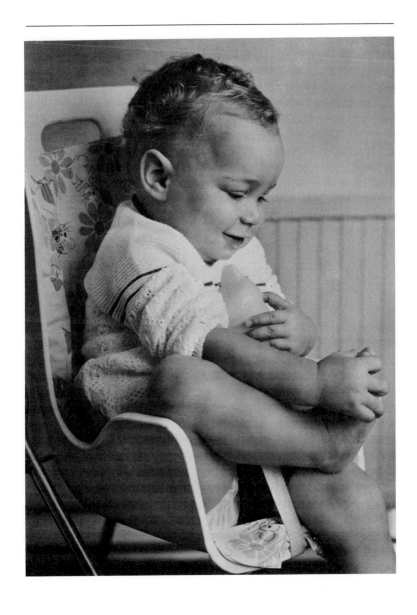

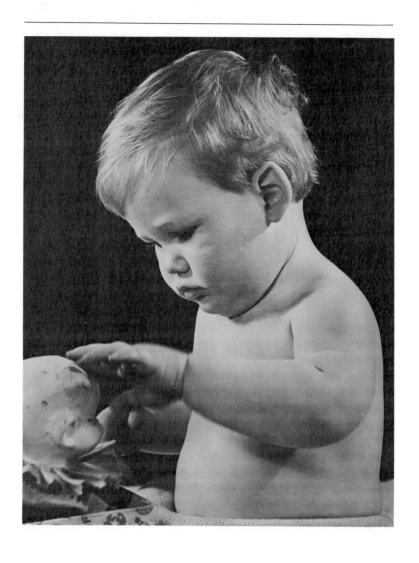

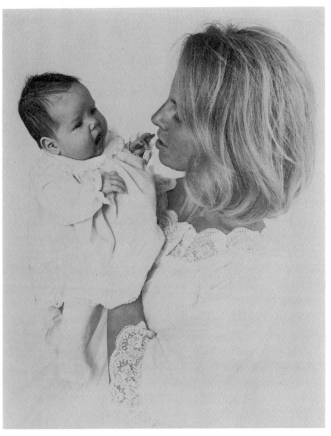

4 weeks old baby, showing the baby's intent regard of his mother as she speaks to
him. Note his open mouth.

'favourite' and therefore 'spoilt'. A child may be a favourite when he had a serious illness, or was born prematurely and had a stormy passage in the first few weeks of life, or is handicapped. So may the child who is blessed with better looks or greater intelligence or a more pleasant personality than his brother and sister. Some children are more affectionate and responsive than others, and most children show much affection for a time to one parent than to another. It is difficult for a parent not to treat such a child differently from the others. The trouble is that when the mother sees that the father is 'favouring' one child, she inevitably takes the other child under her wing and 'favours' him. Grandparents and visitors commonly have their 'favourites'.

Favouritism is shown in many ways. The favoured child 'gets away' with much that is not permitted to the other children. He can do no wrong in the eye of the parent concerned. The father closes his eyes to the wrongdoings and shortcomings of the favoured child, and severely reprimands the unfavoured one for doing the same thing. When the favoured one tells tales about his sister, she is punished. When she tells tales about her brother, the favourite, she is reprimanded for telling tales, and nothing is said to her brother. When the favoured one gets into trouble with one parent, the other comes to his help. When the unfavoured one gets into trouble, he is reprimanded by both parents. The antics of the favourite are laughed at, and his scribblings and sayings are praised, while no attention is paid to those of his brother or sister. When the favoured one asks questions, the father always answers. He is deaf to the questions of the other. The favoured one gets just a little more pudding, a bigger piece of cake, a larger apple, and more presents than the other. There are many other ways in which favouritism is shown — often subtle ways which are by no means obvious except to other children and to visitors.

The effect on the favourite is bad. He is spoiled. He suffers from lack of discipline and he tends to 'lord it' over his brother and sister and make himself thoroughly disliked by them. If the mother shows favouritism to the boy, he may become *too* attached to her and develop what is termed 'mother fixation'; he becomes too dependant on her, and when older, often as an adult, he is unable to make a decision without securing her agreement. The effect on the un-favoured one is disastrous, particularly if he is the favourite of neither parent. He feels that he is not loved. He responds by any of the signs of insecurity — such as temper tantrums, moodiness, nail biting, bedwetting or stuttering. He is resentful of his parent or parents and of his brother or sister who is better treated than he and he feels jealous of them. He longs when he is older to be away from home and he seeks pleasures elsewhere. He never confides in his parents and later becomes estranged from them. A vicious circle is set up, for the less love he shows to his parent or parents the less love they give him. The favoured one, on the other hand, shows more love to the parent who favours him, and so is loved all the more.

It cannot be denied that favouritism is difficult to avoid. It is inevitable that one will come to the help of the younger child when he is being maltreated by the older ones, and scold them. It is inevitable that allowances are made for the younger one, who is not old enough to know better, while the older child is reprimanded or punished for the same act. This looks like favouritism to the older child. Presents may be heaped on to the younger child by visitors and others, the older children receiving nothing. Absolute equality in a house is impossible and undesirable. It would be ridiculous to suggest that when one child has a birthday, all the other children should have presents too. The other children should know that their turn will come, and that they are absolutely secure in their parents' love at all times.

Do you reprimand one of your children or excuse one of them more than another for the same act of misbehaviour?

Are you more willing to play with one child than with another?

Do you hug one as much as the other?

14

Discipline and punishment

It is becominng realized by doctors that the swing away from the excessive discipline of the last century has led to over-indulgence and overpermissiveness, and that these are no less harmful to the child. We should aim at a middle course — but that is by no means easy. Every child has to learn the limits of his freedom. He has to learn respect for the property of others. He has to learn what is safe and unsafe for him. He has to learn to behave in an acceptable way in the presence of others. Habits good and bad are easily created. The aim should be to establish good habits by reasonable and wise discipline. He needs to learn that certain consequences will follow if he fails to do what is asked of him — or does what he is told not to do. Obedience has to be learnt.

Excessive discipline is now universally recognized as harmful. Discipline is excessive if it demands too much from a child — such as excessive tidiness, unquestioning implicit obedience, good table manners before he is old enough to behave well at table, or unselfishness before he can understand what that means. Discipline which involves continual nagging, with constant exclamations of 'Don't do this, don't do that' is excessive, and it makes the child miserable, for he feels that he cannot do anything right. Some parents are too sensitive about what others think of their children, and they try to make them models of virtue at an age when such 'perfect' behaviour would be highly abnormal.

You should realize that if an intelligent visitor comes to your house containing small children, and finds it spick and span and absolutely tidy, he will think that there is something wrong — and rightly so. If you insist on tidiness, you will make the child miserable. There will be constant friction, and the only result will be greater untidiness or insecurity, with all that that means. He has to learn to be tidy, but he can only learn gradually with wise and tactful management, and by imitating the good example of his parents.

Much friction can arise from excessive efforts to teach good manners. Many a mealtime is made a misery to a child by such constant

admonitions as 'Don't chew with your mouth open', 'Don't hold your fork up', 'Put your knife and fork together', 'You can't eat cake till you have had two more pieces of bread', and so on. Such discipline has to be taught, but it must not be taught before the child is old enough to understand. In any case he learns more by the good example set by his parents than by constant remonstrances. Excessive discipline leads to the repression of one form of undesirable behaviour and its replacement by something worse. Many children who are treated in this way develop temper tantrums, become excessively negative or aggressive, and rebel against the treatment they are receiving. It leads to lying in order to avoid punishment. Other children show any of the various signs of insecurity, such as bedwetting, stuttering, masturbation, stealing or biting. Still others become subdued, repressed, cowed and meek. They lack initiative, confidence and independence. We know that in later years such children are more likely than others to become involved in accidents. Their mothers cannot understand why they always prefer to play in other people's houses.

Everyone recognizes the 'spoilt' child, the child who is allowed to do anything he wants, who is never checked by his doting parents, who totally lacks good manners, who is thought by everyone else but the parents to be a horror, with whom they try to prevent their own children from playing because of the bad example which they will see. These children are disobedient and wail when given a simple request. When told to do a thing they either refuse flatly, appear not to hear, or argue about the request, and perhaps eventually mutter and grudgingly do what they are told. Some parents are so afraid of 'repressing" their children that they exert no discipline at all. The children are allowed to do what they want in the house without being checked. They ride round the drawing room on a tricycle, walk along the window sills and climb on to tables. One of us remembers a house which was little more than a slum because the children had been allowed to run wild, draw on the walls, wreck the furniture and walk on the chairs. There were hardly any carpets, because it was expected that the children would damage them. Beds were left unmade all day. It is wrong to allow a child to keep his own bedroom in chaos, and to make no effort to make the room look nice.

Someone wrote:

'I will not criticise my child
Or once repulse her
Or she'll grow up in later years
To have a peptic ulcer.'

Children brought up without discipline become selfish, greedy, uncooperative and insecure. They are prone to temper tantrums, because they know that by having them they can get their own way. When eventually compelled to do what the parent asks, they sullenly obey. They constantly demand attention. They are unpopular at school, and have to learn the hard way. Like those who have been subjected to excessive discipline, they become accident prone.

How then can one strike a happy mean? How should children be taught discipline? Discipline, good manners and good behaviour are taught by setting the child a good example, by love, by sympathy and understanding. The ideal is that a child should behave well because he wants to behave well, because he wants the approval of the parents whom he loves, and because he wants to behave as they do. A child who loves and respects his parents, and who knows that they mean what they say, and that they have a good reason for their demands, is likely to present little difficulty. A child learns courtesy and manners more easily if his parents are polite to him and set a good example, than if they try to inculcate manners by scolding and correction. He will learn more quickly if he is praised for good behaviour, than if he is merely scolded for bad behaviour. He will learn more by rewards for good behaviour, than reprimands for misbehaviour. Too often good behaviour is just accepted and ignored, while bad behaviour is noted and commented upon.

A placid easy-going child may present little trouble even in the

negative resistant stage between eighteen months and three years, while a determined child with a short temper may be very difficult even for the expert.

It is useless to try to teach discipline too soon, before the child is old enough to understand. Attempts to do this lead to endless friction, with resulting insecurity. It is impossible to give the age at which teaching should begin, for it must depend on the intelligence of the child. A year-old child has begun to understand the meaning of 'no', but it would be idle to suggest that a 12 month-old baby can be taught much in the way of discipline. A 3 year-old can learn a great deal. Somewhere in between lies the age at which a serious attempt is begun to teach him essential discipline, customary behaviour and good manners. Little will be taught until after the second birthday. As in many other matters, one has to learn by trial and error. Much friction and many tears are caused by attempts to teach children good behaviour before they are old enough to understand what is wanted of them.

Firmness is essential in the inculcation of discipline. Rules should not be made unless it is possible to see that they are obeyed. They should be as few as possible, but they should not be broken. There should be a good reason for them, such as the child's safety, which he can understand. One must be careful not to dig one's heel in over trivial things which do not matter. He must be stopped from hurting people, or damaging other people's property, at any age. If rules are few, if restrictions are minimal, and there is little nagging, the child in an emergency is more likely to obey promptly, than when he is surrounded by prohibitions, and told so often that he must not do this, that and the other, and warned so frequently to be careful, that he takes no notice. It is most important that when a definite order or prohibition is given, owing to danger to the child, as when he is near an electric fire, or about to play with matches, or playing near a busy road, obedience must be instantaneous.

A further essential in the teaching of discipline is consistency. No child can be expected to learn good habits if one day he is allowed to do a thing which another day he is forbidden to do, or if one parent condones what the other forbids.

Ogden Nash wrote:

'The wise child handles father and mother
By playing one against the other.
'Don't', cries this parent to the tot.
The opposite parent cries 'Why not?'
Let baby listen, nothing loth,
And work impartially on both.
In clash of wills do not give in;
Good parents are made by discipline.'

Grandparents are apt to allow a child to do things which the mother has tried to prevent. In such a case the father should back the mother up and stop the grandmother interfering. We all know children whose manners are appalling, who in the presence of visitors are constantly being reprimanded for bad behaviour and who are eventually sent out of the room in tears. We know that these children would not be constantly jumping down from their chair during mealtime, and running about the room eating, unless they had been allowed to do it at other times when visitors are not present.

Some parents alternate between excessive discipline and over-indulgence. When the child responds to excessive discipline by a temper tantrum he is allowed to do exactly what he wanted to do. Nothing is more harmful than this sort of inconsistency.

Though inconsistency is bad, absolute rigidity is undesirable. An occasional 'just this once' is reasonable, but if it is oft repeated bad habits are inevitable. If a child is allowed on account of some special reason, such as a birthday, to stay up well past his usual bedtime, no harm is done, but if the mother frequently gives in to the child when he complains about going to bed, it is inevitable that difficulties about bedtime will persist and increase. In the same way absolute insistence about any rule is undesirable, except when it concerns protection from physical danger. Insistence on a particular line of action, which a child in a resistant mood is refusing to carry out, is not necessarily right, neither is it always possible. Strength of will and determination are desirable characteristics and must on no account be broken, for he will need them in later life. It is unwise to try to compel a determined child to admit to a heinous crime which he has obviously committed. When your 3 year-old has deliberately spilled the contents of his teaplate on to the floor, and your request that he should clear them up is flatly and firmly refused, it is not necessarily desirable to insist on obedience. You will both of you have to save face somehow, and it is you who will have to devise the means of doing so. He is likely, for instance, to respond quickly if you say 'We'll both do it, and see who can do it first'.

A child has to learn to finish his first course at dinner before he starts his pudding. But if the effort to make him finish the first course is met with resistance, and it is thought that the resistance is because the child cannot understand the reason for the request, it is as well to drop the effort and try again in a month or two. After all, it will be no disaster if he eats his pudding first and his meat afterwards. No harm will result. He will learn the orthodox way of eating a meal when he is a little older, and he will learn without tears and fights. All too often tears and scenes are the result of a stand being made when no stand is necessary, and when the child is not old enough to comprehend. Nothing leads more to unhappiness and insecurity than reprimands and even punishment which the child feels was unjustifiable. No child (or adult) in a furious temper is able to think clearly. It is useless to try to make him obey when he is in such a state. If you have unwisely made a stand in such circumstances, you will have to back out with as much grace as possible. This sounds like weakness and inconsistency. It is not, but such yielding must be only occasional. It is wrong to have a serious scene with a resistant child over anything. He is more likely to obey another time if he is treated reasonably when he is in a resistant, rebellious mood, than if he is smacked into sullen, muttering obedience. It is useless to try to teach a child discipline when he is tired. Attempts to do so are doomed to failure.

The avoidance of punishment

The first essential is to satisfy the child's basic needs for love, security, tolerance and understanding of his developing mind, with the normal features of his behaviour, his need to be recognised as a

person of importance, his normal untidiness, aggressiveness and selfishness.

Much can be done to remove sources of friction. Care should be taken to see that as few breakable objects as possible are left within reach of the 1 to 3 year-old child. It is unfair to leave these about and then to blame him when they are broken. Some friction may be due to unnecessary and peremptory interruption of a child's play, especially at mealtime or bedtime. It is almost always possible to give due warning. Any common sources of conflict should be avoided. If a child has a strong objection to a particular item of clothing, it should be avoided. Direct clashes of will are nearly always unnecessary. It hardly ever pays to try to force a child to do anything against his will.

When one has children, one has to try hard to avoid being in a hurry. Nothing is more exasperating than the two to four year-old's dawdling, but nothing makes it worse than constant efforts to make him hurry. It is difficult for the mother when she has to get her housework done, and when she wants to get to the shops and back as quickly as possible, but if she has a 2 or 3 year-old with her she will have to be resigned to taking three or four times as long as when she is alone. You cannot hurry the small child. You cannot make him quicker, but you can and will make him slower if you try to hurry him.

Much can be achieved by ingenuity, understanding, love and a sense of humour. One can appeal, for instance, to the child's distractibility. The 18 month-old child is unlikely to be controlled by discipline alone. He has to be distracted by offering him pleasant alternatives to what he is doing, in the way of interesting toys. When a 2 year-old refuses to get out of the bath, he may be enticed out easily by a game with a towel, with which a tent is constructed, or by a race with his brother or sister to see who can get the nightclothes on first. When a 4 year-old dawdles in getting dressed, he may be persuaded to be quicker by having a race, or a suggestion that he should try to get his shoes on before the mother counts ten. A little help may be given occasionally, even though a child at that age should be able to dress himself — except for back buttons. Praise and encouragement can work wonders. When a 2 to 3 year-old refuses to tidy up when the floor at bedtime is littered with toys, he is likely to put toys away at speed if a game is made of it. A 3 year-old will often respond to a request which is whispered as if it is a secret, and flatly refuse a mere command. When a child is found to be doing something which must be stopped, such as splashing water out of a sink, he may weep and rebel if he is reprimanded for what he is doing, but he is likely to be delighted if given a bucket and jug with which to play in the garden. It is usually possible to utilize a child's distractibility to stop some undesirable play by offering him or reminding him of a favourite toy.

You cannot control an active and enquiring 18 month-old child by 'No's' and 'Don'ts' from the armchair. In the phase of negativism he is liable to take them as a challenge and do the opposite. You will have to distract him, and if that fails remove him bodily from the temptation.

One often finds that more can be achieved by giving the child a choice of two alternatives, rather than trying to force him to do something to which he always objects. When he habitually objects to washing his hands after going to the lavatory, he can be asked, 'Would you rather wash your hands in the bathroom or in the kitchen?' It is wiser to say, 'We are going out now', than to say, 'Would you like to go out now?' In the phase of negativism the second question would be likely to be met with resistance.

When small children are playing, much tactful handling is required to avoid unnecessary or harmful fights. It is only partially true that children should solve their own disputes. It is wrong to interfere unnecessarily in minor arguments and tussels. But no child should be allowed to harm another. When it is clear that play is deteriorating, much can be done by distracting the angry child, and offering him an attractive alternative game. If one child is seen to be teasing another excessively, so that tears are impending, the teaser should be distracted. When play is becoming too rough, and objects are being thrown about a room, a different game is desirable.

It is no use expecting a 2 to 3 year-old to share his toys and to be unselfish. Unselfishness is a quality which is not learnt in the first four years. When there is a conflict because one child refuses to part with a toy, the difficulty is often solved by suggesting that he find a similar toy which the aggrieved child can have, or else the two can be distracted by suggesting different games. If there is constant quarrelling about a certain toy, that toy should be removed. It is wise to allow a child to put away his favourite toys before a party, in order that friction will be avoided.

It may be argued that this advice is unsound, in that children should learn to find their own solutions to their difficulties. That would be true in an older age group, but 2 or 3 year-olds cannot be expected always to find the solution themselves. Tactful management is required, with a minimum of interference and avoidance of orders and scolding.

Punishment

Punishment of one kind or another is an unfortunate necessity in the upbringing of children. There is no doubt, however, that the wiser the parental management, the less often is punishment necessary, and that the less often punishment is given, the less severe need it be to have the desired effect. A trivial reprimand when punishment is rare is more effective than a major beating when punishment is frequent. Conversely, the more frequent the punishment, the more severe it has to be, and the severity has to be constantly increased to have the desired effect. A trivial punishment of a sensitive child will be quite as effective as a more severe punishment in other children. Punishment by a loving and loved parent is much more effective than punishment by a harsh rejecting one. Physical punishment is much more common in the lower social classes.

Smacking a child is almost always due to loss of temper by the parent, who is merely letting off steam. Smacking is rarely done merely to help the child. If the child refuses to admit that he is being hurt, the parent feels thwarted and becomes even more angry, and smacks him harder. You will lose your temper with your child at times and smack him. Probably everyone does. But you should try to make these occasions few and far between.

Most punishment is wrong — even it its infliction is not merely the result of loss of temper by the parents. George Bernard Shaw wrote that 'to punish is to injure'. In Sweden it is illegal for parents to punish children by boxing their ears or otherwise smacking them. It is not clear how the law is enforced. When a parent hits a child, he is teaching the child aggression. Animals are trained by rewards rather than punishment, and there is no reason to believe that human beings do not learn better by praise, rewards, approval, encouragement and incentives, rather than by discouragement, reprimands and punishment. In any case, most punishment is irrational. Children, like adults, become bad tempered because they are hungry or tired or have been bullied and yet they are punished for it, while adults are not. Children are expected to control their temper while adults can lose theirs with impunity. Children need loving most when they are at their worst, and behaving badly; and they appreciate love and tolerance most when they are feeling tired, cross or unwell. Punishment fails to deal with the *cause* of the bad behaviour. When a child, feeling insecure or unhappy, does something which annoys his mother and is punished for it, he inevitably feels all the more insecure, and all the more certain that he has lost his mother's love — just when he most needs it.

Children (and motorists) are liable to be punished more for the consequences of an act than for the act itself. When a two-year-old playfully clings to the legs of his father, no reprimand is normally given, but when by clinging to his father's legs he causes him to upset and break a pile of plates, the boy is punished. When a child rocks a small table, little is said to him, but when owing to rocking it a prized ornament is broken, he is smacked. The child cannot understand the reason for such different treatment and he does not learn.

Most of the offences for which he is punished are not wrong at all. When a child is being punished frequently it is a good thing to jot down on paper all the 'offences' during the day which have led to reprimands. Their triviality will be just laughable. But it is not laughable for the child. Frequent punishment may seriously disturb him, and lead to troublesome behaviour problems. Furthermore, many of the offences are acts outside his control. He cannot help feeling insecure.

He does not indulge in thumbsucking or nail biting on purpose. Negativism, aggressiveness, fighting and selfishness are normal features of the developing personality. It is far better for the child to learn at home that he cannot get all his own way with other children than to have to learn the hard way at school. He cannot help being jealous, or bad tempered when he comes back hungry or tired from school. He cannot help having a tic or stuttering, or concentrating badly or being clumsy or overactive: he cannot help wetting the bed (or swearing in his sleep). We heard of a girls' boarding school in which the wet sheets of a bed-wetter were displayed by the headmistress to the whole school in an effort to shame the girl. Punishment is often directed at a symptom rather than at the cause.

Lewis Carroll's well-known lines are relevant:

'Speak roughly to your little boy
And beat him when he sneezes.
He only does it to annoy
Because he knows it teases.'

Some reasons for punishment

Friction between child and parent is commonly due to the parents being tired so that they are less tolerant of the child's behaviour, losing their sense of humour. When a parent is becoming short-tempered, the cause should be sought. A mother should do her best to get out in the evenings as regularly as possible — say once a week. A break of two or three days from small children may work wonders in improving tempers. She should be able to get out on an occasional afternoon without the children, her husband taking over, so that she can do her personal shopping, get her hair done, and feel 'free' for a few hours without having to rush back.

A child's behaviour is worsened by fatigue, boredom or hunger. Sometimes an earlier bedtime may make all the difference. A bored unhappy or unwell child is much more likely to get into trouble than a well-occupied contented one.

Frequent punishment is always a sign of failure of management. It is often due to unhappiness in the parents' lives, to business worries, or to friction between the mother and father. It is often due to excessive attempts at discipline, usually before the child is ready. The parents naturally blame the child, and it never occurs to them that they are themselves responsible for their child's behaviour — which is the product of his inherited personality and of the home environment and management.

The different personalities of children have been repeatedly emphasized. Frequent physical punishment is never necessary for even the most difficult children. The wise nursery school teacher never smacks children, but she does teach them discipline.

Nothing is more disturbing to a child than to be punished for something which was purely accidental, especially when he was genuinely trying to help and to be kind. The child must be old enough to understand the *reason* for punishment. If he is not old enough to understand the reason, he should not be punished. When a child asks the reason for a request or for being forbidden to do something, it is futile for the parent to answer irately 'because I said so'. One of us saw a severe behaviour problem in a girl who had been smacked from the age of 4 weeks whenever she failed to have a motion when put on the potty. The girl, as one would expect, refused when older to have a motion, and as a result became severely constipated. No baby is old enough to understand why he is smacked. One often sees a 9 month-old baby being smacked for putting the finger into the mouth. Such a child could not possibly understand what he has done wrong. No punishment should ever be given to a child in his first year.

Threats of punishment should be rare, but if the threats are not heeded, punishment should be the inevitable consequence. If the child finds that the threats are never carried out, it is surely obvious that he will pay no attention to them. Yet it is extremely common to hear children threatened with punishment which the parent has not the least intention of giving, and the child knows it and ignores them. Whenever possible, he should be warned that if he disobeys, he will be punished. The really vital thing about discipline and punishment is the child's need to know that if he disobeys certain consequences will result.

Physical punishment is rarely necessary. It is better in the majority of cases to punish by simple acts of deprivation, fitted to the particular crime. When a child needs punishment for bad behaviour in play with other children, he is isolated from them, either by sending him into a corner or another room for two or three minutes. When he dawdles in getting dressed in the morning (between 4 and 5 years), and the rest of the family has finished breakfast by the time he comes downstairs, he is punished by finding that his breakfast has been cleared away, and the same happens when he fails to come in from outside to his dinner. When the girl cuts a hole in her dress with the new scissors, the scissors are confiscated. When she draws on the wall of her bedroom, her pencils are removed. When the 5 year-old girl dawdles in getting ready to go out, she is left behind (if there is someone left in the house). When a boy starts to throw bread about the table, he is sent away from it. When he breaks his toys or tears his books, they are removed. When he leaves his pencils or books about, they are confiscated. If his room is untidy he gets no pocket money until it is tidied. This sort of punishment is perfectly effective. It does away with the need of constant nagging and reprimands. There is no need for argument. The child just has to learn exactly what the consequences will be if he does not do what he is told, and if he fails to do what he is told after due warning, the consequences will be inevitable. *Constant threats, scoldings, reprimands and nagging do nothing but harm, and they are unnecessary. Attempts to shame the child are always wrong: ridicule should never be used. Threats of withdrawal of love are invariably wrong, and may be harmful. The mother may make these threats half-jokingly; but the child may take them seriously. Such management only leads to insecurity. It is much more harmful to a young child than a single slap on the bottom.*

If physical punishment is given, and it has to be given on occasion, it should be as slight as possible. Nothing but the hand should ever be used. There is never any need for a severe smacking for a properly managed child. It is never necessary to hurt him. Where relevant, the child should make restitution for his wrong-doing. If a boy deliberately destroys one of his sister's books, he should buy her another one out of his pocket money. If he throws his brother's shoe into a pool, he has to go to get it. This is an essential lesson which has to be learnt.

After the punishment has been given, it should be forgotten. The child should not be constantly reminded of what he has done. He should be loved, so that he knows that he has not lost his parents' affection. It is wrong to recite the child's wrongdoings in his presence to the father when he comes home from work. He should not go to bed in disgrace. He should go to bed feeling certain that he is loved. Punishment should never lead to fear.

Excessive and repeated punishment leads to insecurity, resentment, stealing, lying, fears and other bad habits. It may lead to nail biting, bedwetting, stuttering, 'tics', such as blinking of the eyes, shyness, nightmares or showing off.

15

Other basic needs

The importance of example
Children are imitators, and they are likely to model their behaviour on that of their parents, teachers and friends. Parents cannot expect their children to be well-mannered, loving, generous, unselfish and honest unless they set a good example. If you ignore your child when he speaks to you, or merely grunt a reply, you should not blame him for doing the same. If you push your child out of they way in impatience, you must expect him to do likewise. If you fail to say that you are sorry when you accidently knock him or when you lose your temper, you cannot expect him to apologise under similar circumstances. If you snap at him when asked a simple question, you should not expect him to speak politely to you. If you show atrocious manners to him, you must expect him to show equally bad manners. If you and your husband are rude and unkind to each other, lose your temper and argue, you cannot expect anything different in your child. If you say that you do not like this, that or the other food, or that you cannot bear such and such a person, your child is likely to express similar dislikes. You cannot expect your child to be honest if you commit petty acts of dishonesty in front of him or boast of what you have done. If you are unkind to others and criticise others for their faults, he will follow your example. You set a bad example if, when someone us unkind to you or annoys you, you retaliate by doing the same to him.

If you smoke or drink or take other drugs of addiction, you inevitably invite him to do the same. If you constantly complain of various symptoms, or make the most of them, missing work unnecessarily, the child will follow suit. He will follow your example in your choice of radio, TV programmes, records and reading matter. He will be influenced by the example set by his teachers — in coming late to their classes, smoking or losing their temper.

You have a big responsibility. Let him see nothing but love, honesty, unselfishness, tolerance and kindness in your dealings with him and others, and the odds are that he will grow up to treat others in the same way. You set your child a good example when you are kind, loving and unselfish, when you willingly do something for someone when otherwise you would not want to do it, when you look for the good in people, instead of criticising them, and when you come to the defence of someone who is being criticised. When a child finds an excuse for someone's undesirable behaviour, particularly that of a brother or sister, he should be praised, and unkind criticism should be condemned. Children are likely to learn their moral values, which will be theirs for life, from their parents in early childhood.

The atmosphere in the home

Children are profoundly affected by the atmosphere in the home; they are greatly upset by parental friction and discord. Research has shown that when the mother and father become separated or divorced, the children suffer more from the preceding discord and unpleasantness than from the separation from one of the parents. We have seen a six-month-old baby burst into tears when the mother and father pretended to hit each other, or when a brother or sister is punished. We have frequently seen children whose vomiting or asthmatic attacks only occurred when the parents quarrelled. One of the principle features of the background of juvenile delinquents is domestic disharmony.

Making a home a happy place

Every effort should be made to cause the home to be liked and enjoyed by the child. Some parents wonder why their children always prefer to play in someone else's house, and why they do not show enthusiasm about having their friends into their own home. If this happens, it is worth while to take stock. Are his friends really welcomed? Are they criticised when they leave? Do you go out of your way to make them enjoy their visit? How often do you let your child have friends in for the night? When he is older and independent, will he really enjoy coming home — or will he come home merely because he feels it to be his duty?

One is reminded of George Bernard Shaw's comment: he never forgot the misery of his childhood. He wrote 'We children were abandoned entirely to servants who were entirely unfit to be trusted with the charge of three cats, and much less of three children'.

A parent, mother or father, may be highly successful in work or profession, and highly unsuccessful in making the home a happy place, with an atmosphere of love and tolerance and freedom from discord.

Habit formation

Children rapidly develop habits, good and bad. It is the parents' task to try to establish good habits and to avoid undesirable ones. For instance, it should be an understood thing that after a meal the child should help to clear the table and wash up — unless he has homework to do. Boys and girls should naturally and without argument take their share in helping. They need not be asked; it should be automatic.

Sex attitudes

Any time after a year of age the baby begins to show interest in his stools and in passing urine. This interest increases as he grows older. By the age of three or four, children are likely to show interest in lavatories and to talk freely about motions and urination. Between 2½ and 3½ years of age children begin to notice differences between the two sexes and to make comments. At three or four years of age the boy is apt to exhibit his penis with pride. The girl will openly handle the boy's genitals. Children of this age take pleasure in watching the baby's nappy being changed and in helping to powder the buttocks. All this is healthy, normal and natural interest, and should not be discouraged. As long as children of opposite sexes are bathed together and are allowed to run about, if they want to do, without clothes on at bathtime, this natural interest will wane and cause no trouble. It is wrong to tease a small child for playing with the opposite sex or for kissing a child. It is interesting to note that there are wide differences with regard to the management of these sex matters by parents of different social classes. The Newsons at Nottingham* found that in social class one, five per cent of children were being punished for genital play, compared with 48 per cent in social class five. The Newsons discussed the very marked social differences in attempts to protect children from seeing or being interested in sex. They wrote, 'It is in the stratagems chosen for the child's sexual naïveté that the social classes differ so profoundly'.

It is a matter of opinion as to how much the child should be allowed to see his parents without clothes. We think that it is unnecessary and undesirable for parents to go out of their way to prevent their small children seeing them undressed. It will suggest to the child that there is something wrong about being unclothed, and at this age it is better to avoid such a suggestion. It is the child who is brought up in a home in which there is prudery about sex matters, especially if he is an only child, or if he is one of the several children with the same sex, who is likely to show unhealthy interest in sex when he goes to school. Some psychologists claim that it 'over-stimulates' children, whatever that means, to be allowed to see their parents without clothes. We feel that if a child does sometimes see his parents undressed his interest will soon wane. He will show interesst for a few weeks, when he first notices differences in the sexes, but after a time he takes no notice at all. When children have been brought up in a home in which there is no secret about the differences between the sexes, and in which the normal sex interest is not regarded as something disgraceful, and in which questions about sex are dealt with honestly and adequately, there will be no reason for silly and secretive sex talk and sex play in later years.

After the third birthday children are likely to ask elementary sex questions, such as where the baby comes from. They should be answered truthfully, but only told what they can understand, and only what they have asked. When a child asks where babies come from, he is told that they come from their mummies. When he asks how they get out, he is told that they come through a special passage. No more need be said, and that satisfies the child. It is awkward when the child asks such questions in the grocer's shop. A sense of humour is a great help in these circumstances. The question must be answered without shame. It can be shelved until one is outside the

*Newson J Newson E 1968 *Four Years Old in an Urban Community*. London, Allen and Unwin.

shop by a matter of fact 'I'll tell you in a minute'. You will have to be certain not to show any embarrassment or amusement at his question, and not to make him feel silly. The child should be told the truth, for he will find out later in any case, and may seriously lose confidence in his parents if he finds that they have told him lies. He may be caused considerable embarrassment later by his enforced ignorance.

When four or five-year-olds are found playing with each other's genitals, it should be ignored if in the family; if not they should merely be distracted, no scolding or anxiety being shown. There is nothing abnormal about it. It is most important that a child should never be teased or laughed at because of his friendship with a child of the opposite sex. To make jokes about a little boy's behaviour because he has been seen kissing a little girl, for example, is just disastrous.

A sensible attitude to sex is essential. The mother must encourage the boy to become independent from her as he grows up. It is important never to dress the boy in girl's clothes in play. Boys should be encouraged to take part in boyish pursuits and games and not overprotected in case they might receive some injury. Sensible sex management and instruction, without prudery, leads to accept-

ance of sex as normal and healthy. The wise parent has no need to censor the books which the child wants to read, or the cinema or TV programme which the child wants to see. There is no excuse for the ludicrous state of affairs in which the parents dare not take their daughter to the art gallery in case she might see a painting or sculpture of a nude. Studies of female homosexuality have indicated a background of a dominant puritanical father, interested physically in his daughters. There have been threats of punishment for sex play with boys. Studies of male homosexuality have indicated a background of a harsh punitive father, who favours his daughter, or a weak ineffectual father with a dominant mother who has continued to bath the boy and keep him utterly dependent on her for too long. There is often a family attitude of repression of sex interest.*

Steps to self-confidence and independence

Every normal child, after the age of nine months or so, thrives on praise and encouragement and the feeling that he is wanted. He takes pride in the ability to achieve new skills, in being independent and in being able to do things without the help of adults. He needs freedom so that he can learn and obtain experience, but it must be

*A useful book for the young child is *The Body Book* by Claire Rayner, Piccolo Picture Books. Pan Books 1978.

freedom tempered with discipline.

At about nine months of age he begins to repeat tricks which are laughed at. Thereafter this love of attention and encouragement increases, at least up to the age of about four, and all manner of attention-seeking devices may be tried. It is all part of the child's need for love, praise and encouragement. It is normal. Parents need not fear that they will make their three- or four-year-old child a prig by encouraging him and praising him for his abilities. They must admire his drawings, praise his tracings and listen to his stories. If they fail to show any interest in them, the child will be discouraged, stop showing them to his parents, and later on refuse to confide in them.

Children delight in practising new skills. When the seven-month-old baby has learnt to sit, he tends to want to sit whenever he is awake, and fusses when compelled to lie down. Later on he delights in standing, holding on to furniture; in pulling himself up to the standing position; in creeping; in walking with two hands held; in feeding himself, dressing himself and in attending to his own toilet needs. After about 18 months he delights in 'helping' in the house-work, and in doing things with his hands which he has seen his mother doing. All this needs encouragement. In the early days he needs help, but as soon as he can dispense with help, he should do things for himself. When a nine-month-old baby is learning to feed himself he will make a frightful mess. But when he shows the desire to feed himself (from six months or so onwards), he should be allowed to do so. A child given the chance in this way will be feeding himself without help long before other children whose mothers feed them so as to avoid a mess. The two-year-old should be encouraged to undress himself, and to put his own socks, shoes and trousers on. It takes twice as long to get a two-and-a-half to three-year-old dressed if he is allowed to dress himself (as far as he can), as it does if the mother does it all for him, but if given a chance to learn, he will be independent far sooner than children whose mothers never give them a chance to learn. It takes twice as long to set the table, and twice as long to cook the dinner, when the toddler is allowed to 'help', but the helping gives the child a feeling of importance, teaches him to use his hands, gives him confidence, and equips him for bigger tasks in the future. If he is not given a chance to practise these skills when they are new, he will lose interest in doing so, and it will then be found that he does not want to feed himself, dress himself and be independent. He just does not want to make the effort.

Encouragement works wonders. Anger, impatience and discouragement do nothing but harm. It is easy to exclaim 'You're no help. You are more bother than you are worth'. When a child drops a cup in setting the table, it is wise to avoid an outburst of anger at his mishap, for it will make him lose confidence. He could not help it. It would be wrong to forbid him to 'help' in the future as a result of an accident. It is equally wrong to suggest by one's anxiety that he will fail, for it will make him nervous and lose confidence. Constant exhortations to 'take care', to 'mind the step', to 'be careful of the scissors' achieve nothing. The child just learns to ignore such constant admonitions. On the other hand, it is a mistake to give a sensitive child responsibility before he is ready for it, for failure will make him lose confidence.

There are many other ways in which a child learns self-confidence and acquires a feeling of security. Calculated risks have to be taken in order that he can eventually acquire independence. He should be encouraged to think for himself and to take the initiative. A woman said about her daughter 'She was a self-willed little girl. I always had to crush her initiative'. That spoke volumes about the mother. The child should be helped to gain experience, to see and to learn. A half-constructed house may be dull for many adults, but an intelligent four-year-old would learn a lot from watching the method of building. A four-year-old learns self-confidence by being sent into a shop to make purchases — the mother keeping at a judicious distance. He enjoys collecting flowers from the garden and arranging them. Albert Schweizer wrote about his parents that 'they trained us for freedom: they never knew how much we owed them'.

Failure to let a child grow up, to learn to be independent, is one of the signs of what doctors call 'overprotection'. It is due to the mother's desire, often a subconscious one, to keep the child a baby, always utterly dependent on her. She feeds him, dresses him, attends to his toilet needs, inspects every stool he has, long after a normal child has learnt to look after himself. The child then remains immature, mixes badly with other children, and remains 'tied to his mother's apron strings', but often becomes resentful against her for not giving him independence. She convinces him that he is incapable of looking after himself. He learns that it is unnecessary for him to make any effort, because his parents always rush to his help, convincing him that he cannot look after himself. They support him in his criticism of other boys or of his teachers. They take him to school and help him with his homework. They will not let him choose the friends he would like to invite to his home. In a dispute with his older brother or sister, the older ones are always rebuked, with the result that the younger one is spoilt, and deliberately annoys them in order to get them into trouble.

Overprotection is shown in many other ways. The mother will not let her child out in case he gets his feet wet, catches cold, plays with rough children, or picks up their 'accent'. She will not let the child play out of doors in case he should hurt himself. She will not allow him to play on his own, always stepping in to 'help' him in his play. She encourages him to use baby words, and even calls him 'baby' when he is quite a big boy. One of us knew two brothers who had their temperature taken every night for the first 15 years of their life, because their mother was so anxious about them. One often sees children of six and seven who are still dressed by their mothers, because they have never been given a chance to do it themselves. Some parents make the mistake of trying to get their child excused from physical training, games or camp, on the grounds that he is delicate.

Overprotection occurs particularly when the mother has had an unhappy life herself, and she tries to extract the maximum amount of love from her child. It occurs particularly if the father has died, or when there has been a long wait for a child, or the child is of the much desired sex after a long succession of children of the opposite sex. It is a common feature of the mentally or physically handicapped child. Overprotection is often a characteristic of children brought up by a 'nanny', who inevitably has to be careful to prevent accidents. The usual result is the opposite of the effect desired. It is well known that such children tend to rebel against the overprotection as soon as they are able to break loose from home, and they are then 'accident prone' — in other words more liable to be involved in accidents than other children.

Excessive criticism and fault finding does much to undermine a child's self-confidence. It is particularly difficult for him when several relatives live in the house, and all join in reprimanding him. We saw one disturbed child who was being constantly scolded by five adults in the home.

Ridicule is always harmful. A child's failures, fears or shyness should never be laughed at. All too often a child's shortcomings are discussed in front of him, often amongst strangers. A child's fears are serious to him, and it is wrong to laugh at them. His games of make believe, his imaginary playmate behind the sofa, are real to him, and he should not be laughed at or ridiculed for them. We saw a three-year-old reprimanded on the station platform for 'playing trains', on the grounds that it was 'silly'. Teasing is all right up to a point, but teasing which is not liked by the child is harmful, especially if it leads to tears.

Another cause of lack of confidence in small children is the practice of 'labelling' them. The parents and relatives habitually refer to one child as the one who is 'clever with his hands', or 'poor with his hands'; to another as the 'observant one'; another as the 'helpful one', or still worse the 'good looking one'. This leads to jealousy and insecurity.

Nothing should ever be said in the child's presence about his shyness, peculiarities of speech, backwardness, smallness of stature or obesity. No suggestion should be made that he is weak or delicate. Such remarks may have a profound effect on the child, and do nothing but harm.

One frequently hears parents talk in front of their children about his smallness of stature, obesity, appearance, speech difficulties, bad behaviour, poor appetite, timidity or backwardness. A child's wrongdoing, for which he was punished or reprimanded, is described to his friends in his presence in such a way that the boy realises that his parents regard the whole things as a joke or are secretly proud of his escapades. They make the comment that 'he's a real boy'. It encourages him to repeat the performance.

16

Some special problems of management

Mother–child interaction

From the moment of birth onwards a mother's responses, behaviour and attitudes are much influenced by the child's responses to her and by his behaviour: and the child's responses and behaviour, from birth onwards — including adolescence — are greatly influenced by the parents' responses to him. Sometimes this is a pity, because if a child has a difficult personality, inherited from one of his parents, he is likely to come into conflict with his parent — particularly the one with the same awkward personality traits.

In the early weeks a smiling baby evokes smiles and pleasure in his mother, and a mother's smiles and overtures evoke the same responses in him; but an awkward crying baby, or a drowsy baby who responds little, may leave the mother cold and unresponsive. When he is older, and behaves badly, his bad behaviour tends to evoke bad behaviour on the part of his parents, who lose their temper with him and scold and punish him — so making him behave all the more badly. An irritable, tired, worried adolescent, who has 'got out of bed on the wrong side', evokes corresponding bad behaviour on the part of his parents, who rise to the occasion and respond to his rudeness and negativism by loss of temper and by unkind remarks.

Children, like their parents, want love, security and tolerance; they thrive on love; love brings the best out of them, especially when they are at their worst. Difficulties arise when neither child nor parent is at his best. When a child is hungry, tired or poorly he becomes bad tempered, quarrelsome and aggressive. If his mother is tired, worried, hurried, suffering from an attack of depression or premenstrual tension, or is affected by the bad weather, she responds to the child's bad behaviour by anger, reprimands and punishment — and so the child is all the more difficult and badly behaved. Children, like adults, need loving most when they are at their worst: it is then that they most appreciate tolerance and good humour.

The father's part

It goes without saying that the father has a big part to play during the pregnancy, not only in taking some of the load of preparing for the baby, but in doing all he can to help his wife, physically and emotionally, especially during the last few weeks. When the mother is in hospital or having the baby at home, he may have to play an important part in looking after the home.

He can do much to help his wife in the few weeks after delivery, in supporting her, and in sharing the responsibility of looking after the child. The mother needs help at this time — not only physical help, which he can only give in small part, because of the calls of his work, but psychological support, for women in the first few weeks after delivery are in an emotional state. They tend to weep with little apparent reason, to be upset at nothing, and to worry over the most trivial difficulty. The father should be aware of these psychological difficulties of the first few weeks, be patient and loving, knowing that the difficulties are only temporary and common to most women after delivery.

Some fathers hand over the entire management of their child to the mother and then blame her when things go wrong. It is not fair that she should have all the responsibility of bringing up children, neither is it desirable for the children. He can and should help his wife by taking his share, by supporting her when she is emotionally and physically tired as a result of the child's difficult behaviour, or of looking after one of the children in an illness, by helping her to deal with the child's problems and by sharing in the anxiety of illness. When she is becoming tired and impatient it is his job to help in the housework, to ensure that she gets out regularly away from the children and if possible has holidays of a few days away from them. A mother may become stale after continuous contact with her own children for prolonged periods — often with little outside contact with adults. It is a great help to her after a busy and exhausting day with exuberant children if he takes over when he comes in, plays with them, reads to them, baths them and puts them to bed. He may think that he has no time. No father should be so immersed in his work that he cannot devote time to his children. He may have to work after they have gone to bed or forgo an evening out, but his children will be closer to him and will love him more and he will understand them better.

It is a good thing for the father to be able to bath and change the baby, and in the weaning period to be used to feeding him, for it is undesirable, in case of illness in the mother, for the baby never to have been handled by anyone else. He should be left to do it without

a lot of criticism of his methods. The vest may be inside out, but the baby will not be harmed thereby.

The father should take part in teaching discipline, obedience and manners. Not only should he set a good example himself, in the way of love, honesty, unselfishness and politeness, but he should ensure that there is no inconsistency between him and his wife. Nothing is more disheartening and annoying for a good mother, when she has had to take a firm line with her child, than to find that her h﹐ has come in and taken the opposite line, allowing the child to ⁄ she has forbidden. The father may do this in order to cour with the child. It is most unfair on the mother and bad for t﹐ who soon learns to play one parent against the other.

Parental consistency does not mean that whenever a ⁄ something undesirable both parents should pounce on him him. There is a tendency for this to happen. Scolding ⱥ ment should come from one parent only, the other ﹢   t, expressing condonation of the offence by neither word⁄   ᵴs- ion. It is always wrong for the mother to say, 'Wait till   ᵫes in; he will give you a good hiding'. The child is kept ⱼ   all day and regards the father as a man to fear. The fathcⱼ   ᵾuse to have anything to do with this sort of thing. On thₑ   d he should take his part in punishment, if punishment iₛ   It is wrong for one parent to leave all punishment to thⱼ   ₑnt in order to court the child's affection.

Grandparents

Grandparents may be a great help to a mother in the bringing up of children, but they can lead to a lot of trouble. They can be a help because of their love for their grandchildren, because of their experience of rearing children, because of their trustworthiness in looking after the children so that the parents can get out in an evening or for a short holiday, or so that the mother can go into hospital to have another child with the certain knowledge that her children will be well looked after in her absence. They can help by giving extra love to a child who is feeling jealous — to the older child, when the new baby comes, or to the younger child, when the older one goes to school. They can help most by setting a good example — by managing the children with love, tact and wise discipline, without showing irritability or loss of temper, and without punishment. They can help by suggesting play and providing suitable play material which they know from their experience will be appreciated. They can help by reading or telling stories, when the mother has little or no time for it, or by taking the children out.

Sometimes grandparents cause trouble in the home. This is usually due to interference in the management of the children, to spoiling them by indiscipline and giving them all their own way, or to favouritism. Less often it is due to irritability with the children, to intolerance of their noise and constant activity.

It is difficult for a grandmother, who has had considerable experience of bringing up children, to avoid criticizing her daughter's methods of managing them. Criticism or implied criticism or even the mildest suggestions by the grandmother may cause annoyance to a young mother, who has her own views on how to bring up children. She may have vivid memories of unpleasant episodes in her own childhood, of favouritism, or what she considered to be unjust punishment, or restricted freedom and excessive strictness, of constant bickering and criticism — and she is determined to bring her own children up differently. It cannot be expected that two women of different generations, particularly if they are women of character who have decided views on life, will see eye to eye. Ideas change, and each thinks that she alone is right. It is important that each should fully realize this difficulty and try to make allowances for it. Parents are determined not to make the mistakes their own parents made. They will probably succeed — but make a lot of other mistakes which their parents avoided.

The mother must have full responsibility for bringing up her own children and it is wrong for a grandmother to interfere. The wise grandmother will absolutely avoid criticism or interference, knowing

how much it will annoy. She will never condone behaviour by the grandchild which the mother forbids, for a child will soon learn to play one against the other in order to get his own way. She will do her utmost to leave all the training of the child to his parents. She will have to avoid scolding, punishment and threats of punishment, knowing how much it will annoy the parents, and knowing how bad it is for a child to be reprimanded by several people. It should be left to the parents, whenever possible. She must not spoil the child by being so afraid to exert discipline that she allows him to do exactly what he likes — things which his parents never permit. She may greatly annoy her daughter by giving the child sweets, or articles of diet which the mother thinks are undesirable. The grandmother may do this to spite her daughter-in-law (of whom she may be jealous). The grandmother is in a difficult position — a fact so often not realised by the mother — and it is only the wisdom of years which will enable her to avoid friction with her daughter.

Usually grandparents get on well with their grandchildren. They are able to give special treats, nice presents and lots of time — and children like to be 'spoiled'. Grandparents may annoy them, however, by being irritable with them — and by the worst crime of all — suggesting that it is now time for them to go to bed.

Few serious difficulties are likely to arise if the grandparents see little of the children. If they live in the same house, and particularly if they own the house, the problems are greater. It is a help if the mother tries to give the grandparent a feeling of responsibility —

some routine tasks, which make her feel that she is contributing something to the household. But in the best of circumstances the situation is difficult.

The child who is separated from one or both parents

One-parent families present important social problems, and there are many such families. In the U.K. there are over a million children in one-parent families. It is said that in the U.S.A. there are 18 million children under the age of 18 in one-parent families. We have already stated that domestic friction may have a profound effect on a child, and lead to a variety of emotional and behaviour problems, including delinquency. Loss or absence of a parent by bereavement, separation, illegitimacy or divorce may present other problems — notably financial difficulties and housing problems. It has been shown that behaviour problems following separation or divorce are largely the result of preceding discord and subsequent attitudes expressed by the mother about her husband, though the loss of a parent is bound to have an effect as well. A boy most needs a father after the first four or five years, and the absence of a father may lead to difficulties in sexual adjustment: it is sometimes a factor in leading to homosexuality. However careful the guardian parent is, the child is bound to lose something. All that one can hope to do is to give him as much love as possible, to give him treats which normally the other parent would have been expected to give him, and yet not to over-protect him; for such a child is particularly liable to be overprotected and so prevented from growing up.

The great majority of children adapt to the absence of one parent. Relevant factors with regard to satisfactory adaptation include the reasons for the absence of a parent, the presence or absence of brothers and sisters, the personality, energy, stability of the mother (or father) with the absence of overprotection.

The child whose mother is at work

A child most needs his mother's love in the first three years. Many feel that unless it is a matter of economic necessity, it is undesirable for a mother to go out to work when her child is under three years of age. We do not agree with Benjamin Spock who wrote that 'wanting more than motherhood is not natural, but a reflection of her individual emotional disturbance'. Others feel that in the case of a professional woman a long period away from her career (perhaps nine years if she had three children) would make it so difficult for her to get back to her career that there is much to be said for the mother getting back to work as soon as she can, provided that there

is a good mother-substitute, such as a granny, whom the children love.

There are various reasons why a mother may want or need to go out to work. She may want or need the money — especially if her husband has died. She may want more money to raise the standard of living, to pay for a private school, or to have better holidays. But she may want to work for other reasons — for after she has paid tax on her earnings, paid for a home help and perhaps for a private nursery, she will not gain much financially — and satisfactory help is hard to find. Another difficulty is the limited time for which a creche or play group can take a child. She may want to work because she enjoys it, because she wants to keep up with her professional work so that when her children are older she can return to a full-time post suitable for one with her experience. She knows that the longer she is away from work, the more difficult will it be for her to get back to it, and the more likely it is that she will have to accept work inferior to that for which she is trained. She may want to work in order to enable her husband to undertake special training for his career.

The effect on her child will depend on a variety of factors. It will depend partly on his personality; and if he has never been separated from his mother because she has never had a break away from him, it may be difficult for him if his mother goes out to work. It may be difficult for him to go to a nursery school and he may be seriously disturbed by it, while others would thoroughly enjoy it. A child may benefit from having his mother with him until he starts school — if she is a good mother; on the other hand he may benefit greatly from going to a good nursery school, or being left with a loving grand-mother. He may become more independent, more self reliant. Much will depend on the arrangements for him. Another factor is the age at which the separation occurs, and the question of when she returns from work, and in particular whether she is always at home when he returns from the nursery (or school). The presence or absence of brothers or sisters to play with must also make a difference.

It is a mistake for a mother to feel that she can never leave a child (e.g. for a break or other good reason). A child may be positively helped in the step towards self-confidence and independence. Monkeys denied opportunities to leave and return to their mother in the first year are likely to refuse to leave their mother when they reach adulthood.

If the mother is unable to do the work for which she is trained, she may feel bored, thwarted and resentful, so that the child suffers. She may be envious of her friends who are doing interesting work, meeting interesting people, and earning good money, and so she becomes bad tempered at home. If she works all day she may come back tired and irritable — so that the child suffers. If she does work, she will watch for any signs of insecurity, and if she sees them she will act accordingly. In fact extensive research has not shown that children suffer from the mother being at work, provided that suitable arrangements are made for them.

The effect on the mother must also depend on several factors, and in particular on her satisfaction in her work. It must depend on her personality and stamina, for a working mother will have to do many more hours of work than a full-time housewife or her husband, even though he has to help in the house. She has the responsibility of looking after a child who is ill, the responsibility of securing home help, and the responsibility of doing the shopping. If she is lucky, she will be able to take the child to her place of work, if there is a suitable creche. She may have to accept a lower standard of housework and entertaining. She has to do her shopping at inconvenient hours. She may need labour-saving devices in the home. Her husband may have to help more in the house and take over from her. Factors include the attitudes of the husband, mother-in-law, and other relatives.

Research has shown that a mother who works is less likely to have psychiatric problems than one who just stays at home. She has improved self-esteem and self-confidence. She is less likely to be jealous of her husband. Studies have shown that the school performance of the children and the divorce rate are unaffected.

Should he go to a nursery school?

There is no answer to this question, except that each case has to be considered on its merits. Nursery schools under the Local Authority are not likely to be available unless it is essential for the mother to work, and other provision cannot be made for the child, but there are numerous private nursery schools or play groups.

The factors which have to be considered are the age of the child, the extent of his dependence on his parents, the number of children in the house and neighbourhood with whom he can play, and the opportunities for play at home, particularly out of doors. There is something to be said for it if he is an only child, and there are no children in the neighbourhood with whom he can play, if there is overcrowding at home and no garden for him to play in, or if the child is bored, in spite of all efforts to keep him occupied. It would be wrong if the child is seriously upset by being separated from his mother.

One drawback in sending young children to nursery school is the frequency with which they acquire the common infections there, such as colds. This is a nuisance if there is a baby in the house.

The only child

The first child of a family is an only child for a time, and may resent the change when another is born. A colleague of ours coined the

Manipulation. 6 months.
Transfers objects.

40 weeks. Pokes clapper of bell
with index finger.

phrase 'a second only child' for one who is born, often as an "accident", years after his siblings have grown up, and he is likely to be spoilt — not only by his elderly parents but by his grown-up brothers and sisters.

The effect of being an only child must depend partly on the reasons for his not having a brother or sister. The cause may lie in some illness in his mother, in gynaecological conditions, in the death of a previous child, in illegitimacy, in separation or divorce; parents may decide not to risk having another child when there is some unpleasant genetic disease, such as fibrocystic disease of the pancreas, haemophilia or muscular dystrophy, or when the child is spastic or mentally defective. The cause is bound to colour the attitude of the parent to the only child. It would not be surprising, if the mother had lost her husband, or if a previous child had died, that the mother would be excessively anxious about her child's health. For instance, she may overprotect him and fail to let him acquire normal independence — dressing him, feeding him, bathing him, taking him to the lavatory, long after he should be able to attend to his own needs — and she may protect him from trivial risks which a normal child should take and which give him necessary experience.

Problems of discipline may affect the only child. The usual trouble is that he is given all that he wants and never learns to accept a 'no'. He is not taught essential discipline, so that he will have to learn the hard way when he goes to school. Sometimes parents of an only child are so determined not to spoil him that they are overstrict, and make him insecure as a result.

Parents of an only child may be overambitious for him. Their whole ambition is centred on him. They watch his homework and help him with it and check its accuracy. The father may be anxious that the child should go into his business and never think that the child should be expected to choose his own career. The child may be worried about his school report: it is different if a sibling also has a bad report: it is worse if he is the only one.

The only child may be lonely. He has no-one on the spot with whom he can play. He tends to play indoors more than others and to take less part in extra-curricular activities at school. He feels the odd man out. He misses sibling rivalry. At the time it is difficult or impossible for a child to realize how much he is learning and benefiting from the jealousies, fighting and derogatory remarks made by his siblings. The only child has to face this for the first time when he starts school, and may find it difficult. At school he may find it hard to stand up for himself, so that he may be unpopular or bullied. He has not had a chance to learn fair play and give and take. He may miss early friendship with the opposite sex.

As he grows older he misses the friendship of a brother and sister. When his parents criticize him, make unfavourable comments on his friends, especially in adolescence, he lacks siblings who can always be relied upon to come to his help when his parents disapprove. In adult life, when some crisis arises, or a difficult decision has to be made, he has no brother or sister to turn to for advice.

The girl who is an only child may suffer in adolescence and later because an overpossessive parent lets her know in no uncertain way where her duty lies — in looking after her aging parents even though it will grossly interfere with her career and her sex life.

The only child tends to be more mature; he is exposed to purely adult conversation in the home; he associates more with adults than with those of his own age; he is likely to have an adult type of holiday. He may be more comfortable talking to adults than with his own age group.

Many an only child in his early years and later bitterly regrets that he has no brothers or sisters. But there is no typical only child. When the only child in later years ascribes some of his personality problems to not having had siblings, one wonders whether he would have been any different if he had had; one wonders how many of his difficulties are part of his inherited personality or merely reflect the personality of his parents. Certainly no parent should ever feel guilty because she has only one child: it is hardly ever her fault and knowing some of the difficulties which the only child has to face, steps can be taken to avoid the usual problems — especially over-anxiety, overprotection, and faults of discipline.

The child who arrives after a gap of years
The problems of the child who is born many years after the previous one are similar to those of the only child. The particular danger is that he will be 'spoilt' by his parents, and by older brothers and sisters, being treated as a baby and so prevented from growing up. He is likely to have all his own way, and to be overprotected.

The child of elderly parents
The child of elderly parents, particularly if he is an only child, is apt to be spoiled and overprotected. He is less likely to mix with other children of his age, because his parents' friends are more likely to have older children.

The eldest child
The eldest of two or more children has his own problems. Jealousy is

his first. Like every other child who has a baby brother or sister, the discovery that he is not the only one is a painful process, but nevertheless good for him. Other problems are not quite so obvious. He is liable to be given troublesome chores in the house and often too much responsibility in the way of looking after his young brother. When the younger child gets into mischief, he is blamed for not preventing it. He finds it difficult to understand why his young brother gets away with things (on account of his age) for which he himself is reprimanded. The activities of the elder child are often restricted on account of the younger one. Walks are shorter. His parents have less time to play with him than when he was the only one.

The youngest child
The youngest child is apt to be spoilt and kept a baby, but he gains by having an older brother or brothers with whom he can play and by acquiring their toys. He finds it difficult to understand why his older brother has treats and does things which he is not allowed to do.

The boy in a family of girls
The only boy in a family of several children may be overprotected and the subject of favouritism. He may be domineering in his ways towards the girls. Occasionally a boy in this position takes on the ways of girls and becomes effeminate in his behaviour.

The girl in a family of boys

The only girl in a family of boys may be overprotected and the subject of favouritism, just like a boy in a similar position. She may become a 'tomboy', or be rejected by the boys.

The adopted child

There is no reason to feel that the adopted child is more likely to have behaviour problems than any other. He may be adopted by elderly parents, and develop certain problems as a result of this. If parents know that he has had an unhappy time before they took him, they may pity him so much that they are overindulgent with him and spoil him.

It is better to adopt the child when he is a small baby than later. Even a young baby misses a lot of mother love if brought up in an institution, and it is possible that after a good many months of this deprivation his future character may be affected. It is difficult for a two- or three-year-old to change homes, so to speak, and to settle down in a new home. Babies adjust to the change well and with little difficulty. The only trouble about early adoption is that it is less easy to be sure that the child is mentally normal. It should be easy to tell that, however, by the time he is six to nine months of age, before adoption is clinched.

It is easy for the parents to ascribe his behaviour problems to his family background. He will have behaviour problems, like any other normal child, but they are more likely to be related to his management than to the character of his real parents. Any normal child after the age of three is apt, in a rage, to say to his mother and father 'I hate you'. Adopting parents should not be disturbed by this normal behaviour.

It is better to tell the child as soon as he is ready to understand, usually about four years of age, that he is adopted. It has been suggested that the child should be told in the form of a story, about a mummy and daddy who badly wanted a child and looked all over for one, until eventually they found just the child they wanted. If he is not told, he is apt to find out later and be seriously disturbed, particularly if he finds out at a time when some friction is occurring in the home, or if he is told by someone other than the parents.

It is important that the child shall always be certain that he is loved and wanted. It would be wrong to remind him when he is being naughty that he is adopted, for he would then gather that he is not really loved.

Special problems facing the handicapped child

The child who is physically or mentally handicapped has many problems, but we shall mention only a few and very briefly. The handicaps include physical ones, such as cerebral palsy or muscular dystrophy, congenital heart disease, severe asthma and diabetes, amongst many others. When the child is old enough to understand, he feels different from others. This is particularly relevant in early adolescence. Partly for this reason we think that special schools (e.g. for the delicate, partially deaf or partially sighted) are to be avoided where at all possible.

Handicapped children are liable to experience favouritism at home; partly as a result they are viewed with jealousy by their brothers and sisters: the handicapped child has good reason to feel jealous of them. He is particularly liable to be overprotected, whereas every possible help should be given to make him independent and acquire self confidence.

He is liable to be lonely, because of difficulty in establishing friendships, and in adolescence, depending on the handicap, there may be special sexual problems.

Parents when aware of these problems, can do much to minimise them.

17

Sleep

We propose to discuss the management of sleep in some detail, because such conflicting advice is given, and because most babies and small children sooner or later present a sleep problem, which if badly managed may persist for many months and cause anxiety and inconvenience. Many a mother feels to be at her wit's end about the problem. On the one hand, she finds that she is unable to make her child go to sleep, and on the other hand, she knows perfectly well that he needs more sleep, because he is tired out and cross and irritable during the day.

Where should be sleep?
The importance of open air has been discussed elsewhere. During the day the baby should sleep outside if there is a suitable place which is reasonably protected from draughts, and provided that it is not wet or foggy. At night he should sleep in his parents' room until he has stopped demanding night feeds (normally about ten weeks), and then be put into a room of his own, if this is possible. In cold weather it is reasonable to warm the cot or pram before putting him into it. The hot bottle is then taken out, in case he should be burnt.

Keeping him warm
Active babies, after about 6 months of age, often kick their bed-clothes off. They are likely to be found lying transversely across the bed, or lying the wrong way round. A year-old child will often be found asleep on top of the bedclothes. In winter this is a nuisance. One way to get over the difficulty is to put the child into a sleeping bag. It is unwise to tie it near the neck, because of the possibility that he will wriggle into it and suffocate. Another method is the use of clips, which clip the blankets and are tied by tape to the bars of the cot. The disadvantage of these is the remote possibility that the child will wriggle under the blankets and suffocate. At about 2½ years of age children learn to pull the bedclothes over them at night. In cold weather you should also consider the possibility of putting a low-

powered nursery radiator into his room to keep it warm at night. It must be absolutely safe so that he cannot possibly get a burn or shock from it. Such radiators take little electricity but they do take the chill away.

The older baby will often refuse to keep mittens and socks on, even in cold weather. Hands can be kept warm by sewing the mittens to the dressing gown or other article of clothing.

The 2½ to 3 year-old may climb out of the bed or cot and be found asleep on the floor. Many babies and small children sleep on their stomachs. This is harmless, provided that they have no pillow and the mattress is firm, and it is probably a position to encourage. Babies sleep more if placed on the abdomen, they cry less, and it is safer for them, because if they are sick they are less likely to inhale vomit than if they are lying on their back.

Cot or bed?

It is not possible to lay down a rule about the age at which a child should change from a cot to a bed. The change should not take place just at the time that a new baby arrives, for a child becomes attached to his own cot. The essential point that should decide the mother is the possibility that he may climb out of the cot. We have known a 1 year-old baby climb out of his cot, but it is unusual for a child under 2 to do it. The risk will depend partly on the height of the side of the cot. A child who falls to the floor after climbing over the side of his cot is more likely to hurt himself than a child who rolls off a low bed. One of use saw a child of 4½ years who had fallen out of his cot and broken his arm. This is inexcusable. If he has a bed, it is possible for him to attend to his own toilet needs.

When the change is made, the safest bed is a low one, with a soft mat at the side to break his fall. It is not desirable to tuck the bedclothes in too tightly, because of the habit some children have of wriggling under the bedclothes, but it is unusual for a child to fall out of bed at all. It may occur on holiday if the bed is in a different position in relation to the wall. If, for instance, the child is accustomed to having the right side of the bed against the wall, he may fall out if on holiday there is nothing to stop him falling out at that side.

Some feel that a child should not be allowed to have toys in bed. We do not agree with this. We see no reason why he should not have some of his favourite toys, as long as they are not toys which may hurt him in the dark. They will give him something to do in the morning when he awakens. We do not think that they will keep him awake in the evening.

Duration of sleep

Many books lay down the exact duration of sleep which children at various ages require. What they do not say is how to make the child go to sleep when he decides to stay awake. It is usually impossible to make a child sleep longer than he normally does, provided that his bedtime is at a reasonable hour — and without drugging him. What these writers have failed to realize is the obvious fact that not all children are the same, but that all children are different. Some babies and small children require much less sleep than others. We cannot help feeling that those writers who state exactly how long children at various ages must sleep have never themselves had to deal with determined characters in the resistant phase who have their own views on the matter.

The amount of sleep required by children depends largely on their personality and possibly on their intelligence. Most placid babies present few sleep problems. They sleep the large part of the day even at 6 months of age. The wiry, active, determined type of baby behaves differently. Even at 3 months his naps are short ones, and at 6 months of age he may only have about half-an-hour's sleep during the day. Yet he is perfectly well and possesses boundless energy — and will continue to have, as the mother will in due course find out.

The exhausted mother who possesses an active baby who is awake nearly all day should take consolation in the thought that such babies are usually the more intelligent ones. We certainly would not say that because a 6 month-old baby sleeps most of the day he is unintelligent, for that would be wrong. But many babies of superior intelligence seem to be born with a more mature nervous system than others, so that they need less sleep and yet are more awake and alert than the average child. The variations in the sleep requirements of babies and small children are so great, and it is so impossible to force them to go to sleep, that rigid statements about the exact duration of sleep which children should have are impractical and senseless.

On going to sleep

It is important to remember that while the baby in the newborn period cannot help going to sleep after a good feed, the older baby can. Many babies at 1 or 2 months of age cry for a few minutes before lapsing into sleep, probably due to fatigue. Later on, after about 6 months of age, children commonly cry for a few minutes when put to bed. Some have termed this the 'testing cry', implying that the cry represents an attempt to get the mother back into the

bedroom. Some determined babies of even 6 months seem to find it difficult to get off to sleep, and scream and resist for prolonged periods. This resistance is more often met with in the toddler between 15 months and 3 years in the phase of negativism. A child can resist sleep for two or three hours, even though obviously exhausted. The placid child presents little problem in this way, for he just lapses into sleep without effort.

Naps

All babies have one or more naps in the first few months of life, and these naps present little difficulty. The active, alert baby of 3 months onwards, who wants little sleep and is intensely interested in his surroundings, will find it difficult to sleep in a place where there is any movement to be seen. Babies learn to watch the window for their mother, and to scream as soon as they see her. Such babies have to be placed in a quiet spot where they will not be disturbed.

It is a help to the mother if the naps are as near as possible to the same time every day, but it is no use saying that they should be at exactly the same time, because the baby may think otherwise. Some children need their nap in the late morning, and some in the afternoon.

It is always better to put the baby or older child to bed, whether for his nap or night's sleep, before he is too tired, for an overfatigued child may sleep badly and find it difficult to get off to sleep. On the other hand, it is no use expecting a child to have a nap if he is particularly wide awake.

By about 2 years of age many children become awkward about the midday nap. The placid ones do not object. The active, alert ones often do, even though they are obviously tired. This stage is troublesome, for when the child misses the nap he is tired out for the rest of the day, and the parents do not want him to fall asleep at 4 p.m. or 5 p.m. because even a short nap at that time is likely to postpone considerably the time at which he is ready to go to bed at night. It is not always possible to avoid a late nap in such cass. It can sometimes be prevented by giving the child his evening bath unusually early (perhaps before tea) and letting him come down in his dressing gown, for a hot bath often serves to restore his flagging energy. Sometimes the use of a little imagination will enable the child to have his midday nap even though he is much against it. The suggestion that he should lie 'in a little house' constructed on the floor or sofa, instead of putting him to bed, may persuade him to lie down and have a rest. The word, 'sleep' should be avoided. Even if he does lie down, he is apt to have a boisterous and noisy time, and may not sleep at all, though he gets some rest. He cannot be made to go to sleep. However, most children accept the midday or afternoon nap until about the third birthday, and may accept it for some months after that.

No rules can be laid down about the duration of the nap. It is an obvious temptation for the mother to let the child sleep as long as he will, but it is not reasonable to expect a child to sleep from, say, 2 p.m. to 5 p.m., and then be ready for his night's sleep at 6 p.m. On the other hand, if the nap is too short he may be over-fatigued in the evening and so fail to go to sleep. The correct duration of the nap can thus in many cases only be found by trial and error. It depends on his age and sleep requirements. In many cases the child himself supplies the answer by awakening and getting up.

Habits in connection with sleep
One sees habits in connection with sleep in babies as young as 3 months, when it is obvious that crying in the evening, which began as '3 months colic', continues when there is no more pain. The baby becomes used to being picked up every evening, and continues to demand it. This crying has to be ignored, so that the habit is broken. As early as 16 weeks old a baby may object to strange surroundings, as on holiday, and refuse to go to sleep. Thereafter as the baby gets older he becomes more and more liable to habit formation.

Any time after about 9 months a baby may rub his eyes when tired, and put his finger or fingers into his mouth. We have seen a 2 year-old deliberately take his gloves off when tired, in order to insert his fingers into the mouth. Removal of the fingers from the mouth by the mother (which is unnecessary) is likely to be resisted till about 2½ to 3 years of age. From about a year or so sleep often becomes associated with a particular teddy, rag or toy, so that when tired he looks for and hugs the teddy, and demands it before going to sleep. Often the child not only hugs the teddy, but puts the fingers into the mouth as well.

Between 9 months and 2 years many babies rock on hands and knees before going to sleep, shake the bed, or roll or bang their heads in bed. This is normal, and no steps should be taken to stop it.

Between about 21 months and 3 years most children develop what are called *sleep rituals* — demanding this, that and the other before going to sleep. They may demand that the door should be opened to a particular point and no further, and that the blind be drawn half-way down, no more and no less. They ask for a drink and then the potty and a series of stories. Some children have learned to prolong the process of going to bed in this way by as long as half-an-hour. These rituals are harmless enough if they only occupy a minute or so, but the mother must not let the child keep adding to them, for sooner or later she will have to put her foot down and stop it. This will cause resistance and crying, but it will have to be ignored.

We often think that a clever child with a high degree of intelligence must learn habits, good and bad, quicker than a child of low intelligence. An intelligent baby quickly learns various means of getting his parents just where he wants them — if he is given the chance. He learns that all he has to do in the evenings is to cry out and make enough noise to get his mother back to him, and that if he does it often enough, as soon as her back is turned, she will eventually sit with him until he has gone to sleep. The toddler learns that if he lies awake when put to bed his mother will come in to see him every few minutes and he stays awake for the next visit. He may get both parents to sit with him and play games with him, and as a result a thoroughly enjoyable evening passes quickly — for the child. He may find that if he screams out later in the night he will be given a hot drink. He finds a hot drink at 1 a.m. every morning most pleasant and refreshing. Even so, he prefers company, and an hour later he decides that he would like to be in his parents' bed. He was taken there once when he cried and he liked it very much, so he demands to be taken there every night. He screams out again and this time refuses to be quietened by anything, until finally he is taken into their bed. Then he sleeps, but he has had a disturbed night, and is thoroughly bad tempered and cross all day as a result. He finds the day difficult, but he really enjoys himself at night. He loves the fuss and attention, and after all, considering his age, he has achieved quite a lot, for he has the whole house revolving about his sleep.

We often see striking examples of the success of small children in achieving what they want at night. We see mothers who are compelled, so they say, to spend three hours with a child at night, because whenever they go away he cries. One frequently sees children who have their mothers going in to see them twelve or more times in the night. They often have the idea that the child has 'wind', or some such discomfort. Even older children of 6 years or more still successfully secure a warm drink in the middle of every night by calling out and making enough noise.

A mother must realize that habits are readily produced in children. The best managed children develop them, but a wise mother soon realizes that a habit has started and she promptly puts her foot down — and the habit is then broken.

The difficulties which may arise as a result of illness are discussed in Chapter 27.

The usual age at which troublesome sleep problems begin is 9 to 12 months — when the baby discovers that if he howls when put to bed (or when he awakens) he will be picked up, cuddled, taken downstairs to the nice warm sitting room, where the rest of the family is, or into his parents' bed. It is wise not to start this habit. Once started, it is not easy to break. If it is not broken, it may continue for years — so that the parents will have years of broken nights.

Bedtime

We do not think that it is sensible to lay down an exact time at which children of various ages should go to bed. We would certainly agree that some small children are put to bed far too late, and are tired next day as a result, but there are so many variable factors that it is impossible to lay down rigid rules. We have already discussed the importance of the personality of the child in connection with his sleep requirements. The length and the time of his afternoon nap, the question of whether he has discarded the nap, and the time of getting up in the morning, must have an important bearing on his bedtime. So must the amount of exercise and excitement which he has had in the daytime. A nap of as little as a quarter-of-an-hour at 4.30 p.m. may postpone the two-year-old's bedtime from the usual 6 p.m. to as late as 8 p.m. We do not think that one should expect an active, determined 2 or 3 year-old to go to bed willingly and sleep when he is not at all tired. Commonsense should be used at all times in child management.

On the other hand, it is important to inculcate good habits — and as has been repeatedly emphasized, habits good and bad are learnt rapidly, particularly by intelligent children who learn quickly. Every effort should be made to ensure that the bedtime is as regular as is reasonably possible, and in the case of a placid child it is not necessary to alter the bedtime. But for other children under special circumstances the bedtime should be put forward or back, according to the dictates of commonsense.

One would expect a 2 to 4 year-old to go to bed at about 6 p.m. One would not be horrified, however, if one heard that because of an unavoidable late nap a 2½ year-old had not gone to bed till 8 p.m., but we would certainly think that this should not be the rule, and that every effort should be made, if for nothing else but the interests of the parents, to put the bed-time back to a more usual hour. In this connection there is nothing like healthy out-of-doors exercise for bringing about fatigue and readiness for bed.

Preparation for bed

When the child is reasonably fatigued and bedtime has come, every effort should be made to make it a pleasant time which he will enjoy. Threats of bed for wrongdoing are always wrong, for they are bound to suggest that bed is a punishment and unpleasant. The child should have warning that he will have to stop playing with his toys.

It is common for the mother to be in a hurry at the child's bedtime, and to tend to snatch the toys from him, with resulting tears. There should be no fight about tidying up. He has to learn to tidy up, but the 2 to 4 years-old should be given a helping hand.

On no account must there be any argument about bedtime. This must never be allowed to begin. Once the child discovers that by a display of resistance or by throwing a temper tantrum, he can postpone bedtime, he will inevitably do it every night. One often sees children who are allowed to make ridiculous scenes about going to bed. One of us saw a 10 year-old boy who refused every night to go to bed, and the parents tried all manner of methods for four hours every night to get him off. Once the mother has said that it is bedtime, the normal amount of time is allowed for the child to stop what he is doing and to tidy up, but no further procrastination is allowed. The parents must be consistent over this matter. It is fatal for the father (often in an attempt to court favour from the child) to say 'Let him have another half-hour' when the child, having been told by the mother that it is bedtime, seeks his opinion. If the parents are absolutely firm and consistent about this, the child will know that the parents say what they mean, and there will be no fight and no tears at bedtime. (There may be tears and some resistance if the child is overtired, and in that case he should have gone to bed earlier).

There is a danger that the process of getting the child off to bed will be rushed when both the parents are going out for the evening, or are having friends into a meal, or are feeling tired, so that he will be put to bed a little before he is ready for it. The child soon senses that an effort is being made to get him out of the way, and may be difficult as a result. Patience and absence of hurry will win in the long run.

Bathtime should be a time of pleasure, which the child will enjoy. He should be given time to play with the bath toys and to splash. The determined, independent child should be allowed to help in preparing the bath and to undress or help in undressing. If the mother is in a hurry, she may cause tears by ripping the child's clothes off herself, because it is so much quicker, instead of letting the child do what he wants, and undress himself. Tears should be avoided at all stages, so that bedtime is pleasant. The same applies to dressing after the bath. It is often difficult to get the child out of the bath. Once more firmness and refusal to argue is essential. Once the child finds that by argument and resistance he is able to stay longer in the bath, there will be resistance every night. He should be allowed, as soon as he is old enough (say, 3 years), to dry himself, to brush his teeth and to put his pyjamas on. He then goes to bed — and this is another time at which trouble often occurs.

He is put to bed, kissed, tucked in and left. Or is he? Many a 1 to 3 year-old springs up like a jack-in-the-box when he has been laid down. He stands up, and the unwise mother lays him down again. Up he jumps, and he has a thoroughly enjoyable game. Once he discovers that he can have this bit of fun, he will have it every night. The mother should ignore his refusal to lie down. If he jumps up, he is left standing up. It will be necessary in the case of the young child to go into his room later to cover him up, for he is likely to be found asleep on top of his bed-clothes. It is a wise thing to have a blanket or two on a chair, so that they can be put over him when he is asleep. When we have told mothers about this treatment, they exclaim that they are afraid that he will fall out of his cot. In that case he should be in a bed. If he is already in a bed, they say that they are afraid that he will open the door and fall downstairs in the dark. (Children can turn the door handle between 2 and 2½). In that case a catch can be placed on the door so that he cannot get out. It is wrong to lock a child in his bedroom, but during this temporary phase it may be wise to put a catch on the door.

It often happens that a toddler, aged 2 to 3, will go to bed easily for the father and refuse for the mother. Naturally, the father claims that this is simply because he knows how to manage the child. In fact, it is more often due to the greater attachment to the mother. Children at this age often go through a stage of increased dependence on the mother, and they are loth to be left by her at night. If the mother hesitates or shows anxiety, and lets the child know that she is uncertain whether he will lie down and behave when put to bed, he will certainly leap up and be difficult. The problem is not usually difficult to deal with, once its nature is understood. It may be desirable for the father to put the child to bed for a week or two, and then let the mother take over. Whether he does not, the essential thing is to realize that this is largely an attention-seeking device, and that it must be dealt with by letting the child see that the mother is not interested whether he lies down or stands up in bed, and that if he cries it will not benefit him. There is no denying that a determined child can be difficult in this way.

Crying when put to bed

The so-called 'testing cry' has already been described. When the 1 to 3 year-old child is put to bed he may cry for a minute or two, partly in the hope that the mother will come back to him. It must be ignored.

The baby can be rocked to sleep on occasions, but if it is done regularly, a habit will be created, so that he will not be able to go to sleep without rocking.

This section concerns a real problem, that of the child who not only cries but screams, and keeps on screaming, when put to bed. It is common, and no easy matter to deal with. It is usually due to a bad habit — the child having learnt that by screaming he can get his mother back to him. It may be due to putting him to bed before he is reasonably fatigued. It may be due to the fact that he has been taught to regard bed as an unpleasant place, because he is sent to bed as a punishment when he has been naughty. He may be crying because he is afraid of the dark, or of shadows on the wall, or of the curtains billowing in the wind. It is normal for children of 18 months to 3 years to develop this fear. He may be afraid of a peculiar shadow cast on the wall by a street lamp. In most cases the crying is basically due to his love for his mother and his unwillingness to be separated from her.

A two-year-old, crying when put to bed, was clever enough to say to her mother 'I love you, mummy, and I feel lonely in my room all by myself without you. Don't you feel lonely downstairs without me?' It is wrong when a child cries out at night to accuse him of being 'naughty'. It is not naughty to want to be loved. Adults too like to be loved — and dislike being lonely.

Many small children cry out because of their desire for fuss and attention. Many may cling to their mother if she has been out at work all day and they have seen little of her.

Some mothers refuse to be tied by their small children, and continue with their outside interests just as they used to do before having children. An insecure child is likely to be difficult if he finds that his mother is going to go out in an evening. It is wrong not to tell a child who is old enough to understand, for he might be greatly disturbed if he awoke in the evening and found a strange person in his bedroom whom he did not know.

Crying when put to bed is often due to attempts to make the child go to sleep. Any such attempt is bound to fail, for the child deliberately does the opposite of what is wanted of him. Appeals to him to 'be a good boy and go to sleep' or threats of punishment if he does not, will almost inevitably make him do the opposite and stay awake. He senses his mother's anxiety and he enjoys the fuss and attention his sleep refusal causes. When there is overcrowding, or there are unkind neighbours who complain whenever the child cries, or when the child is on holiday, and other people have to be considered, the problem is an extremely difficult one. But the mother must realize that efforts to make the child go to sleep are bound to fail. Often there is no discoverable cause for the child's behaviour. Children have phases of good and bad behaviour at night.

Much depends on his age. The 9 month to 2 year-old child can be rocked to sleep. The child who is 2½ to 3 years old or more should be told to stop the noise and then left. The child from 18 months to 2½ or 3 who is not old enough to understand, cannot be dealt with by punishment. Exceptionally, he can be taken downstairs, if it appears that he is not as tired as was thought when he was put to bed, but if this occurs on successive nights a habit will inevitably be created and the habit will have to be broken. It is unwise for the mother to sit with the child because he cries when she goes out, and still more unwise to read stories or play with him, or to get into bed at his side. If this is done a habit will inevitably be created.

If a bad habit has developed, it is no use thinking that he will grow out of it. Children do not. Sleep problems of this nature may persist for years unless firmly dealt with, and the sooner they are dealt with the easier it is to stop them. When a 2½ to 3 year-old child has developed a habit, the habit has to be broken by leaving him to cry. He will then have to learn that he will achieve nothing by crying. Unfortunately, it is not easy to teach him.

A good mother finds it painful to hear her child screaming prolongedly without going to soothe him, but she has to realize that it is in his interests so that he gets more rest. She will have to look in (for a second only, preferably without him seeing) at infrequent intervals, to see if he is safe, for he may be strangling himself, or in some awkward position (e.g. with his legs hanging through the bars of the cot) from which he cannot extricate himself. Some babies and small children have the unfortunate habit of making themselves sick by crying — largely by swallowing air, and so making the stomach

distend with wind. But having made sure that he is safe, he must be left.

The difficult thing is to say how long he should be left crying. It is no use saying that every child, if he is left to cry it out, will get over the habit in three or four days. Most do, but some do not. Neither is it possible to say that he will not cry longer than an hour if left. Some children show incredible powers of resistance, even though tired out, and can scream for hours on end. In such obstinate cases there is only one possible line of treatment — to give a medicine which will make him sleepy. This is a matter for the family doctor. In our experience phenobarbitone does not help. Chloral is the best drug in that it is the safest, and it always works if given in sufficient dosage. This has to be determined by trial and error, because although a small dose works for some children, a large dose is needed for others. It should be given not after the crying has begun, but before he is actually put into bed, so that when he is put into the bed he is very sleepy. The crying, if any, is ignored. The effect of the medicine does not last long. The point of the medicine is merely that he cannot help but fall asleep. Medicine should only be used for about a week — long enough to break the habit. It is always wrong to 'drug' a child night after night, and a lamentable confession of failure of management. It should be noted that when medicine is given every night, the child gets into the habit of expecting it, and will not go to sleep without it. It becomes part of the so-called 'sleep ritual'. This habit must then be broken.

The importance of being consiste.   .ust be emphasized. Good habits can be taught as readily as bad habits, with proper management. The mother who 'tries out' various methods of management, and who takes the child downstairs one night when he cries, leaves him to cry it out on the following night, and on the night after sits and plays games with him, is not likely to teach him a good habit. Neither will he taught a good habit by being left crying on one night only.

It is important to remember that every child from a year onwards loves fuss and attention, and likes to feel important. For this reason it is essential that she should never discuss the sleep problems in front of him, so letting him realize how interested she is in them.

The soundness of sleep

The soundness of sleep varies from child to child. Most children waken up at some time in the night, but they go to sleep again without trouble. It is common enougn for an 18 month-old child to lie awake for an hour or two talking, and for a 2 year-old to awaken at 1 a.m. and sing nursery rhymes for an hour. No attempt should be made to stop this. He should be left strictly alone. If the mother goes in to see him, and the process is repeated on successive nights, a habit is formed, and he will cry out for his mother as soon as he awakens. Even if he is tired next day as a result of lack of sleep, there is nothing which she can do about it. It may be that he is a long time in going to sleep because he was not tired when put to bed, perhaps as a result of too long a midday nap, or too late a nap. You may try the experiment of adjusting the nap, but the odds are that it will not make any difference.

It is said that girls sleep more soundly than boys. It has also been suggested that the more intelligent child sleeps less soundly than others, but we do not know whether this is true. Some young babies awaken at the slightest sound. Others sleep through anything. The young baby sleeps soundly after a good feed. This is a nuisance in the late evening, when the parents want to give the baby his last feed before they go to bed. It is annoying, after trying in vain to awaken him, to hear his shrieks for food half-an-hour after they have got into bed. Older babies are more easily awakened.

It is undesirable for the parents to have to creep about on tip-toes for fear of awakening the baby, though it is easy to understand why they do this, when a baby, once awakened, is awkward about going to sleep again. A child has to get used to the ordinary household noises.

Causes of awakening

The young baby is awakened by hunger, cold or excessive heat, by noise, a bright light or by discomfort, as from 3 months colic. Hunger is not a cause of awakening in the night after about ten weeks of age, except occasionally for the first few days after weaning has begun, or for a day or two after some infection, when he has an unduly big appetite.

Though the pain of teething may be severe, so that the crying continues even when he is picked up, it often seems to be trivial discomfort which is enough to awaken him, or to keep him awake once he has awakened, so that he begins to cry. The crying stops as soon as his mother comes in, and she is apt to think that he is merely being 'naughty', or has got into a bad habit. It is difficult to be sure. Any grown-up knows that a trivial discomfort may keep him awake, and it is reasonable to suppose that the same thing will happen to a baby. If in doubt, you should pick him up, being careful to break a habit once you are satisfied that it is nothing more than that.

After the age of 6 months or so he may awaken with what appears to be a nightmare, letting out a sudden shriek. The shrieking continues till the mother goes in, when it promptly stops. He is found to be asleep or almost asleep, and as soon as he has been comforted (in a minute or two) he is left.

A common cause of sleep disturbance in older babies is the sharing of the bedroom with the parents. When the baby is still having feeds in the middle of the night (usually the first 10 weeks) it is more convenient for the parents to have him in their bedroom, and he sleeps more soundly at this age. But after that it is wise to put the baby in a bedroom of his own if possible, so that he will not be disturbed by them, for he is now more easily awakened. He is easily disturbed by their coming to bed, or by their coughing, making the bed squeak, or snoring. The intelligent child, who would readily go to sleep without difficulty in a room of his own, is soon likely to realize that his parents are there, and demand attention. He is particularly likely to be awakened by them early in the morning. The parents sleep less well, for they are disturbed by the baby, and the mother may lie awake wondering if the baby is all right, and she may even get up to see him. If there is not a room for the baby, it is often possible, at least in a flat, to carry the cot out of the bedroom into another room, such as the kitchen, so that he has an uninterrupted night. Some mothers do not like to have their baby in another room. They like to have him near them, but it is in the interests of both that they should be separated at night. When two children of different

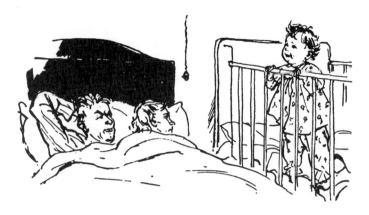

ages share a room, the one in bed first may be awakened by the other child, but this cannot necessarily be prevented.

The question of whether or not to awaken a 2 to 3 year-old child to put him on the potty, is discussed elsewhere (Chapter 19). A child who is 2 or more years of age may cry in the night because he wants to pass urine or to have a motion. This must not be discouraged.

Early morning awakening
Though the presence of parents in the same room is one of the cause of early morning awakening, it is not the only one. There is not usually any cause for it. Most young babies go to sleep after they have had a feed, but the older baby and the toddler are apt to think that the day has begun when they awaken at 5 a.m. They have had an excellent night's sleep, and they feel wide awake and very pleased. They have no idea of time. The toddler finds it difficult to understand why his parents are not as pleased to see him as he is to see them. The 3 year-old is likely to get up in the early hours of the morning and wander about the house. Early morning awakening of a child who had previously awakened at a reasonable hour is often most troublesome on holiday, possibly owing to the change is surroundings.

If he merely wakens up and sings, he should be left, but if he wakens up and cries, it is not so easy. It is useless to leave him crying, because he is wide awake and will cry for two or three hours on end, and still not go to sleep. It is undesirable for the parents to take him into their own bed, except as a 'treat' just before they get up, for this will inevitably lead to a habit, so that the child will demand it every day, and it will be a habit which will be difficult to break. In the case of a baby the parents should never take him into their own bed (except to feed him), for there is a serious danger that they will lie on him when asleep and suffocate him. If the baby will go to sleep after a feed and after his nappy has been changed, then he should be left to do so. The baby usually will. The toddler will not.

It may be thought that if the toddler goes to bed later in the evening he will awaken later in the morning. This may be tried, for it may work, but it will often be found that the reverse is the case — he will awaken earlier still, or else it makes no difference. In the case of the baby aged, say, 6 to 9 months, the parents may try awakening him for his 10 p.m. feed, even though he has outgrown this, but this is not likely to help. You may think that it would be a good idea to fix a blind in his room, so that in the summer months the room will be dark in the morning. It is worth trying, but it is not likely to work. It is annoying, after fixing a blind, to find oneself buying a night light because he has become afraid of the dark!

There is, in fact, nothing that one can do about the problem. One should see that he has some toys in bed with him, so that he has something to do when he awakens in the morning. It is often a temporary phase, and after a few weeks the child begins to awaken later, but one cannot promise this with certainty. By the age of 2½ to 3 years the child is old enough to understand that he must not awaken his parents in the morning. He should be told firmly when put to bed at night that he must not awaken them, and if he does awaken them, he must be reprimanded and told to stop it.

Awakening and crying
Some children go to sleep without difficulty, only to waken up, often after about a quarter of an hour, though sometimes not until the early hours of the morning, and call out for the mother or cry and scream. Children who have gone to bed thoroughly tired may show wonderful recuperative powers and be wide awake after a mere 15 minutes' sleep. This is a difficult problem. If the child goes to bed overfatigued, he is liable to sleep badly. One may therefore try the experiment of lengthening his afternoon nap or putting him to bed earlier. It has already been pointed out that a child cannot be expected to sleep well unless reasonably fatigued, so the opposite may be tried too — putting him to bed later, unless it is obvious that he would be too tired, or shortening his nap. It is a matter of trial and error.

When a child awakens and cries, the action depends on the nature of the cry. If it is a mere half-hearted cry followed by a whimper, he is left. But if it is obviously increasing to a full throated roar, or if it begins with a shriek, the parent should go in to see him. If left, he becomes almost hysterical, and cannot stop. The cry which began as a call for his mother becomes a cry of distress; long after the crying has stopped, even though he is happy in his mother's arms, the irregular gasping respirations known as sobbing may persist. It hardly ever pays to put a child back to his bed, after picking him up, if he has not stopped sobbing.

If he has had a night terror, he needs comforting. He may have fallen out of bed, or have got into an awkward position, or have been sick or feel poorly, so he must be seen. The parent should only stay long enough — usually a minute or two — to comfort him. One has often seen mothers who stayed an hour or two every night with their child, because every time they tried to leave him he cried.

If the crying out is repeated, and it is obvious that it is merely a habit, the habit must be broken. The younger child is merely left to cry, though the parent may have to glance at him at infrequent intervals in order to make sure that he is safe. The older child, of 2½ onwards, is told in no uncertain language that he must stop the nonsense, and if he does not he is smacked, and any further crying is ignored. If the habit has been allowed to continue for a long time, it is not an easy one to stop.

Some psychiatrists think that it is always wrong to leave a child crying at night. But it is very much in the child's own interests that his lack of adequate sleep because of prolonged crying should be remedied. It is very much in the interests of both parents that a bad habit of repeated crying at night should be stopped: the parents get worn out, tired and irritable, domestic friction may occur, and the child suffers for it. The habit has to be broken.

Crying on being awakened

It is usually at about 2½ years of age that a child cries and screams after he has been awakened in the morning or from the midday nap. It is a peculiar difficulty which resolves itself soon after the third birthday. It seems that he feels terrible when awakened, and he screams and screams and nothing seems to please him. He cries when picked up, he cries when put down, he refuses his favourite toy, he refuses his dinner. Everything is wrong. The crying may go on for as long as an hour.

It can be avoided in part by making the awakening a gradual process, by going into the room, pulling the blind up, then leaving him and returning in a few minutes. There is nothing much otherwise to do about it except to give love and to avoid scolding him and trying to force him to behave. He cannot help it. It is not a habit. It is normal, and he will stop after a few months.

If, when the child has reached his third birthday, there is still trouble about awakening him, you may try the effect of letting him miss his nap. The difficulty is that the may be excessively tired as a result, and if you try to restart his midday nap he may object violently.

Sleep walking

Sleep walking is only rarely a problem in the first 5 years. It occurs in 10 to 15 per cent of older children. It is thought that there is a hereditary tendency: it is six times more common in identical twins than in non-identical ones. Injury during sleep walking is unusual. Some children only do it when they go to bed soon after a meal. In that case care must be taken to time the meal differently. Otherwise no treatment makes any difference.

Sleep talking

Some young children and a few older ones often talk in their sleep. It is of no importance and no treatment is necessary.

Nightmares

Most children sooner or later have nightmares or night terrors. Some have them more than others. It is impossible to say how soon they begin, but we suspect that they can occur by 6 months of age. They tend to occur in particular when an infection is beginning, or when there is a sudden noise, or when the child has been particularly tired. They may be due to having a heavy meal before going to bed. Unless they are frequent, there is no need to do anything about them, except that you should go to see the child when he suddenly cries out, so as to comfort him and give him the security which he needs.

If the nightmares are really frequent, say, every day, they are likely to be due to insecurity, some unhappiness at home or school. The cause should be looked for and removed.

Conclusion

Sleep problems can be very trying for the parents. It would be wrong to suggest that they are easy to deal with. But from experience of many hundreds of children with such problems we have done our best to suggest the best way of managing them.

18

The appetite: obesity

> What is the matter with Mary Jane?
> I've promised her dolls and a daisy chain,
> And a book about animals, all in vain.
> What is the matter with Mary Jane?
>
> What is the matter with Mary Jane?
> She's perfectly well, and she hasn't a pain.
> And it's lovely rice pudding for dinner again.
> What is the matter with Mary Jane?
>
> (A.A. Milne. When we were very young)

Food refusal, which is called by mothers 'poor appetite', is probably the commonest of all behaviour problems. One is asked to see more children with this problem than with any other.

We have seen scores of mothers who are distraught because they cannot get their child to eat enough. They seriously believe that he is in danger of starving. They have tried everything to get him to eat. The essential fact is that if only they had not tried anything, the child would have been eating normally, for the child's poor appetite is nothing more than food refusal caused by the mother. The child has discovered a wonderful way of attracting attention to himself, and of making others realize his importance. He has succeeded in getting the whole house revolving around what he will deign to eat — and, of course, he loves it. He hears his mother discuss the problem with her friends. His terrible appetite is almost the sole topic of conversation which he hears. He thoroughly enjoys the scenes which occur at every mealtime. Furthermore, by making a fuss he gets his mother to give him just what he wants to eat, and he secures all manner of excellent bribes. He is allowed to develop a variety of food fads because of his mother's anxiety.

When a mother tells one that she has tried everything, she certainly means it. She has tried coaxing him, but he will not be persuaded.

She beseeches him to eat a little more. She watches every mouthful which he takes. She asks him to take a bit for Aunt Lizzie. She tells him that it is good for him, but apparently he could not care less. She asks him to eat just a little more so that she can tell his daddy when he comes in from work. Then she threatens him. She threatens to give his dinner to the girl next door, but he knows that that never happens, so he does not take any notice. She threatens to smack him if he will not eat. She says that he will not grow up big and strong like Uncle Tom unless he eats, but he does not care.

She tries to distract his attention, so that he will eat when he is thinking of other things. She reads stories to him and puts a mirror in front of him so that he can race the child in the mirror. She turns on the wireless, gramophone or television set. She lets him run about the garden, eating, so that he has something else to think about. She buys him comics. One has seen fathers creep on all fours pretending to be a horse, dog or bear, and several other fathers pretending to be dive bombers, in order that each time the bomber zoomed down the child would take a spoonful of food. One of us saw a 10 month-old baby whose mother, father, aunt and two uncles crept about the room after him with spoonsful of food, trying to get him to eat something. We have seen the brother roped in to set off an alarm clock near the child at frequent intervals, so that each time the boy wad distracted by the clock the mother could put a spoonful of food into his mouth. We heard of one child who would only eat when his father's car passed the window. As a result the father had to drive the car backwards and forwards, so that each time it passed the mother could put a spoonful of food in.

Most mothers faced with the problem try the effect of bribes. They offer him money if he will eat. They offer sweets, trips on the bus, trips to the park, or new toys. One of us saw a little girl who was making a lot of pocket money out of food refusal, with the consequent bribes. He has not forgotten her look of disappointment when he told her mother that it should stop. One boy refused to eat unless he was given a toy motor car, and his mother said that he had acquired nearly 300 cars in that way. If the child has any intelligence, he will put the price up and demand more and more. It pays him to be awkward about his meals, because otherwise he will not receive the bribes. So he continues to refuse his dinners.

Most mothers have tried so-called 'tonics'. They are useless, for the problem is simply one of food refusal. One of us saw a small child who would only eat his dinner if he was given a drink of Ribena and brandy before it.

All mothers faced with this problem try to force the child to eat, by putting the food in with a spoon. Any intelligent child hits the spoon with a well-directed blow, sending the contents on to the floor, or refuses to swallow the food and spits it out, or swallows it and deliberately vomits it up. Most children with this problem are smacked for refusing to eat, but the mother soon discovers that this does not help.

It almost inevitably follows that the child is allowed to have something to eat when he wants it between meals. The mother encourages this, for she genuinely fears that otherwise he will starve. One mother said that she always kept her boy's dinner warm, so that if ever he would eat some, it would be warm and ready for him. Another mother proudly displayed a bag of biscuits in her handbag. She said that she never went anywhere without those biscuits, so that if ever the boy said he would eat something she could give him one. One mother, who complained that her 2 year-old had a bad appetite, was giving him seventeen meals a day in an effort to keep him alive. We saw another child, aged 21 months, who was having 25 feeds of milk a day.

Children all over the country have a tremendous amount of fun out of refusing to eat. In poor homes, where there are numerous children, it is practically never a problem. The home in which it is a problem is the one with an only child in which a mother has time to devote to her child's eating. If she had not time, or had little love for the child, the problem would never arise.

What is the cause of the problem? There is no one factor. It often

arises in the weaning period (Chapter 5). The factors are those
mentioned in connection with other behaviour problems, his love of
fuss and attention and his desire to feel important, together with his
normal negativism and resistance between 9 months and 3 years or
so, which makes it impossible to force him to do things against his
will. *By far the commonest cause of food refusal and poor appetite in an
otherwise well child is food forcing. Coaxing and efforts to make him eat
inevitably have the opposite of the effect desired. The child refuses, and
the more fuss made over his appetite the more he will refuse.* We often
think that it is quite an achievement for an 18 month-old child to
cause his grandmother to dance a jig and his father to creep about on
all fours pretending to be a dog, in their efforts to get him to eat,
when he would hate to do without.

Another important cause of trouble is the fact that appetites vary.
Some children, like some adults, have a small appetite, but it is by
no means always the case that children with a small appetite are
below the average weight. The appetite is affected by the amount of
exercise which the child gets. If he is kept indoors all day, his
appetite is not likely to be as good as if he is playing out of doors. It is
well known that if a child is unhappy for any reason, because of
friction at home or school he may eat badly. Some normal children,
like some adults, have a particularly poor appetite for breakfast. One
of the commonest reasons for a mother's complaint that her child has
a poor appetite is the fact that he is small for his age, and so eats less
and wants less than children who are big for their age. The usual
reasons for a well child being small are that he takes after one or both
of his parents who are small, or that he was small at birth,

especially 'small for dates'. We are repeatedly impressed by the number of mothers who are seriously worried about their well active children being small for their age (and therefore commonly having a small appetite), and who have never thought that their children's smallness of stature is related to their own small size — measuring perhaps, under 5 feet in height and weighing seven stones. As a result of the child's small appetite the parents try to make him eat, and so he refuses. They may go further, and cause so much unpleasantness at mealtimes, with food-forcing, coaxings, threats of punishment or actual punishment, that the child becomes 'conditioned' against food, associating all food and mealtimes with unpleasantness, and so genuinely loses his appetite. This is a common and difficult situation to treat.

Many mothers are worried because their 9 to 12 months old baby seems to have lost his appetite. Whereas the average baby gains about 7 oz (198 g) a week in his first 3 months, he gains on average only 2 (56 g) to 2½ oz (71 g) a week in the fourth three months — with an associated falling off in appetite. The mother then tries to make him eat, and so he refuses. The same thing happens when a mother thinks that her child is 'delicate' or needs 'feeding up' after an illness. After an illness a child is particularly likely to be difficult. He has been pampered while poorly, and given just what he likes, and would like this to continue. His mother, anxious that he should eat 'strengthening' foods, tries to force him to take more — with the opposite of the effect desired.

There are many books which lay down the exact quantity of foods which children should eat at various ages. We know a well-known Textbook of Diseases of Children which says exactly how many spoonsful of this, that and the other the child should have at various meals. This is sheer nonsense. No one in their senses measures the amount of food which a 1 or 2 year-old has. He is given what he wants, with usually a bit to spare. With a baby in the first 5 months it is different, up to a point. One has to know the average amount which babies take, in order that one does not underfeed them, but no rigid rules are possible at any age.

Another frequent cause of trouble with the appetite is the way in which children dawdle with their food between 9 months and 3 or 4 years. They have no sense of time. They see not the slightest need for hurrying. They do not know why the mother needs to hurry to get her washing up and other work done. They love to play about with the food. The 1 year-old puts his hand into the food, and likes to run it through his fingers. He hits it with the back of his spoon, lifts a spoonful up and drops it down again. The mother thinks that he is playing with it because he does not want it, and she tries to hurry him up and attempts to feed him herself with a spoon. She needs to get the table cleared and to get washed up, so that she cannot leave him indefinitely. For both reasons she tries to make him take the food — and any intelligent, determined child promptly objects and refuses it. We are sure that this normal dawdling is one of the chief causes of food forcing and so of food refusal. Some mothers make the mistake of talking to friends about his poor appetite in front of him. They let him know that they expect him to eat badly. He does.

The mother cannot be blamed for her attitude. She loves the child dearly, and is convinced that he will starve if he is not forced to eat more. She has heard that children need greens, meat and milk pudding, and so insists that her child shall have all that the books say he ought to have. The child soon realizes how anxious she is that he should eat these foodstuffs, and so he refuses. If a mother insists that the boy shall finish his meat course, he will object and refuse to eat it. If she insists that he shall finish his pudding, and does not care what he eats of the first course, he will prefer the first course.

It is annoying for the mother, when she has gone to a lot of trouble to prepare something really nice for the child to 'tempt' him and he refuses to have anything to do with it. Mothers go to a great deal of trouble to find something which the child will eat. It leads to loss of temper and impatience. The child is reprimanded for not eating and possibly smacked. The mother may try to make him eat it — and the child refuses. It is not surprising that she feels at her wit's end. If she is of a domineering nature, and is used to being obeyed, it is annoying for her to be completely defeated by her small child — and she *will* be defeated if she tries to make him eat.

Another cause of food refusal is the constant nagging which goes on at so many dinner tables. Not only is the child constantly assailed by requests to eat a little more of what he has in front of him, but he is not allowed to have what he wants — his pudding, so insistent is his mother that he should eat the meat and greens, which she says are good for him, and so anxious is she that he shall not learn bad habits. A child has to learn to eat his first course before his pudding, because that is the custom, and he has to learn to do what others do. But he cannot learn until he is old enough to understand, and efforts to make him learn before he is ready lead to constant friction. Mealtimes become a sheer misery to the child and after a time a genuine distaste for food develops. One of us saw a 4 year-old who started to cry everytime the gong sounded for a meal. It is a pity that mealtimes, which are such a source of pleasure to a properly managed child, should become a battleground as they do. After all, what harm will it do if the 18 month-old child has pudding first and meat afterwards? He is too young to understand why he should conform to custom. Even if he leaves the meat, he will get enough protein in other ways — in egg and cheese, for instance. At teatime it is no use insisting on a child finishing his bread before he has a cake, until he is old enough to understand. Rather than have friction at every teatime it is better merely to put what he is likely to eat on his plate, and let him choose the order in which he eats it. When he is 2½ years old or so he will be ready to begin to learn the customary order in which the various items at tea are eaten. It is not worth while having a fight about it. It is different in the case of a 3 or 4 year-old, who is old enough to understand, but even at that age undue insistence on the meat course will do nothing more than turn him against meat. Food forcing is a potent cause of food fads. If constant efforts are made to force a child to take meat or greens or milk pudding against his will, he may dislike those foodstuffs for the rest of his life. It is difficult for a small child to eat his first course when an attractive-looking fruit dish or pudding is within his sight on the table or in the background. A child may eat his first course well until he catches sight of the pudding, and then refuse any more until he gets what he wants. The moral is obvious. The pudding should be kept out of sight until it is time for it.

Dislike of foodstuffs is readily suggested by careless remarks made by the parents. If a child hears his father say that he does not like a thing, he is likely to dislike the same food. It can be suggested in another way. Some parents, in their anxiety to teach their child about everyday matters, go into such detail about how meat is obtained from animals, even describing from what part of the animal it comes, that he will have nothing to do with it when it is put before him. You should be careful what you say to your child if he is of the imaginative type. It is easy to allow a child to develop fads about his foods. They should not be suggested by the parents and should not be allowed to develop.

There are many reasons why small children come to be coaxed and persuaded to eat, and why attempts are made to force them to eat. It is essential to realize that this food forcing is the cause of food refusal. There is nothing wrong with the child's appetite. He only refuses food because he is being forced. The trouble lies entirely in the parents, and not in the child.

No well child ever starves for not being forced to eat. It never happens. Persuasion is never necessary and should never be started. The vast majority of children are born in working order, and they have appetites which are sufficient for their needs.

Treatment

The treatment of poor appetite and food refusal is implicit in what
has been said. The appetite is ignored. The mother must take not the
slightest interest in what he eats. There must be no anxious looks at
the plate, and no remarks about it.

He should be given the food in a take it or leave it attitude, giving
him the impression that no one cares whether he eats it or not. He
should normally sit up to the table until everyone has finished. He is
not praised for eating his dinner. There is no more need to give him
praise for eating his dinner than there is for splashing in the bath. It
is normal behaviour and it is just taken for granted. He is not told
that he is naughty for not eating it. He is not naughty, and it is
useless in any case to say so. There should be no angry looks at him.
If he leaves the food, it is ignored. But if he refuses his dinner, there
should be nothing between meals. We do not think that it matters in
the least if a child who is eating normally has occasional oddments in
between meals, but if he is being difficult he must learn that there
will be nothing at all until the next mealtime, however hungry he is.
He can leave the whole meal if he wishes, but there will be nothing
else for him. A child quickly learns this. At the next mealtime the
same treatment is given. He can leave it if he wishes, and no one
cares. He will not starve and no harm will befall him. The mother
may say 'How long can he be left?' It is unnecessary to answer the
question, for no child ever does continue to do without meals. It
never happens.

It is essential that no interest should be taken in his food refusal.
All bribes should stop. It is no use taking half or three-quarters of
the above advice and not all of it. If, for instance, the mother stops
trying to force the food in with a spoon, and yet tries to persuade him
verbally or merely by her looks, the food refusal will continue. The
entire advice must be taken, and if it is, the appetite problem will
disappear, but it may take time, particularly in the case of those
children who have come to associate mealtimes with smackings and
unpleasantness.

It is reasonable and desirable to make the food look attractive.
Children like bright colours, and the appearance of the food is
important. It is important not to overload the child's plate. He may
feel so overfaced by it that he does not begin to eat it. He should be
given small helpings and left to ask for more if he wants it.

So much for the appetite in general. What of refusal of particular
foods? Mothers hear so much about the importance of a balanced

diet that they are seriously concerned about this. It has to be treated in the same way. It must be remembered that children from about 5 months onwards have genuine likes and dislikes. On rare occasions a particular food really upsets a child, just as may happen in adults, so that up to a point his dislikes should be respected. But only up to a point. The 4 year-old has to learn that it is bad manners to say 'I don't like that' at a mealtime, and it must be stopped.

Although no effort should be made to force a child to take a particular foodstuff, certain tricks can be legitimately employed. A child who refuses to drink milk may drink large quantities of it if he is allowed to pour it out himself. Children between the ages of 2 and 4 love to 'help' to cook, and if they are allowed to 'cook' for themselves, they are likely to eat the product of their own handiwork with relish. A 'tea party' in the garden, in which the children are allowed to pour milk out and get on with their meal without the mother being present, may well lead to the disappearance of an unusually large amount of food; but we do not want to suggest that the mother should set about thinking of ways to make her children eat. It is not necessary, for they will not starve. The child should become used to taking what the parents take, and as long as they take a reasonable diet themselves, and spend the available money wisely on substances of good food value, the child will obtain all that he requires. The child who refuses to eat greens, for instance, will come to no harm as long as he has plenty of fruit. The child who refuses meat will receive plenty of protein if he eats fish, eggs and cheese. The child who refuses eggs will be adequately nourished if the rest of his diet is well balanced.

Refusal to chew solid foods

This is an unusual but troublesome problem which commonly arises from lateness in weaning from the breast or bottle, with consequent food refusal and so food forcing. Children normally begin to chew at about 6 or 7 months of age, and if the year-old child has developed normally in other ways it is exceedingly unlikely that he will be unable to chew. We have never seen such as case, though we frequently see mentally defective children at that age who are retarded in all fields of development and are unable to chew. The difficulty is that if the child is not given solids (as distinct from thickened feeds), to chew when he has become able to chew, he may refuse to chew later. Psychologists are interested in the so-called sensitive period — the time at which the child has become able to carry out a particular act. If he is not given the chance to carry out the act then, he may prove unwilling to do it later. There are numerous examples of this in the animal kingdom. For instance, if the red squirrel is not given nuts to crack for a period after he has become able to crack them, he will never learn subsequently to do it. Babies must be given solids to chew when they are ready — usually at 6 to 7 months.

In the weaning period, refusal of solids is common. No forcing must be used. If the child over 12 months is still refusing solids, one may have to compel him to eat ordinary food by withholding everything else. He should not have his appetite so satisfied with milk and strained foods that he does not want anything else. This drastic treatment should only be given under the supervision of the family doctor.

Obesity

It is difficult to define obesity, and to distinguish the normal from the abnormal. One has to distinguish a big build from fatness.

We have advised mothers to weigh their babies and young children regularly — but not too frequently; one can then detect excessive weight gain (or inadequate weight gain) and take the appropriate steps.

One must do one's best to prevent a baby becoming significantly overweight; but this may be very difficult. If the baby is fully breast fed, and is putting excessive weight on, one cannot deal with the matter by giving him less time on the breast or giving him less frequent feeds: the determined hungry baby may announce his displeasure in no uncertain way. We would tend to begin weaning fairly early — say at four months — and would certainly not continue full breast feeding into the latter part of the first year — especially after about eight or nine months. The point about early weaning is that one can fill much space in the baby's stomach by puréed vegetables and fruit (on no account adding sugar or starchy foods or cereals). In fact the great majority of fully breast fed babies thin out in the toddler stage and shed their excess weight.

When a baby is bottle fed, in some ways it is easier to deal with the problems of excessive weight gain. We would certainly not allow him to exceed two pints of milk a day: as in the case of the breast fed baby he is weaned by giving him puréed fruit and vegetables and meat, but keeping all cereals to a minimum. In Chapter 4 we mentioned that tins of puréed food are liable to have a high carbohydrate content: if a mother has a liquidiser she should prepare the food herself, not adding sugar or starchy foods. When he is able to chew (at six or seven months), one must continue to avoid starchy foods, fried foods, potatoes and bread, as far as possible.

Although some of the factors responsible for obesity are not fully understood, it can be said confidently that no child (or adult) can become obese without eating more than he needs. This does not necessarily mean that the obese child is eating much more than others, but it usually means that. Some children have a tremendous appetite and do not become fat: others seem to become fat although their appetite seems to be merely moderate. This tendency to obesity often runs in families — as does the tendency to overeat, to avoid exercise and to have frequent snacks between meals.

Much obesity is due to the habit of overeating and of sweet-eating. The habit of overeating, of always demanding a second helping, perhaps because a brother does, should not be started. It is thoroughly foolish to encourage children to eat a large quantity of sweets. We see fat children who are given far too much money for sweets. These have a bad effect on teeth by causing dental decay; they take the appetite away and so reduce the intake of more valuable foods, such as protein, and they tend to make a child fat. Most fat children can be seen to be constantly eating sweets, lollipops, ice creams, potato crisps, peanuts and other foodstuffs. The grandmother and other relatives tend to give a child sweets as a token of affection, or a method of courting favour.

The cause of overeating is not always obvious. Psychologists say that it is often a behaviour problem — a reaction to a feeling of inferiority or of insecurity or a reaction to jealousy. Mothers may cause a child to become obese by giving him excessively starchy or fatty foods, particularly bread, potatoes, and fried food. They may cause it by giving him rich food because they fear that he is delicate as a result of some illness which he has experienced. Some mothers offer food to the baby every time he cries or has any discomfort. Some want their child to be fat. Some think that the child will sleep longer if given a large feed at night. More often, in our experience, there is no discoverable cause for the condition. It is of interest that most obese children are tall for their age.

As a rough guide, one can say that all fruit and vegetables, even baked beans, have low food value, as has rice, and therefore need not be restricted. Meat and fish have a relatively low food value. The following foods have a high food value: sweets, chocolate, cakes, jam tarts, puddings, sugar, butter, margarine, all nuts, cornflakes, biscuits, spaghetti, cheese (except cottage cheese) and especially cream cheese, cheese straws, bacon, sausage rolls, potato crisps, ice cream, peanut butter.

For mild overweight you should merely cut out sweets, and slightly reduce fried foods, bread and potatoes, and considerably reduce or eliminate cereals and rusks. Milk should be restricted to a pint a day.

For severe overweight, not only should sweets be eliminated but fried foods as well. Bread and potatoes should be severely restricted. It is then difficult to satisfy the child's hunger. Green vegetables can be given in unlimited quantities. Fruit can be given in considerable amounts. Plenty of protein, in the form of meat, fish, and cheese should be supplied. Excess of milk must be avoided. Before initiating any strict diet, it is essential for you to consult your doctor.

You should also do your best to see that your child gets plenty of exercise. Though it is true that exercise increases the appetite, and therefore partly loses its value in keeping weight down, it is a matter of common knowledge that lack of exercise is an important cause of obesity.

When the child is old enough to understand, certainly from three onwards, an attempt should be made to explain why the restrictions are imposed, without making him self-conscious about his obesity. The obesity (and still less the overeating) should never be discussed with others in front of him. The four- or five-year-old child may be rendered very self-conscious by careless conversation or by ridicule. Not only is obesity bad for health, but it leads to difficulties and embarrassment at school, and it is far better to treat it in the early stages than to wait until it is really advanced.

We do not advise the use of drugs to reduce the appetite. They have unpleasant side-effects, and usually the result, if any, is only temporary.

It is largely true to say that it is only the heaviest babies which have a significantly greater risk of obesity in later years: the heaviest ones have a two or three times greater risk than others of becoming overweight adults. But the majority of fat adolescents become fat adults.

19

Toilet training

Most children begin to acquire voluntary control of the bowel and bladder at about 18 months. Many babies are clean long before that age, but it is 'involuntary', and not intentional. Doctors call this 'conditioning'. By that they mean that when the baby is put on the potty regularly he acquires the habit of passing a stool or urine at the feel of the rim of the potty, but he does not do it on purpose. Many babies learn this as early as a month or two of age. That this emptying of the bladder can be 'involuntary' is shown by the way the older child, say, 2 or 3 years old, passes urine when placed on the potty on being lifted out of bed in the late evening fast asleep. He is put back to bed still fast asleep. This could not be 'voluntary' because the child has never wakened.

It is unusual for a child to tell his mother that he wants to use his potty before he is about 15 months old. The first indication that he is beginning to learn control is that he tells his mother when he has wet his nappy. Later he tells her when he is wetting it, and later still when he is just about to do so. Shortly after this he tells his mother in time, and can be more or less relied upon to say 'No' if he does not want to void when asked. He will need constant reminders for a good many months if accidents are to be avoided, for when concentrating on an interesting game he will forget to go to the lavatory until it is too late. In the meantime he will sorely test his mother's patience at times by passing urine immediately after he has left the potty. This should not be regarded as naughtiness, but a normal thing which will soon stop if it is ignored.

It is important to realize that in the early stage of learning control he cannot wait when once he feels the urge to empty the bladder. This urgency normally disappears in a few months, and by the age of 2 years most children can be relied upon to tell the mother in time, and some will fetch the potty themselves. By the age of 2½ most children learn to pull their pants down themselves and to climb on to the lavatory seat, attending to their own needs if wiped. Some awkward children are unable to have a bowel action unless they are

fully undressed, but that is unusual. By the age of 3 years, accidents
in the day are rare, though it is common for a child to wait until the
last minute, and then, feeling the urge, to shriek. He stands, rooted
to the spot, clutching himself down below, and often allows a few
drops of urine to escape into the pants. This is only a temporary
phase. By the age of 2½ most children are dry at night if lifted out
late in the evening, but accidents are liable to happen till 4 or 5 years
of age. By then children learn to get up in the night when they want
to pass urine. Some learn much sooner.

When should training begin? How should it be done?
Doctors differ as to when the 'potting' should begin. Some think
that it should not begin until the child is able to sit well and securely
— say, 9 months. Others think that it is best avoided until the child
begins to tell his mother that he wants to pass urine. We do not think
that it matters when it begins as long as it is done calmly and without
fuss or force, and as long as it is realized that it is not until after
about 18 months that he begins to learn control and to hold urine or
a stool back if he wishes. It will save dirty and wet nappies, for most
babies 'learn' to pass urine or to empty the bowel when placed on the
potty regularly after a meal, or else the baby is found to have a
motion at certain fairly fixed times in the day, and the mother is able
to 'catch' him by 'potting' him at these times. It would be reasonable
to put him on the potty when he is 2 or 3 months old. We saw one
mother who was so determined to 'train' her baby that she began to
put him on the potty on the day after birth!

The essential point is that there should never be a fight about it. If the baby screams when put on it he should be taken off immediately. *It is always wrong to force any baby or child to sit on a potty against his will. This is by far the commonest cause of the various troublesome behaviour problems in connection with the eliminations.* Children who have been forced to sit on the potty against their will are the children who refuse in later months to use it — deliberately wetting or soiling their pants as soon as they get off it, or deliberately withholding their stool and becoming seriously constipated as a result. Others become bed wetters later. At whatever age, it is time to take the child off the potty as soon as he tries to get off it, whether he has passed anything into it or not. Most babies sooner or later develop phases of pot resistance. They should be respected, and no attempt at potting should be made for a few days. Some babies refuse to sit on the potty, but are willing to sit on the lavatory seat, and only then will they pass urine.

Many babies who have been successfully 'conditioned' to use the potty when placed on it, seem to the mother to forget its purpose after a time. They sit contentedly on it for a long time and then have a motion as soon as they have been taken off it and had the nappy restored. Others do not seem to 'learn' the use of the potty at all in the first year. Both these difficulties are common, and they do not signify that voluntary control is going to be learnt late. As long as no anxiety is shown about this problem, and no effort is made to force the child to void, he will learn control in the usual way in due course.

It is usually enough to place the young baby on the potty for a few minutes after each feed. The older baby may show that he is going to pass urine or have a motion by wriggling movements, and the observant mother may avoid a wet nappy by promptly potting him. Doctors have said that in the first 15 months of a baby's life it is the mother who is 'trained' and not the baby. Never try to make the baby have a motion by inserting the finger into his bowel. It is unnecessary and may be harmful.

As soon as the child begins to tell his mother that he is about to pass urine, then is the time when she helps by giving him the potty immediately. She should on no account scold him if he tells her too late, for at this stage he cannot wait when once he feels the call. She reminds him at frequent intervals, so that he does not leave it too late. The capacity of the bladder is small at this age, and she must remind him frequently. She should certainly offer him the potty after meals, after coming in from outside, and before going to bed.

It is unwise to cause the child to discard his nappy until he is able to let you know with reasonable certainty when he wants to use the

potty, and until he can be relied upon not to wet his nappy immediately after he has said 'no' to your question of whether he wants
to use it. It is different if the child is later than usual in learning
control. If he discards the nappy too soon, accidents will happen,
and they may disturb him. The nappy should be discarded as soon as
he shows himself ready to do without, so that he has the responsibility of keeping dry. He is likely to be ready for this at about 18
months or a little later, though the normal variations must be remembered. The sooner he is able to attend to his own toilet needs,
the better. A child's 'lavatory seat', which fits over the ordinary one,
may help if the child shows anxiety about falling in.

The nappy should not normally be discarded at night until it is
found that if he is picked out of bed in the late evening at the
parents' bedtime, it is dry. Most children who have reached the 2nd
birthday are dry if picked out at 10 p.m. If it is wet, there is
practically no chance that he would be dry in the morning if he were
left without one. If it is dry when he is picked out in the late evening,
he should be left without, and if after two or three nights it is found
that his bed is wet in the morning, the experiment should be stopped
and retried in a few weeks. There is no point in picking him out in
the late evening until there is a reasonable chance that by so doing he
will be able to discard the nappy and be dry in the morning. A child
does not learn anything by being picked out.

If the nappy is discarded too soon, the bed will be wet, the child is
likely to be upset, and more harm than good is done. If it is not
discarded soon enough, the child retains the habit of passing urine
into his nappy instead of taking responsibility for remaining dry.
Some children object to being lifted out in the late evening. In that

case it should not be done, but it is usually only a temporary phase.

We do not agree with those doctors who say that the child should be awakened when he is lifted out. He may be awkward about going to sleep again. Children empty the bladder when fast asleep, and they can be put back to bed, still asleep. We are convinced that there is nothing to be gained by awakening the child. The sole purpose of lifting him out is to make the bladder less full in the morning, because when the bladder is distended up to a certain point, urination will occur. By lifting him out at night one aims at preventing the bladder becoming so distended that he cannot hold the urine longer.

The age at which lifting out can be stopped can only be found by trial and error. After lifting him out for a few weeks one misses it for a night or two. If, as a result, he is wet in the morning, the lifting out is continued for a few weeks, and the experiment is then repeated.

When a child has an accident by day or night, it is essential that no fuss should be made about it. The child is often distressed and he needs comforting rather than scolding. He should never be told that he is naughty and punished. If a fuss is made, he will be likely to repeat the performance and control will be delayed.

Difficulties may arise

Most children sooner or later in the first 4 years develop some problem in connection with their 'training' to be clean. Sometimes these problems are troublesome and cause a great deal of anxiety. Some of them, like problems of appetite, are brought on by the mother following the instructions which she has read in a book — instructions which led her to try to train her child in a way she would never have dreamt of if she had merely used her own commonsense.

As with all other behaviour problems, the personality of the child is one of the chief factors. A placid, easily managed child usually presents little difficulty. A determined, independent child can be difficult to manage. The phase of resistance and negativism has strong bearing on the problem, for it is just at the time that a child is normally learning clean habits that he is reaching the height of his phase of negativism, and any effort to force him to use the potty will meet with strong resistance. In addition, he is at the age when he most wants to assert himself and show his importance. He loves a fuss, and likes to be in the centre of the picture. If he can cause anxiety and have the whole house revolving round his bowels, he will.

It is particularly annoying for the mother when it is obvious that the two-year-old *could* control the bladder if he tried — particularly when there have been no efforts at compulsion and no unpleasant-ness over the use of the potty. It is totally wrong to suggest that lateness in controlling the bladder is due to faulty management: it may be related to the child's personality, and it is commonly a familial feature.

It is important to realise that you cannot accelerate the process of learning to control the bladder, but that you can certainly slow down the process by over-determined efforts to 'train' the child to be dry and clean, so that you meet with resistance, the usual negativism and the child's normal enjoyment of fuss and attention getting.

In the case of habit training there is another factor which is often of even greater importance — the wide normal variations in the age at which control of the bowel and bladder is acquired. Some children acquire control early and some later. A mother whose first child was 'dry' early will almost certainly use the same method of training for her second child and expect the same 'success'. She was proud of her 'success' in training the first child to be clean from an early age, and boasted to her friends about it. The second child is different. Not only is the second one a different character and more difficult to manage in almost every other way, but he is later than the first in learning to use the potty. The mother cannot understand this. She knows the second one is more advanced in other ways than the first, and she assumes that he ought to be equally advanced in learning clean habits. She thinks that he is just being naughty, and so smacks him, only to find that he responds by becoming worse, and refuses to sit on the potty at all. What she does not realize is that all children are different. They are different not only in personality, but in the age at which they learn various skills. She does not realize that her 'success' in the early training of the first child was simply due to the fact that the child was naturally able to acquire control early, and that in reality she has played little part.

It has been explained that the age at which various skills are learned depends largely on the nervous system having developed far enough. If the nervous system has not developed far enough, no amount of practice and training can make the child learn the skill. If a mother fails to realize this she makes more and more determined efforts to teach him. He is not ready for it, he cannot help it, and he resents any effort at forcing him, so he rebels. The age at which a child learns to be 'clean' is by no means always related to his intelligence. We have known mentally defective children acquire control early and many children of superior intelligence acquire control later than the average. Girls tend to acquire control sooner than boys, and bowel control is usually learnt before control of the

You should never allow your child to play with the tap — he may scald himself.

bladder.

Relapses of control

A few babies continue to be clean from about 6 months onwards. They have no relapse, and they acquire voluntary control at the usual time, about 18 months. The owners of those children are lucky; but such children are few and far between. They are lucky, for about three out of every four children who have been 'conditioned' to use the potty in their first year 'relapse' sometime between 12 to 15 months. This may lead to trouble, for the mother is likely to think that her child is being 'naughty', and she smacks him and compels him to sit on the potty when he is trying to get off. He begins to associate the potty with discomfort, with smackings and scoldings — and so will not use it.

Relapses of control, once control has been learnt, are common, as are phases of refusal to sit on the potty. These troubles arise from a wide variety of causes — teething, infections, changes of surroundings, jealousy. As often as not these phases are unexplained. They just happen. They are soon over, as long as no anxiety is shown about them. It is remarkable how teething upsets the child's habits. Some children steadfastly refuse to sit on the potty each time a new tooth comes. Many children, after a long dry phase, wet the bed when they acquire an infection such as a sore throat, or when they go away on holiday or go into hospital or return home after being in hospital. Any emotional disturbance, such as the arrival of a new baby, or the removal to a new house may cause a relapse. It is a form of jealousy and insecurity. Emotional stress at around the time that a child has recently acquired control is particularly liable to cause a relapse.

All scolding and punishment must be avoided, while praise and encouragement must be given when the child is dry. With wise management these relapses are only short lasting.

The child who is late in learning control

Some normal children, who have no disease of any kind, are later than the average in learning control. These are trying for the mother and occasion much anxiety. About 10 per cent of children still wet the bed at least occasionally when they start school at 5.

When a child has reached 21 to 24 months without having shown any sign of telling his mother that he wants to pass urine, the experiment of making him do without his nappy should be tried. He will then need constant reminders that he should use his potty. If accidents are too frequent the experiment should be stopped and repeated later. If 'training' has been mismanaged, and undue fuss has occurred, the child has been compelled to sit on the potty against his will, and he has been punished for accidents, then there is good reason for lateness in learning control. All one can do then is to try to undo the harm that has been done by completely changing one's tactics. Accidents must be ignored. Punishment and scolding must cease. No interest is shown in his refusal to sit on the potty, and he is on no account compelled to do so. If there has been serious rebellion against the potty over a period of time, it is better not to attempt to put him on it for a few weeks, hoping that he will largely forget the troubles of the past. It is no use thinking that it is easy to make amends when management has been wrong and behaviour problems of this nature have resulted. The child may respond quickly to wise and calm management, but often the re-training is a slow, painful business requiring much patience and tact over a number of months.

When there has been no mismanagement, and control is still delayed, so that there is no sign of control by the 2nd birthday, there is rarely any reason for anxiety. In the case of wetting, there is no reason to suspect that there is anything wrong with the bladder or kidney but it is important to have the urine cultured in a laboratory in order to exclude an infection in the kidney. But if it is found that there is an infection in the urine (and therefore in the kidney), it would be a mistake to assume that treatment of the infection may stop the bed wetting. If often does, but not always. It is not even clear whether the infection causes the bed wetting or vice versa. It is true that rarely certain diseases of the kidney and of the urethra after it has left the bladder cause incontinence, but they are rare, and should not be considered until after the 3rd birthday except in the presence of one symptom — constant dribbling of urine all day and night — meaning that drops of urine trickle away every minute. That is a symptom which should be fully investigated by an expert, for it may be due to a condition which can be cured by appropriate treatment. The only other symptom which could suggest disease would be the passage of an unduly large quantity of urine, associated with excessive thirst and water drinking. In this connection, one must remember that small children do pass urine frequently, and that it is normal for them to be unable to hold it long once they have felt the urge. This sort of disease can be readily eliminated by simple examination of the urine by the family doctor. In the absence of those symptoms one should do nothing but wait, with the knowledge that control will be acquired in due course.

If the child reaches his 3rd birthday without acquiring control, the condition can no longer be considered to be 'normal', though usually it is not due to any disease. In the majority of cases in which there has been no mismanagement, the mother or father or other near relative had the same complaint. Doctors use the term 'Enuresis' for lateness in acquiring control after the 3rd birthday. It is usually found that a child of this age who wets his bed at night is unable to wait during the day when he wants to pass urine. He has the same sort of urgency by day which the 18 month-old child has. Daytime wetting without wetting at night is unusual. One line of treatment which may help consists of training the child to hold out longer and longer during the day when he feels the urge to urinate, so that he trains the bladder to hold more before it empties. This training takes time, but it is worth it. The treatment otherwise in no way differs in the essential points from that of the younger child, except only that the nappy has to be discarded. The mother has to do her best to protect the mattress by waterproof sheeting. Scolding and punishment have to be absolutely avoided, for the child cannot help it, and it is in no way deliberate, so that punishment only increases his fear of failure. No one has voluntary control over what he does in his sleep, and it is easy for the mother to see that her child's bedwetting occurs when he is sleeping and not when he is awake.

An electrical device is often useful for the older child say 5 years-old or more, when no cause has been found, and it has been shown by laboratory culture that there is no urinary infection. The child sleeps on a special pad, and as soon as it is wet by a few drops of urine a buzzer sounds, which awakens the child, who then gets up and passes urine. Many of these electric buzzers are marketed. They differ widely in price. A satisfactory one, amongst others, is that obtained from N. H. Eastwood Ltd., 70, Nursery Road, N. 14.

Buzzers often succeed, but not always. Failure may be due to the fact that the buzzer does not awaken the child, in which case a louder buzzer may be obtained or the buzzer can be put into a metal bin, so that it makes more noise. Failure may be due to the fact that the child can switch the buzzer off without getting out of bed. He must get out of bed, turn the buzzer off, and then go and pass urine. The buzzer method may fail if it is not given a long enough trial. Most children should use it for three months, and some need it longer. Some doctors use a tranquilizing drug, imipramine ('Tofranil') or amitriptyline ('Tryptizol) to try to stop the wetting. These drugs may succeed, but their use should be discontinued as soon as possible after they have cured the problem or have been given a fair trial. It is no use trying one if the other has failed, and it is useless to continue giving it after a month or two if the child is still wetting. In an overdose it is a dangerous drug, and it must be kept out of the child's reach.

If the wetting occurs during the day, it is not deliberate either, unless there has been serious mismanagement which has caused the child to resist the training methods used and to do the opposite of what he is asked to do. The less said about it the better. Encouragement and sympathy do much more to help than scolding, which does nothing but harm. If the mother or father had the same complaint, there is all the more reaason to be sympathetic with the child, who cannot be blamed for hereditary characteristics.

At night encouragement is the only thing which will help. Appeals to the child when he is put to bed are useless, for they only make him worried and anxious. Many doctors advocate the 'star chart', a piece of paper with the days marked on, and a square for each day. The child puts a cross against each day on which he has been dry. With suitable praise when a star is earned, the child is encouraged and helped to be dry.

It cannot be emphasized too strongly that anxiety or insecurity will perpetuate the bedwetting. Not only should scolding for accidents be avoided, but the whole management of the child during the day should be reviewed. The mother should ask herself whether she is impatient with the child, expecting too much of him, and failing to show him all the love which he requires. Jealousy, excessive restrictions at home, lack of real love, friction between the mother and father and favouritism, all lead to insecurity and so may lead to enuresis. Even premature attendance at a nursery school may be the cause of the problem, as a result of separation from the mother. The problem should never be discussed in front of the child.

Excessive frequency of urination

Many mothers are disturbed by the frequency with which children of about 18 months pass urine by day. The bladder capacity at that age is small, and children therefore empty it frequently. Once they feel the urge to empty it they cannot wait. In addition, children often genuinely try to avoid mishaps, and so use the potty unnecessarily frequently.

There is a common behaviour problem which develops at this age. The child deliberately asks the mother for the potty every few minutes, because he has discovered that by so doing he can make her drop everything which she is doing and perhaps even carry him upstairs to the bathroom. The mother should be on her guard against this, and if she suspects that this is happening she has to put her foot down, giving him the potty only at reasonable intervals.

When a child begins to pass urine excessively frequently, it is always as well to ask the family doctor to examine the urine, in order to make sure that the frequency is not due to an infection or other cause.

When a baby girl has discomfort ('scalding') on passing urine, the usual cause is a nappy rash, rather than an infection in the urine.

Withholding of urine

A less common problem occurs in the 2 year-old — the deliberate withholding of urine. The child discovers that his mother becomes anxious and disturbed when he has not passed urine for a long time, so deliberately holds it back longer. It occasionally happens that after a time the child genuinely finds it difficult to pass urine, but he can do it if placed in a hot bath. Otherwise the problem is treated by ignoring it.

The problem sometimes occurs when a child visits a friend's or relative's house and refuses to use the lavatory to which he is not accustomed. It is wise to get a small child accustomed to using the lavatory when he visits friends.

Deliberate urination after being 'potted'

This is an attention-seeking device. It usually results from compelling the child to sit on the potty against his will, and smacking or anxiety when he has had an accident subsequently. It is treated by ignoring it, but the problem will not resolve itself quickly if mismanagement has occurred for a long time.

Conclusion

Delay in controlling the bladder and bowel, or loss of control when it has been acquired, present considerable difficulties: we have tried to give parents an understanding of the problem — and most children do have some problems — which should help them to deal with problems as they arise.

20

The bowels

The breast-fed baby

In the first two or three days the stools passed by a baby are black and tarry, and are called 'meconium'. They change colour as the breast milk comes in, becoming less intensely black, then brown, and finally yellow. Before they become yellow they often go through a stage of being bright green. They usually contain some slime (mucus), and always contain curds in the early days — and often later.

Stools are frequently green and this may worry doctors, nurses and mothers. A striking green colour does not suggest an abnormality: it is normal — either in the newborn period (after the meconium stage has passed), or in later infancy.

Many mothers fear that their breast-fed baby has got diarrhoea, because he has loose frequent explosive stools, often green in colour, containing slime and curds. As long as the baby is well and thriving, they need not have fears on that score. The stools of a fully breast-fed baby are always very loose. They are nearly always explosive in the early days. They may be very frequent. We are constantly being asked for advice because a young breast-fed baby is having 12 or more stools per day. They often do when they are young. A breast-fed baby may have up to 20 or more motions a day, but the stools are small ones, merely a few drops. Such frequency is unusual, though not abnormal, unless there has been a sudden increase in the frequency of the stools and the child is poorly and vomits. If that happens, you should consult your doctor: but we have never yet seen gastroenteritis in a *fully* breast-fed baby who is receiving nothing else by mouth. Otherwise, the all-important fact which should reassure you is that the baby is well and gaining weight. If he has gastroenteritis he certainly would not gain weight.

Such frequency of stools is only temporary. It is unusual after 6 to 8 weeks of age. The stools become less frequent as he grows older. At any time after 2 or 3 weeks of age he may miss a day — and then several days. *It is normal for a fully breast-fed baby to pass only one stool every four or five days, or even less frequently.* We have known babies have a motion as infrequently as every 12 days, but that is rare. The baby is well between the motions. His abdomen is not distended. He is contented. Then the motion occurs, and the mother knows about it, for it will be a big one. It seems as if the fluid intestinal contents do not provide sufficient bulk to initiate the ordinary bowel movements. It is normal, and if it happens to your baby, you should be thankful that you have so many fewer soiled nappies to wash.

Breast-fed babies do not necessarily have such infrequent stools. They may continue to have three or four a day. Often the rhythm changes, so that a baby who has had infrequent stools begins to have three or four daily motions.

This infrequent bowel action is not constipation, and you should on no account give the baby medicine for it. We have known scores of unfortunate babies who have had medicines poured down them one way and enemas pushed up them the other way, whereas there was nothing wrong at all, and the mothers should have been heartily thankful! It does not occur when a baby is on cow's milk — unless there is something wrong.

Constipation in the bottle-fed baby

The bottle-fed baby does not have infrequent stools, like many breast-fed babies do. He may miss a day, but not usually more. Constipation in bottle-fed babies is common, and is characterized by hardness of the stools. Hard stools cause pain when they are passed and sometimes some bleeding from the bowel by damage to its lining. The stools of a bottle-fed baby are much firmer than those of a breast-fed baby. His stools should never be loose, like those of a baby fed on breast milk, but they may be green and that is normal, unless there is diarrhoea. The greater firmness of the stools of a bottle-fed baby are due to differences in the chemical composition of the milk.

The commonest cause of constipation is underfeeding. Make sure that you are giving your baby enough food. It may be due to insufficiency of fluid. It may be due to excessive perspiration, due to hot weather or to overclothing. The body loses so much fluid in perspiration that the stools are hard.

If in spite of attending to the above points, the stools are still hard, try adding two teaspoonful of brown sugar to the feed. You may increase the amount of orange juice which you are giving, by an additional teaspoonful per day. If he is still constipated, you can give him a small amount of puréed prunes. You should begin with a teaspoonful, and increase up to a dessertspoonful or more twice a day if necessary.

Only if all else fails will you give some medicine for the bowels. The safest is milk of magnesia. Begin with half a teaspoonful, and increase the dose if necessary, only giving enough to make the stools reasonably soft. Do not give so much that he has diarrhoea. There is never need to give stronger purgatives, such as castor oil, which is a violent irritant to the bowel. The routine use of purgatives is unnecessary and thoroughly undesirable. Enemas should be avoided unless they are absolutely necessary, for they may have a bad psychological effect on the child. Suppositories are equally harmful, and should only be used if they are essential. We have never prescribed one.

Any child may miss a day or two without having a stool. This is normal, and does not matter as long as the stool is not hard. It will do no harm and no medicine should be given.

If your child suddenly becomes constipated, having previously had normal bowel movements, and begins to vomit or becomes poorly, and does not even pass flatus, you should consult your doctor immediately, in case there is intestinal obstruction.

The colour of the stools
Apart from the green colour, whether the baby is breast or bottle fed, the stools may show unusual colours, such as the following:

Black — normal meconium in the first two or three days. Iron or bismuth medicine, liquorice, charcoal. Blood from the upper part of the intestine.

Red — blood. Red gelatin dessert.

Pink — diazepam (Valium syrup).

Pale stools sometimes occur in recurrent vomiting attacks (commonly migraine), and always occur in infective hepatitis (jaundice).

Other drugs may cause colour changes.

Constipation in the weaning period
Constipation is sometimes a minor problem in the weaning period. It can usually be treated easily by adjustment of the diet, allowing more fruit, increasing the amount of fluid, and if necessary giving puréed prunes. Only if these fail should medicine, such as milk of magnesia, be given. So-called 'roughage' is unlikely to make any difference. Some doctors prescribe rectal suppositories, but we prefer never to prescribe them: children dislike them and they are rarely if ever necessary.

Genuine constipation must be distinguished from refusal to use the potty, as a result of mismanagement (Chapter 19).

Constipation in older children

Constipation in older children is not usually due to simple feeding difficulties. The deliberate withholding of a stool is usually due to the same cause as the refusal to urinate — namely the mother's determined effort to make the child void. In this case there is an underlying cause — the mother's anxiety about constipation. She tries to make him use the potty, and so he refuses.

The child resists, and screams. As he grows older, he finds that he can derive a great deal of satisfaction from the fuss created, and becomes more and more difficult. He violently resists the potty, and deliberately empties the bowels as soon as he is removed from it, or else he continues to refuse to empty them. Soon he has the whole house revolving round his bowel actions. After some weeks of this he becomes grossly constipated, the motions become hard and hurt him when he passes them, and there is then an additional reason why he should withhold them. Soon the bowel becomes so distended that it stops letting him know when it should be emptied, and he reaches the stage when he cannot empty it if he tries. At this stage it is a difficult problem to treat, and admission to hospital is often necessary. A further complication commonly arises at this stage — incontinence of faeces. The hard stools irritate the bowel and loose faecal matter constantly dribbles out of the anus. It is then thought that the child has chronic diarrhoea, when in fact the trouble is constipation. At this stage the constipation and the resultant faecal incontinence are involuntary, so that punishment and scolding is never justified. It is a common picture. Constipation of this nature sometimes develops in the first place without mismanagement — as a result of the child passing a hard stool with consequent discomfort, or developing a fissure or crack in the anus which causes pain. The child refuses to empty the bowel as a result. If this is not promptly managed, by ensuring that the stools are soft by giving a suitable laxative, and by avoiding fuss and anxiety and forcing methods, refusal may persist. Although there is some disagreement amongst doctors about the matter, we feel ourselves that severe constipation is by no means always due to over-enthusiastic potting, or to pain on passing stools. One often sees severe constipation without any such history, and we do not know its causes.

Although in 19 out of 20 cases of severe constipation the trouble is due to one of the causes mentioned above, there is a rare type of constipation dating from birth due to a defect in the bowel (Hirschsprung's Disease). The diagnosis is made by X-ray examination. We do not propose to discuss the treatment of this condition, which is a matter for the doctor.

Lateness of acquiring control as constipation
This is due to the same factors as those discussed in connection with bladder control, and the treatment is the same. Loss of control of the bowels, when once it has been acquired, may be due to jealousy and insecurity, just like incontinence of urine.

Soiling without constipation
Although the most common cause of soiling after the age of 3 or 4 is constipation with overflow (liquid material escaping round solid masses of stool in the bowel, and leaking out from the anus), it is not the only cause. Soiling may result from over-enthusiastic potting in infancy, or may be a sign of insecurity. If the child has never been clean, the odds are that the mother has never given him a chance to use the potty when he wanted to, but if soiling develops after a period of bowel control, an emotional factor may be the cause, and it is often associated with wetting of the pants and of the bed. The cause for this should be sought, and the problem is not an easy one. Your family doctor may refer the child to a paediatrician for advice.

Stool smearing
This is partly due to the natural curiosity of the child and his desire to handle things, and partly due to his natural and normal interest in the excreta. It only becomes a problem when the mother shows horror at what he is doing and punishes him for it. It then persists as an attention-seeking device. It may be the result of a feeling of insecurity, arising from jealousy or excessive strictness, or other reason. We suggest that you should consult your doctor about it if it is troublesome.

Blood in the stool
Much the commonest cause in a well child, who has no diarrhoea, is the passage of a hard stool, which has caused bleeding by damaging the lining of the bowel. Bleeding may be caused by a rectal thermometer.

If the child has diarrhoea, it is likely to be due to dysentery. If the child is having regular attacks of screaming, is pale and vomiting, blood in the stool may be due to intussusception (intestinal obstruction). In all these cases your doctor should be consulted at once.

Diarrhoea in the bottle-fed baby
When a bottle-fed baby has diarrhoea, doctors always fear that he has an infection (gastroenteritis), which may be due to carelessness in preparing the feeds. It may be due to putting too much sugar into

the feed. It might result if you mistakenly added sugar to one of the modified milk preparations (e.g. S.M.A., Cow and Gate Premium, Babymilk Plus, or V Formula, S.M.A. Gold Cap, Ostermilk Complete Formula). Sometimes it results from orange juice. In that case you can give your baby synthetic vitamin C in its place (ascorbic acid tablets), or give vitamin C in other forms (e.g. rosehip syrup). Overfeeding is an exceedingly rare cause of diarrhoea, and must only be considered when the quantities taken are excessive. As the danger of gastroenteritis is ever present in the bottle-fed baby, and early treatment is essential, you should consult your doctor immediately if your baby develops diarrhoea.

Diarrhoea will not be due to the particular dried food which you are using. It is useless to change to a different milk preparation.

Diarrhoea in the weaning period
One often finds that stools become more loose when solids are added. Certain fruit, such as bananas, oranges, pears and plums sometimes cause looseness of the stools.

If there is vomiting, or if the child is poorly, or if the stools do not rapidly return to normal when you have removed the offending fruit, you should consult your doctor immediately in case the baby has an infection which requires treating. In the meantime you should cut out solid foods altogether and give him plenty of water to drink.

Diarrhoea in the older child
As in the younger child, diarrhoea is usually due to an infection such as food poisoning, though it may be due simply to indiscretions of diet.

Diarrhoea with incontinence of faeces (dribbling from the anus) in a child who had acquired bowel control, is usually due to gross constipation and has to be treated by your doctor.

You should remember that worry and anxiety can cause diarrhoea. Adults sometimes have it when acutely anxious about an impending interview or examination. Children may have it if they are seriously worried about going to school or nursery school. Do not make the mistake of ascribing diarrhoea to teething.

Unless the diarrhoea is only slight, you should consult your doctor. This is particularly important when the baby is young, for it may become rapidly worse and endanger his life.

The stools in the weaning period
Do not think that there is anything wrong if you see undigested foods, such as peas or fruit, in the stools. It will not do him any

harm, but it does indicate that you should be more careful to give him digestible foods. Vegetables, for instance, should be mashed or more finely cut up, if this occurs.

Threads of banana may pass through the stools and resemble worms. They may cause anxiety if not recognized.

Offensive stools
Offensive stools when the child is well may be due to excess of meat and egg. You should try cutting these down, but if you are still worried you should consult your doctor.

Pain on passing a stool
This is often due to hardness of the stools as a result of constipation. It may be due to a small crack or fissure in the anus. This is usually treated by keeping the stools soft for a week with liquid paraffin (about a teaspoonful twice a day), and applying 1 per cent lignocaine to the anus before he has a motion.

21

Other behaviour problems

Fears

Fears are normal, unless excessive. Only severely mentally defective children are fearless. An intelligent, imaginative child is likely to develop fears more readily than others.

In the first year babies show fear by crying when there is a sudden noise, or when they feel that they are falling. At six months they often cry when they are faced by a stranger. Children usually develop fears between two and three years — fear of dogs, cars, noisy machines, the hole in the bath or the lavatory, sudden noises, thunder or the dark. To a small child objects around seem to be enormous. Even a small dog does not seem so small to a child. Children may fear being left alone, or being left by their mother, or being locked up in a cupboard. If they have had an unpleasant experience in hospital, they may be afraid of doctors or nurses. They show less fear when their parents are with them to reassure them. Jealousy represents fear of the loss of the parent's love or loss of importance. All these fears are normal, and all normal children have many of them. Between the ages of two and three years children commonly awaken with 'night terrors' and frightening dreams.

Fears are due in part to the child's lack of experience and understanding. They are often suggested by adults. Fear of the dark, of thunder, of empty houses is readily suggested. Fear is suggested by the admonition 'Don't be frightened'. When a child is being taken to the doctor or dentist for the first time, he has no means of knowing that there is anything to be afraid of until his mother says 'Don't be frightened'.

A mother should do her best not to let the child see that she is afraid of the dark. Fears may be suggested by efforts to teach the child necessary caution, as in crossing the road, using scissors or a knife, or in running or climbing. They are implanted by foolish threats. It is wrong to threaten to leave the child if he does not do what is asked of him, to threaten not to love him, to threaten to take him to the doctor or hospital, to 'cut his tail off', to send him to school if he does not behave. Mothers may say 'You wait till you get to school. The teacher will soon smack you for doing that sort of thing', or else, 'Wait till I tell daddy what you've done'. Some foolish mothers, on finding their boy handling his penis, say, 'It will fall off if you do that'. It is wrong for the mother to threaten that if he is naughty she will bring a 'bogeyman' or a 'policeman'. Fears are readily suggested by such foolish threats, and they may persist for many years.

Fears are often suggested by unthinking visitors, or by careless conversation about fires, burglaries and assault. Imaginative children may develop fears as a result of fairy stories. They may be afraid not only of the dark, but of shadows on the wall in the bedroom. It is said that small children may develop fears as a result of seeing their parents having intercourse.

Excessive fears are largely prevented by wise upbringing, by giving the child love, self-confidence and security. A child should never be told lies. If he is told that 'it won't hurt', when it does hurt, he will certainly be afraid in the future. We have seen children of three and four years of age seriously disturbed after admission to hospital, because they had never been told that they were going to be admitted and what it meant. When a mother has to go into hospital herself and leave the child in charge of a relative, it may cause a lot of disturbance if it has not been explained to him. Explanations should be given as long as he is old enough to understand.

Treatment is not easy. He should never be laughed at, teased or ridiculed for his fears. This never helps. His fears are real to him and they should be respected. It is wrong to try to force him to face the object he fears, with the idea of making him 'tough'. It will not do that, but it will make him still more afraid. He should be removed from the object which he fears, and given the feeling of security which he wants. It is silly to say 'Don't be afraid', because he cannot help it. If he is afraid of the dark, he should be given a light which he can switch on and off himself. A low watt electric light is the best for the purpose. As he grows older he will stop using it. The mother may help by making a game of going into a dark room with the child. If he is afraid of dogs, it is no use trying to force him to face them. He should be shown other children playing with dogs. As soon as he is old enough, he may be given a puppy as a pet, so that he will gain confidence in dealing with it. If he is afraid of the vacuum cleaner, he may be helped by being allowed to play with the component parts, and to fix them together, putting the switch on by himself.

Do not be anxious about his fears. He will grow out of them.

Shyness

Children have phases of shyness. These phases seem to be inexplicable. They come and go without apparent reason. Children at six months are often afraid when strangers talk to them. At a year they characteristically hide behind their mother when spoken to, or cover their eyes up with the arm. Later on they become strangely silent when they feel shy.

Some children are more shy than others. It is partly due to ingrained character and partly the result of environment. Shyness is in part an inherited characteristic. If a child is not given a chance to meet people, adults and children, he is likely to be shy, but some are shy in spite of ample opportunities to mix with others. It is greatly increased by insecurity. Boys tend to be more troublesome than girls — particularly at parties. It is common for the young boy to sit in a corner watching, refusing to co-operate, when the girls are thoroughly enjoying themselves.

An effort should be made to prevent undue shyness by letting the child have plenty of contact with other children, even when he is a small baby. He should frequently have friends in to the house and if possible go out to the houses of other children. This may be a nuisance for a busy mother, but it is essential for the child. In addition, he needs all the love, security and self-confidence possible. Effusive visitors should be asked to take no notice of the small child for a few minutes after arrival. The child will then make his own approach to the visitor.

Shyness must never be treated by ridicule or teasing. It is useless and harmful to try to force a child to meet people and talk when it is painful for him to do so. It is futile to say 'Don't be shy'. 'Have you lost your tongue?' It can never help, for he is not shy on purpose, and cannot help being shy. His shyness should never be discussed in his presence. It should be respected, and in time usually it disappears.

Jealousy and its prevention

All children have fears, and all children are jealous. Some mothers may not agree with this, but it is true. They may not agree because they may not have recognized some of their children's actions and problems to be manifestations of jealousy.

When a boy hits his baby brother on the head and tries to hurt him, or when he cries when he sees his mother pick his brother up in her arms or when he objects to his mother putting her baby to the breast, anyone can see that that is jealousy. But jealousy shows itself in many obscure ways, which even the expert may not recognize as basically due to fear of loss of his parents' affection — the basis of all jealousy. These manifestations include the development of bedwetting, habit spasms (such as blinking of the eyelids), stuttering, passing urine unduly frequently, clinging to his mother excessively, constantly asking to be picked up and carried, asking to be fed by his mother long after he has learnt to feed himself, demanding the bottle again, talking baby talk, becoming aggressive, quarrelsome or destructive, hurting the dog, refusing food, or becoming unduly negative. The mother can learn a lot, as doctors do, from the boy's doll play. He can often be overheard saying things to the doll, or seen hitting it or 'hurting' it, as if it were his baby sister.

It is easy to see how jealousy arises. The older child has to move out of his cot and sleep in a bed so that the baby can have the cot. He may have to move out of the 'nursery' into a different bedroom. He may be sent to a nursery school just before or after the new baby comes. He may be sent away from home for a time and come back to find the new baby. His mother may go to hospital and leave him in charge of someone he does not know, and then he finds that when his mother returns, and he is particularly anxious to have a great deal of her time, she has no time for him, for she is fully occupied with the baby. When she comes back she is tired, and as a result she is short tempered with him, just when he needs her love. He tentatively plays with the baby, but is immediately reprimanded and told not to touch him. Nothing seems to be right. He wants to be picked up and loved, but the baby seems to be always in his mother's arms. Everyone makes a fuss of the new baby, and people coming to the house admire it and bring it presents, but ignore him — and he is just at the very age at which he wants to feel 'someone', to be recognized as a person of importance. When the father comes home the first thing he does is to pick up and kiss the baby, and then sometimes he kisses him. All day long the mother seems to be occupied in doing something for the baby. The last straw comes when he finds that she no longer has the time for the usual romp and story before bedtime. He goes to bed unhappy, certain that he has lost his mother's love.

When his brother is older he finds that his parents always seem to come to the defence of his younger brother, while he gets into trouble. He is punished for things which his young brother is permitted to do. He is sent out of the room if he makes a mess at the table, while his brother's greater mess is ignored or laughed at. Jealousy is increased when 'comparisons' are made — when, having misbehaved or failed in something, he is 'compared' with his brother or friends. It is greatly increased by favouritism. Jealousy may arise in the younger child when the older one starts school — particularly when he has to be taken to school by one of his parents.

Apart altogether from management, some children show much more jealousy than others. It depends on their personality. Another factor is the age of the first child when the second arrives. The younger the first child the more likely he is to be jealous when the new baby comes. This is partly because it is so difficult, if not impossible, to prepare the 18-month to two-year-old for the arrival of another baby. But the management has a big part to play. Excessive discipline, impatience, irritability, failure to allow the child to grow up and to acquire self-confidence, all lead to insecurity and predispose to jealousy. Anything which lessens his happiness — boredom, constant corrections and scoldings, the fear of spoiling, will increase the likelihood of serious jealousy. It is minimized if he is managed wisely and lovingly, and he is always thoroughly certain of his parents' love. The handicapped child may be jealous of his normal brother and sister, who are able to do things which he cannot do: or the normal brother and sister are liable to be jealous of their handicapped brother because of the favouritism shown to him.

Every effort should be made to prevent excessive jealousy by an understanding of its causes, by avoiding changes in the first-born's life and routine when the newborn arrives, and by giving him love and security.

Treatment can be difficult. The first essential is to realize that it is normal, that there is nothing wrong with the child, that jealousy is not a wicked, evil thing. It is the inevitable result of the child's developing personality and he cannot help being jealous, but every effort should be made to keep it to a minimum, for a jealous child is an unhappy child. It is more important to go out of one's way to show the child love, to pick him up more frequently, to be sure that none of his 'treats' are cut out because of the new baby, and to arrange special treats for him which give him a feeling of importance. The father should make a point of making a fuss of him before picking up the baby. The child is more likely to love the baby if he is allowed to play with him with as few warnings as possible.

When he tries to hurt the baby, the problem is more difficult. The way not to treat the problem is to attack the problem direct. In other words, he should not be smacked or scolded for trying to hurt the baby. It will only increase his feelings of insecurity and injustice. He should be distracted when about to hurt, rather than warned and reprimanded. If he asks to pass urine frequently, it is useless to try to prevent him doing it. If he becomes destructive or aggressive, he is not punished for it. Every effort is made to keep him occupied, but above all things he is given love and affection — for love and affection is his basic need, and punishment and scolding will merely make him worse. It is most difficult to avoid being angry with him — but it is most necessary.

Other signs of insecurity and jealousy

These include attention-seeking devices, rudeness, temper tantrums, thumb sucking, masturbation, disobedience, bedwetting, stuttering and destructiveness. These problems are not deliberate. The child reacts in these ways because he cannot help it — because the trouble lies in what psychologists call his 'subconscious' mind. It is futile and harmful to treat these behaviour problems as deliberate naughtiness, for they are no such thing. The treatment in each case must consist of treatment of the cause of the insecurity. The problems are discussed elsewhere in the pages to follow.

Negativism. The phase of resistance

Many mothers are seriously worried because their 18 month-old child seems to resist all efforts to teach him and train him, and he always seems to want to do the opposite of what he is told. They are liable to think that there is something wrong with the child, or with their management of him. If they attempt to be more strict as a result, he responds by resisting more.

It is normal behaviour. All normal children between about 9 months and 3 years, and especially between 18 months and 2½ years

of age, go through a stage of 'negativism'. They are all nonconformists. If the mother suggests that it is now time to go out, the child says he wants to stay in. If she asks him whether he wants to use the potty he says 'No', and promptly shows that he really did want to by wetting himself. He makes a scene on the bus when the mother wants to get off it. When the mother tries to make the child get ready quickly to go out, he dawdles, and the more she hurries him the slower he becomes. He objects to new clothes. He becomes difficult about what he will eat. He takes every possible opportunity of resisting his parents' wishes and requests. Often when he refuses to do a thing, such as to go out into the garden or to put his wellingtons on, it is obvious that he is only saying 'NO' on principle, for he does in fact want to go out very much. He is difficult at night, refusing to lie down when put to bed, and screaming when his mother leaves. Active, determined babies are worse in this respect than placid ones. Some pass through this negative phase with little trouble. Others nearly drive their mothers to distraction. All are worse when they are tired or hungry or feeling poorly as a result of an infection, such as a cold and cough or when his mother wants to show him off to the mother-in-law. In all cases the negativism is increased by forcing methods, criticism, jealousy, or lack of love. When a child is excessively negative, it is well worth while looking round carefully for a possible factor in his management: but it is probably just his personality, his developing mind; he is taking after his father in his awkwardness and obstinacy. A mother told us that her two-year-old was 'just a walking disaster'.

Once the mother realizes that this behaviour is normal and a passing phase, she will be more tolerant and good humoured about it. A sense of humour is a great help, for the child's stubborn resistance to authority often has its humorous side. With tact, tolerance and patience the phase will pass without difficulty, but if the mother is determined to break his will, there is likely to be considerable trouble in the way of behaviour problems, such as temper tantrums, bedwetting and other forms of insecurity.

It is essential to realize that negativism is normal in this stage of a child's development, and is not just 'naughtiness'. There will be good days and bad days. The bad days will become fewer and fewer as he gets older. But then there will be a recurrence in adolescence.

Further aspects of the treatment of negativism are discussed in the section of 'The Avoidance of Punishment' in Chapter 14.

Attention-seeking devices.

Another characteristic feature of every normal child from about 9 months to 3 or 4 years is his desire for attention, his desire to be in the limelight and to be recognized as a person of importance. Up to a point it continues throughout life. We all know adults who are constantly trying to show off, but it is particularly obvious between 1 and 3 or 4 years of age. A 1 year-old baby is likely to repeat any performance laughed at. He loves an appreciative audience. After that he will find innumerable ways of attracting attention. He delights in anything which causes consternation and anxiety in the house. He may find that refusal to eat, to chew or swallow causes a great deal of fuss, that if he is sick over the table there is much interesting activity, or that there is great excitement when he puts pebbles in his mouth, or eats soil or snails. He finds that refusal of a particular foodstuff, such as greens, arouses great interest and distress in his mother. He may succeed in getting the whole house to revolve about what he eats, about his bowels or his sleep. He deliberately drops food all over the floor if people laugh at him. He may demand to use the potty every three minutes, if he finds that he can make his mother drop everything each time he asks for it. He causes consternation by refusing to empty the bladder or the bowels, or by emptying them under the carpet. He makes a funny noise, or coughs on purpose, and efforts are made to stop him doing it, so he continues it. He finds that if he bangs his head, sucks his thumb or pulls at his penis, his mother is intensely interested. There is immediate activity when he turns the gas tap on, and still more when he pulls up the best flowers in the garden. If his mother is slow in giving him what he wants, he finds that there is tremendous interest in him if he lies on the floor and screams and kicks. His mother is furious when he spits on the floor or spits at her, and so he repeats the performance. If he cries and screams when he receives the most trivial knock on the arm or head he knows he wil be picked up and given a chocolate or else he sees his sister reprimanded for it, and so he cultivates the habit. It is well worth while. He is surprised to see so much fuss when he gives another child a gentle knock on the head. He repeats the performance to see if it is as successful another time. He discovers innumerable ways of attracting attention if his mother is unwary. A boy of 3 was brought up because his mother seriously feared that he was showing signs of becoming a sexual pervert, for he had developed the trick of lifting ladies' skirts up at his mother's tea parties; another made a practice of drinking drain water (only when his mother was watching), and another of eating roundworms or snails, thoroughly enjoying the consternation which he caused. He is delighted to find that if he claims that he has got a pain in his abdomen during the night his mother will come and sit with him, kiss him, rub his tummy, and give him a hot drink. It recurs every night. He can get dressed quite quickly, but he finds that it pays to dawdle over it, because of the fuss and annoyance which it seems to arouse. He was about to discard some of his tricks, until he heard his mother discussing them at tea, and found that she was greatly concerned about them, so he naturally continued them.

The parents have to be constantly on their guard against this sort of behaviour. Every intelligent child tries tricks on, and the more intelligent he is the more likely he is to try them. The majority of the tricks are effectively dealt with by ignoring them and by distracting his attention when doing them. The less fuss and attention shown over them the quicker they will stop. Punishment rarely achieves anything. It is not enough to ignore them. Every effort should be made to see that the child gets adequate praise, attention and encouragement when it is justified. If he does not get this encouragement, he will be likely to seek praise and attention in other ways. He should be given responsible tasks to do, and enabled to develop self-confidence and a feeling of security.

Negativism, with the desire for fuss and attention, is at the root of most behaviour problems, and an understanding of this is essential in managing them. None of these attention-seeking devices should be regarded as mere naughtiness. They are part of normal development.

Temper tantrums
The commonest age for temper tantrums is 18 months to 3 years —

the age of negativism and resistance. The placid child is hardly likely to have them. The determined, independent, strong-willed child is very likely to have them, for he finds it difficult to learn that he cannot always have his own way, and that he has to conform to the will of his parents. To a certain extent, therefore, they are normal. If they are frequent, they are usually due to the fact that by means of a tantrum he has found that he can get his own way and can attract attention. They may be due to imitation of other children or of his parents. They are increased by fatigue, hunger, jealousy and insecurity, by excessive strictness, constant criticism, inconsistent discipline, overprotection, and efforts to teach him good behaviour and polite manners before he is ready to learn.

The usual form of temper tantrum need hardly be described. The child hits, kicks and screams. He may kick his mother or the table. He may deliberately throw objects to the floor and break them. The more consternation the outburst produces, the longer it will continue. Attemps to remonstrate with him make no difference. Smacking is useless, for it only makes him scream louder.

The management of temper tantrums can be summed up by saying that the tantrums must achieve nothing or they will be repeated; and that the cause of the tantrum — the insecurity, faulty management or fatigue, should be looked for. The child will have to learn that howls when he is thwarted will get him nowhere. If they cause the parents to show anxiety, and if they do their utmost to persuade the boy to stop his outburst, they will continue. If they are completely ignored and the parent leaves the room, they will stop, provided that the child does not think that the parents are within hearing distance and are likely to return if the noise continues. On no account should the boy be given what he wanted, for if he finds that he can get what he wants by having a tantrum, he will certainly go on having them. He should, on the other hand, be given love, and the episode forgotten and not mentioned again. Efforts to reason with him in the attacks are futile. Although the obvious and natural reaction of the mother is to give the child in a tantrum a good smacking, she is the first to admit that it rarely helps. The child is punished more than anything by the complete lack of interest and indifference of his parents to the outburst. Unfortunately it is not always possible to ignore attention seeking devices and temper tantrums. We saw one child who in a tantrum would get hold of knives and forks and throw them into the fire, or else he would take a running kick at any adult within reach. Another would turn all the gas taps on; another would get hold of a poker, make it red hot in the fire, and make interesting holes in the lino or sofa. An intelligent child can tax his parents' imagination to the utmost in their efforts to deal with him: as stated above, physical punishment is rarely the answer.

Breath-holding attacks

Breath-holding attacks, often termed 'kinks', are common in children from about 12 months to 3 or 4 years of age (see chapter 26). When a child is thwarted in getting something that he wants, or when he receives a bump (as a result, for instance, of an unexpected fall), he cries for a second or two, and then holds his breath after breathing out. In other words, he fails to breathe in. He rapidly becomes blue, and if he holds his breath for 10 or 15 seconds more he becomes limp. If he holds it for 10 or 15 seconds more, which is unusual, he has a convulsion — which looks just like an epileptic fit. The attacks have no connection at all with epilepsy, and do not occur in older children. It is a mistake to regard all breath-holding attacks as behaviour problems: some are, but those due to a sudden pain or fall are not. The latter are more like the faint which an adult may experience when he suddenly has severe pain, such as when he sprains an ankle. Some babies, when hurt, instead of becoming blue immediately become white and have a fit.

Breath-holding attacks are not easy to deal with. On the one hand, it is essential that as little fuss as possible should be made, and it is vital that the child should not get what he wants as a result of his tricks. On the other hand, it is not sensible to advise that nothing should be done about a breath-holding attack which may go on to a convulsion. Some mothers learn to make the child take a breath by blowing into his face, throwing cold water over him or holding him upside down. The difficulty lies in doing this soon enough: by the time he has become limp or started to have a fit, it is too late: he will come out of it spontaneously.

Boasting

At the age of 4 most children become boasters. They have learnt a great deal in the previous year and they feel that they know everything and can do anything. It is normal behaviour, and there is no need to do anything about it.

The child who will not sit still. Overactivity

Many mothers complain that their children will never sit still. This is normal, but some children are much more active than others, and tend to get on the nerves of their harassed mother.

It is difficult to define overactivity. That which is normal at one age is not normal at another. It is normal for the 3 to 7 year-old to be active, always on the go, and never able to sit still. The child of 6 or 7 cannot walk along the street with his mother without hopping or skipping. Most children grow out of this as they grow older — but some remain 'overactive'. It is often just a feature of the child's personality, and one frequently finds that one of the parents was exactly the same in childhood. It has been shown that children of mothers who were addicted to alcohol or smoking in pregnancy, or who had toxaemia in pregnancy or a difficult delivery involving a deficiency of oxygen for the baby, are more likely than others to have 'overactivity' in school years. Mentally retarded children are later than normal children in losing their early overactivity. Other related factors are boredom, excessive restraint, insecurity, domestic discord, poor teaching at school with defective motivation, or in the case of immigrant families, language problems at school. The frequency of this problem cannot be stated, because it depends on one's definition, and on the parental threshold of tolerance. That which many mothers regard as overactivity is in all ways normal.

In the United States some thought that a few cases of overactivity are due to food additives (such as tartrazine), and a special diet was prescribed, but if there is any truth in this it applies to only a very small minority. Certainly drugs, notably barbiturates, can and frequently do cause significant overactivity.

Overactivity is more common in boys. In boys or girls excessive overactivity is commonly combined with poor concentration, distractibility, clumsiness and sometimes with difficulty in learning to read. Up to a few years ago doctors and particularly psychologists worried mothers by incorrectly terming the condition 'minimal brain damage'. 'minimal brain dysfunction', or 'birth injury'. It is now recognised that there is no evidence of brain damage or birth injury in these children. Numerous books have been written about the condition.

In the United States it became a widespread practice to prescribe certain drugs for it. That is unwise — apart from the side-effect of causing a stunting of growth. Any causes such as boredom or insecurity should be treated. Parents should receive some comfort from the knowledge that the great majority grow out of it as they get older   and that it is not due to disease.

The clumsy child
All toddlers are clumsy, but as they get older and mature, they lose their clumsiness. Some remain awkward with their hands and fall a lot, long after other children have got out of it. It is likely that it is

due to a variety of causes.

All children are different. Some are nimble on their feet, expert at school at physical training, and good with their hands. Others are the reverse, and there are all degrees in between. Some degree of clumsiness may run in the family. Sometimes the child is just late in maturing in motor co-ordination, and he is likely to be if he were late in learning to walk. A child who walks without help at 10 months is likely to be walking well and securely at 20 months; but a child who first walks without help at 18 months, may be unsteady on his feet for a long time, until by 36 months he is walking well.

Some degrees of clumsiness in school children may be of emotional origin. The child feels insecure, and is perhaps teased at home or at school for being awkward, and so he behaves as he is expected to behave — like a clumsy child.

Some medicines given to prevent fits cause unsteadiness of the gait, and may make a child behave as if he is drunk. Several other medicines may have the same effect. Mentally backward children are often clumsy in their movements when compared with normal children. Some children display what we call mirror movements — making movements with the opposite hand when the other hand is performing some action, such as buttoning a coat. This may lead to considerable clumsiness. It is possible that some clumsy children are examples of minimal cerebral palsy. This does not mean that they are spastic.

If a mother is seriously worried about her child's clumsiness, at an age when others have got out of it, she should consult her family doctor, who in turn may refer her to a child specialist. In fact no special treatment is usually available. The most important thing is that he should be accepted for what he is: he should not be blamed for his clumsiness and bad writing, because he cannot help it; he should rather be given encouragement and praise for what he can do well. He may grow out of it completely — or remain somewhat clumsy all his life, like his father.

Hitting and bitting other children. Quarrelsomeness

These three problems are so closely related that they can be discussed together. Most normal children are aggressive, particularly boys. They like games of fighting and shooting. There is nothing wrong about this. It is normal for children from about 2 years of age to find it difficult to get on with each other in play, because they have not learnt to share, and if they are of a determined character, always wanting to lead rather than to be led, friction with others is inevitable and normal. Occasional hitting of other children is equally

normal when there is provocation. When the quarrelsomeness and hitting is excessive, however, the cause should be sought.

Both difficulties are increased by fatigue, hunger, boredom, insecurity and jealousy. They are increased when a child is surrounded by prohibitions, or has insufficient freedom and not enough opportunity for vigorous play inside and outside. They are increased by over-indulgence and lack of discipline. They often occur as an aftermath of Christmas or other parties — after a period of excessive excitement.

Hitting and biting other children is often an attention-seeking device, for it naturally attracts attention and puts the child in the centre of the picture. Mothers often say that they have tried everything to stop the habit. Therein lies a common cause of the perpetuation of the problem. The child is fully aware of the mother's anxiety about it, and so it continues. One line of attack, therefore, is to take as little action as possible, but rather to rely on distracting the child when it is seen that he is likely to hit other children.

One cannot allow a child to be hurt. If distraction fails he should be removed bodily from temptation, and punished by being left alone until he feels able to behave better.

If he has already hit someone, smacking is still inadvisable though difficult to avoid, for it increases the feeling of insecurity which is the underlying cause of the trouble. It should be remembered that this insecurity is in his subconscious mind, and that the aggressiveness is not deliberate. He cannot help it.

If the hitting is not a habit, the action may have been accidental, and punishment would then be harmful. It is unwise to ask the child to promise not to do it again, at least till he is about 5 years old, because he is not old enough to understand the significance of a promise or to remember it.

Hitting and other aggressive behaviour may be due to imitation — imitation of badly behaved friends, or imitation of the parents. A father who frequently hits the child in anger should expect to see his child hit others in anger. It behoves the parents to see that they always set a good example. Whatever the cause, the problem should never be discussed in front of him.

Children may learn aggressiveness and violence from watching television. Research has shown that television tends to teach violence, retaliation and aggressiveness. The more children watch television, the more they accept aggression as a normal part of life. Various drugs, notably barbiturates, may cause aggressiveness and bad behaviour.

It is essential that all possible causes of insecurity should be removed, especially overdomination, and excessive efforts to make him good mannered and well-behaved before he is old enough. Especial efforts should be made to make him feel that he is loved, wanted and important, and that he has his place in the house, and receives plenty of praise and encouragement, so that attention-seeking devices are reduced to a minimum. He should be given plenty of outlet for his energy with hammer toys and outdoor play, which will allow him to give vent to his normal aggressive tendencies. With love, patience and understanding, the problem usually soon solves itself.

When one's children are fighting, it is difficult to decide whether to leave them to it, or to step in and stop it. There is a natural tendency always to stop the squabbles. Determined efforts to make children nice and kind to each other can lead to a lot of unpleasantness, and so to the opposite of the effect desired. On the other hand, one feels that they need guidance in relationships with each other. We feel that the usual mistake is to step in too frequently, instead of letting them fight it out themselves and find their own solutions. When children in a family are being thoroughly rude and abusing each other, even if they come to blows, they are each learning something which the only child misses — give and take with others. Children have to learn to stand up for themselves: one has to avoid too much discouragement from their normal aggressiveness.

It is difficult to know what to do about the boy who constantly teases his brother or sister — and leads to tears and anger. Unless it is excessive, it is normal. Parents can innocently increase it by showing amusement, even though he has gone too far with it, or by such comments in his hearing as 'he's a real boy' or 'a dreadful tease'. It is aggravated by fatigue, boredom and hunger. Unless it is excessive, it should be ignored as a normal feature of the growing child.

Destructiveness

The causes of destructiveness are similar to those of the hitting of other children and excessive quarrelsomeness. Usually, like aggressiveness, it is not in any way deliberate. Any child accidently breaks objects, because of his relative inco-ordination of movement, his boundless energy and exuberance, and his lack of experience of holding friable objects. Deliberate breaking of objects may be due to curiosity and inquisitiveness. He has no idea of their value and is ignorant of the consequences of his acts. The apparent deliberate breaking of objects by a mentally normal child is usually due to a feeling of resentment, to insecurity and jealousy. It is common in mentally defective children, because they do not understand what they are doing: but in most cases of destructiveness there is no question of mental defect. Like the hitting of other children, it is apt to be an attention-seeking device, to occur when there has been over-indulgence and lack of discipline, or where discipline has been excessive and the child is surrounded by prohibitions. It may be due to imitation — if he has seen others throw things about in a rage.

The tendency should be prevented by the removal of all breakable objects, as far as is possible. From the earliest possible age (say, 18 months to 2 years of age) the child should be stopped throwing objects about the room. A toy which he tries deliberately to destroy is removed from him and put away for a few weeks. He will enjoy it when it reappears. He should be given other outlets for his energy, particularly out of doors, and distracted from play which is likely to lead to destructiveness. Every effort should be made to keep him occupied. He should be able to play with friends in his own house and in those of others. Any cause of insecurity should be attended to. A destructive child needs love, confidence, security and happiness. Punishment is more likely to do harm than good.

Bad language

Bad language in children is almost always due to imitation of their parents or of other children. They do not know the meaning of the words which they are using. It will be repeated if it is laughed at. It is often an attention-seeking device.

Provided that the child has no opportunity of hearing similar language in the home, it is best ignored. The less fuss made about it the better.

Telling lies

Many parents expect truthfulness too soon. It is normal for the 3 year-old to make up 'tall stories' and to enjoy pretend games. The more imaginative, intelligent children excel at this. This is not untruthfulness, and no attempt should be made to stop it.

Deliberate untruthfulness as distinct from 'tall stories' is natural in the small child, as a result of his love of fun, desire to tease, normal boastfulness, a desire not to be outdone by his friends, or fear of punishment. It may be an attention-seeking device, if the parents show concern about it. It may be due to imitation of his parents.

In the first 5 years there is no need to feel anxiety about untruthfulness. Truthfulness can only develop slowly. It is wrong to insist on truthfulness and to set about proving to a child that he is lying. No anxiety should be shown when he tells a palpable untruth. The parents should themselves set the example of honesty and truthfulness. When the child is 4 years-old and the 'untruth' is more than mere boastfulness, imaginativeness or a joke, it is enough for the mother to suggest that unless he speaks the truth she will never know when to believe him. Over-severe punishment leads to untruthfulness in order to escape blame.

Stealing

Stealing is not a problem in the first 5 years. Every child should learn what it means to possess things, and he should learn that he cannot take things belonging to others. This is learnt best by letting every child have his own possessions and pocket money as soon as he is old enough, and preferably his own room and drawers. When attempts are made by other members of the family to raid his possessions, they are reminded who is the owner of the property. He has to learn that he can borrow only when permission is given. Each child then learns to respect the property of others. There will be lapses, but as long as they are not taken too seriously, and no fuss is made about them, honesty will gradually be learnt. The parents must set a good example themselves, not borrowing without permission.

Tale-telling

When there are two children of different ages, and the younger is at the age when he can be expected to be getting into constant mischief, say, at 2 years of age, it is unfortunately helpful if the older child keeps an eye on the younger one and tells his mother when he is doing something wrong. The mother has almost to encourage the older one to tell, and she may even scold him for not telling when his brother is misbehaving. This can hardly be avoided, but it must be stopped as soon as possible, certainly by school age. By that time tale-telling should be definitely and firmly discouraged, and action against the wrongdoer informed against should be avoided.

Selfishness

Unselfishness cannot be expected to begin to develop until well after the third birthday. A child cannot be forced to learn it. He will learn it gradually by imitation and wise guidance. It is useless to expect a 2 or 3 year-old to share his toys with another, and wrong to try to make him do so. He will not learn unselfishness by force. Small children regard themselves as all-important, and it takes time for them to learn that there are others of equal or greater importance. There is a natural tendency to try to make a child share his toys with visitors or with younger children, but the 2 or 3 year-old child cannot understand why he should be expected to share with them.

The parents should go out of their way to set an example of kindness, unselfishness and generosity, and to encourage and praise the child when he shows signs of exhibiting the same qualities. Scolding for not showing them should be avoided. When he offers sweets, they should be accepted. He should have his own property which he can eventually learn to share.

Masturbation

Masturbation has to be distinguished from the handling of the genitals indulged in by all babies.

Babies learn to grasp objects and parts of the body at five or six months of age, and it is natural that a boy should frequently grasp the penis, just as he grasps his toes or other parts. This will continue as the grows older, and he may deliberately pull at his penis. This is normal, and no attempt should be made to stop it. Many mothers are shocked when they see their child handle the penis. They fail to realize that they handle the boy's genitals themselves to wash them, and they may try (unwisely) to retract the foreskin. It would seem surprising that they should feel that it is wrong for the boy to touch his own parts.

Some babies from the age of one month onwards obtain some satisfaction by rocking backwards and forwards, or by rubbing the genital area on the corner of a chair or on part of the play-pen. It is more common in girls than boys. The child may sway his body backwards and forwards, cross his legs, grunt and become flushed. He often stares straight forward. This is following by sweating, and he then relaxes and often sleeps. He is annoyed if interrupted. It is

harmless, except that if indulged in to excess some local irritation may result. It is dealt with by distracting the child, if old enough, and giving him something else to do — giving him a toy, for instance, to play with. Punishment is wrong and harmful.

Rhythmic handling of the genitals is unusual before the age of 2½. It is extremely common in older children, and it is usually agreed that about 99 out of every 100 men and women have masturbated at one time or another. Some have done it much more than others. Masturbation may begin with some local itching, but more often it begins with natural experimentation. It sometimes results from irritation, or from excessive efforts on the part of the mother to clean the parts, especially the penis.

It is essential to realize that this habit is harmless. It does not lead to insanity, epilepsy, or anything else. It does not even tire the child, unless he is doing it continually all through the day, which is extremely rare. The only danger posed by masturbation is that of foolish and harmful parental attitudes. If mothers realize that all children do it, and that it is harmless, they will be helped to stop feeling anxious about it. It is a mistake to go out of one's way to 'catch' a child doing it, and it is a still greater mistake to scold or punish him. Some mothers are foolish enough to threaten the child in various ways. One of us talked to a mother who had told the boy that if he did it again his penis would fall off. This sort of silly threat may cause serious worry and anxiety in a child. The older child may be mildly told that some people do not like it and regard it as rude. It is far better to ignore it, or merely to distract the child by giving him something else to do, and then say nothing else. Neither by word or facial expression should the mother show that she is shocked. There is no need for her to be shocked anyway, because all children do it. It will continue to increase if he is scolded and punished for it, though he may well take care not to let his mother see him do it.

Finger and thumb sucking

Thumb sucking is harmless. All babies do it. Yet many mothers are anxious about it, and many books still advocate that firm methods should be used to stop it. Babies are known to suck their fingers or thumbs *in utero*, and occasionally a baby is born with a blister on a finger or on the wrist as a result.

Some babies suck their fingers so much that they make them sore or make the skin thicken. Some suck the wrist instead. Many combine thumb sucking with the stroking of dolls, blankets or other materials.

Some suck their fingers more than others. Almost all newborn babies do it. Children have phases of increased finger sucking. Most mothers think that it means that the baby is hungry. This is only occasionally true, and more often than not it is unassociated with hunger. The idea probably arose in the young baby, because thumb sucking occurs almost entirely when the baby is awake, and in the first month babies sleep most of the time, only to awaken when they are hungry. We do not think that thumbsucking is usually an indication of hunger.

About half of all children suck their fingers when they are one year old. After nine months or so it is commonly associated with sleep, and as soon as the baby feels sleepy he puts his finger into his mouth. This habit continues for many months, and efforts to make him remove his fingers are strongly resisted — at least until he is about three years old. Some babies suck their thumb each time a new tooth comes through. Others do it when they feel shy or bored or get into trouble. It is common at about 18 months of age. Most children get out of it by the age of about four years.

The cause of thumb sucking is unknown. We think that it may be something to do with the baby's personality, for some do it more than others. One of twins may indulge in it more frequently than the other.

Research has shown that thumb sucking is harmless as long as it stops by five or six years of age. If it continues after that, it *may* lead to deformity of the teeth. If it stops before that, the teeth are unaffected. As it is harmless, it should be ignored. No attempt should be made to remove the fingers from the mouth or in any way to stop it. The baby will not understand in any case. The older child, from one to three or four, will resist pressure on him to stop it and do it all the more, especially if a great deal of fuss is made about it. Efforts to stop it will only increase it. The child will get out of the habit if nothing is done to stop it. No appliances to prevent thumb sucking should ever be used in the first five years, and bitter substances applied to the nails are useless and unnecessary. In the exceptional case, in which thumb sucking persists after the third or fourth birthday, it is reasonable to try to stop it, with as little fuss as possible, by suggesting that it is a babyish habit which people think does not look nice.

Head banging, body rolling and head rolling

Some babies between nine months and two years bang their heads when about to go to sleep, and sometimes during the day. They rarely harm themselves, though the noise which they make is annoying. Some babies rock their bodies when about to go to sleep, and occasionally they continue to do it in their sleep. It commonly begins at about six months of age but rarely continues after the age of three. Others in the same age period roll their heads from side to side, and wear the hair off the back of the head in the process. It is commonest between the ages of three months and two years, but is rare after that.

These habits are best ignored. Efforts to stop them only have the opposite of the effect desired. If the habit of head banging continues past the third birthday, in spite of following the advice given above, it can be stopped at least at night by letting the child sleep in a hammock.

Hair plucking, ear pulling, lip bitting, tongue sucking

Some babies pull their hair out. Sometimes they seem to combine this with thumb sucking. Others pull at their ears, bite their lips or suck the tongue. Lip sucking is a particularly common habit, usually beginning between four and eight months of age, and disappearing by the first birthday. Toe sucking is common at about six months of age. They are all harmless habits, and should be ignored.

Nail biting

Nail biting is unusual before the age of three or four, but we have seen it as early as 15 months of age. It may be an indication of insecurity — due to excessive strictness in the home, constant repri-

mands, jealousy or lack of real love, or perhaps boredom. It may be due to imitation. It is not always possible to find a cause for it, and it occurs in more than half of all children.

The best treatment up to the age of three or four is to ignore it, but the whole management of the child should be reviewed, so that any feeling of insecurity can be removed. Thereafter one can try to appeal to the child's pride, by suggesting to him that he is making his nails look ugly. In the case of a girl, a manicure set may give her some pride in her nails and show her how much she is spoiling them when she bites them. It is mainly girls who bite their toe nails.

Nail plucking
Some children pluck their finger and toe nails, giving them the appearance that they have bitten them.

Tooth grinding
Tooth grinding is more common in sleep, but may occur when the child is awake. It is unlikely to continue for long, and nothing can be done about it. It has nothing to do with worms.

Nose picking
This is an annoying habit, in that it makes the nose sore. It occurs chiefly after the age of two or three. You should try to stop it by gently telling him not to do it, and by distracting him when he is

doing it. As in all other habits of this nature, the less fuss made about it the more rapidly is it likely to stop. Again, it has nothing to do with worms.

Habit spasms and tics

Most children sooner or later develop some sort of tic or habit spasm. The common tics are blinking of the eyes, twitching of the nose and shrugging of the shoulders. Others include sniffing, clearing the throat, coughing or complex movements. It is difficult to say why they begin: often there is insecurity for some reason, and this should be looked for. They cease in sleep, and are aggravated by nervousness and tension. The peak age for tics is six to seven years. They often disappear in a year or two, only to be replaced by a different tic. They occasionally persist into adult life.

They are annoying for parents, who sometimes say that the child's habit 'gets on their nerves' — and the trouble is that the more determined parental efforts to stop the tics, by reprimands, sarcasm, disapproval or punishment, the more certain it is that they will continue.

Treatment is unsatisfactory. It is certain that all medicines are useless. The best that the parents can do is to try to ignore the child's tics, and to attend to any discoverable cause of insecurity.

Dirt eating

Dirt eating may be an attention-seeking device. The child discovers that by filling his mouth with pebbles, or by eating snails, earthworms, bits of soil or other unclean objects, he can cause a great deal of anxiety and fuss.

Dangers of dirt eating include lead poisoning, infections such as diarrhoea or worms. If it is not a mere attention-seeking device it may be an indication of insecurity or parental neglect. It may arise by imitation of a parent. Medicines are useless: the best thing to do is to ignore it as far as the child's safety will permit.

Parents' problems

I don't know what's got into him.
I could wring his neck. I could strangle him. I could shake him.
At times I could just scream.
Sometimes I feel like running miles away.
How many times have I told you?
Will you never learn?
What's the matter with you?
Can't you hear me?

I'm absolutely fed up with you.

When your first baby has just been born, and he is handed to you to cuddle, you could not believe that you will not always love him all the time, and that you will not always enjoy him. But it will indeed be surprising if you do not have bad patches. In the days or early weeks after delivery he wears you out with constant crying and his constant demands for attention. He takes all your time — and you feel that you cannot cope with all the other work that has to be done — the shopping, cleaning, washing up, the cooking. You may burst into tears for the most trivial thing or for no reason at all. He is difficult to feed. He wakens up two or three times in the night, and you cannot get a decent night's sleep. You are more tired than you ever believe it possible to be: and the milk boils over, the dinner burns, the clothes line breaks or the refrigerator breaks down. It is not surprising that you are worn out, could scream, run away. Babies and young children do not realise how tired the mother is.

Occasionally when a baby is born the mother does not feel the usual love for him; perhaps he was not really wanted, or the pregnancy was particularly uncomfortable. When everyone around her admires her baby, it is difficult for her to say that she feels differently and that she may even feel afraid of injuring him. If you feel like that do tell people — your husband, the nurse, the doctors looking after you — because you need help. These feelings about the baby may be short-lasting and followed by love for him, but there are some women who find that they cannot feel love for their baby. For the sake of both mother and baby this should be known. It happens particularly if the baby has had to be separated from the mother and placed in an Intensive Care Unit, perhaps because of prematurity, or kept in hospital for a long time because of illness or handicap, so that the normal process of bonding has been interfered with.

Tell people how you feel and ask for help. Even a few hours of relief can make all the difference. Most paediatricians and health visitors are well aware of these feelings. Even talking about your feelings to someone sympathetic can help a lot. If relatives cannot help, and you feel desperate, it is often possible to admit the baby for 48 hours to let the situation settle down and for plans to be made to help you. It is much better to discuss your feelings before you reach a pit of tiredness, despair and desperation.

Feeling like this does not mean that you are abnormal or psychotic. If all common causes of the baby's crying have been eliminated, and crying is excessive, and you are becoming tense and tired, you should consult your doctor. You probably need a break from the baby.

It is not just in the first few weeks after delivery that you feel that you cannot carry on. A baby and small child continues to be most exhausting and annoying. When the mother is most anxious to go out in the evening he chooses that evening to misbehave and to refuse to go to sleep. Just when she is about to take him out to the shops he has a motion in his nappy, or possets over his clean clothes, or over her new shirt. After about nine months he begins to creep — and is constantly in trouble. He favours the coal bucket and the waste paper basket. He tears the paper into scores of fragments and leaves them all over the floor. He tugs at the table cover and the lamp flex, and pulls all the books out of the bookcase. He is put in his play-pen, but he pushes it about the room or creeps under it. After his first birthday he becomes more mobile. He takes his shoes and socks off every few minutes. The constant noise gets on his mother's nerves. A small child always seems to shout, and loves hammer toys, drums and other musical instruments. He makes a horrible mess when eating, and deliberately empties the contents of the pudding dish on to the floor. He refuses the dinner which his mother has taken particular trouble to prepare. After a long session on the potty he immediately wets his pants or does it on or under the carpet. He is thoroughly negative, and nothing seems to please him. When his mother takes him out to tea, and wants to show him off, he is at his worst, cries, hits other children and clings to his mother. When his sister has friends in to tea, he shows off, and is thoroughly unkind and unpleasant. He never stops talking, however exhausted his mother is, and asks her all manner of questions, many of which she cannot answer, and repeats them over and over again. When he has difficulty in getting his own way he has a temper tantrum, kicking and screaming so much that his mother fears that the neighbours will complain, or think she is being cruel to him. He is constantly fighting his sister, and she is compelled to intervene because of her loud screams.

He gets a cold, his nose runs all day, and he cannot be persuaded to blow it. He sniffs constantly, and is more than usually bad tempered. His face seems always dirty, and he leaves dirty marks on the walls. He cannot sit still for a minute. On cold days he opens the door every few minutes, comes in and goes out, leaving the door wide open. The girl constantly loses her hair clip. He may develop an annoying tic, which gets on his mother's nerves. Punishment does not seem to help, because he does not understand what it is for, and it merely seems to make him worse. His lack of remorse for his wrong-doing exasperates her. She knows that part of the trouble is that he is tired because he has slept badly, but he flatly refuses his afternoon nap, and is thoroughly unpleasant all the afternoon as a result. One of the most annoying things is her inability to make him do what she wants him to do. He will only do what he wants. She cannot reason with him. He just does not seem to understand. She often wonders whether he is deaf, because he takes so little notice of what she says. Just when the cake for tomorrow's party is requiring urgent removal from the oven, there is a crash in the next room and it is found that he has upset and broken the best flower vase. However busy she is, he always demands immediate attention. In however much of a hurry she is, he dawdles and has not the least sense of time. He will not sit still for a minute, but is always on the go. She is overwhelmed with work all day, and just when she has got the baby into the bath the postman knocks at the door. Just when she has started the breast feed the rent man arrives. Wherever she moves she falls over his toys. She knows that her temper would be better if she could get out in an evening and away from the children, but there is no one she can leave with the children, and even if there were anyone available, they are so badly behaved at night that she could not leave them.

Ogden Nash* understood this sort of problem when he wrote:

'Oh sweet be his slumber and moist his middle.
My dreams, I fear, are infanticidle.
A fig for embryo Lohengrins.
I'll open all his safety pins.
I'll pepper his powder and salt his bottle,
And give him readings from Aristotle.
Sand for his spinach I'll gladly bring
And Tabasco sauce for his teething ring,
And an elegant elegant alligator
To play with in his perambulator'.

In the U.S.A. there is an organisation of psychologists who run a service for what they term 'debratting' troublesome children. The psychologists study in detail all the child's offences and crimes, and plan a suitable punishment for each, with the aim of curing his horrible behaviour.

There are bad days and wet days. On a bad day everything goes wrong. The milk boils over because she has to attend to his wet pants. He is particularly obnoxious, and the baby chooses that day to howl without ceasing. Nothing seems to occupy his attention for more than five minutes, and she just cannot get her work done. Every five minutes he comes and says 'Mummy I don't know what to

*Ogden Nash in 'The Face is Familiar'. London, Dent. 1943

do!' She just does not know what has got into him. Finally, her husband returns from work in a bad temper because of trouble in his business. When the children are good, they are 'very, very good, but when they are bad, they are horrid'. Yet many mothers do not want them to grow up. They want to keep them as babies, and when they have grown up they want another! And remember, these things are most annoying, but they are not naughty. They are just part of the growing child. Innumerable mothers are surprised to find that their really difficult, unmanageable and uncouth child has grown up into an altogether delightful adult.

Trying to understand the problem

As we have said earlier, a child's behaviour problems represent a conflict between the child's developing mind and the personality and attitudes of parents, teachers and his friends. Fatigue, hunger, worry, boredom, the weather, and probably biochemical changes causing depression, tenseness, marital relationships and many other factors affect the parents' own behaviour and therefore the management of the child and the interaction between child and parent. Parents feel thwarted at features of the child's behaviour which they cannot control — his appetite, sleep, tics, potty refusal, wetting, fidgeting, overactivity, dawdling, crying, stuttering, jealousy and general awkwardness. They worry about what people (particularly relatives and neighbours) will think about their child's behaviour.

It is an unfortunate fact that difficult parents are likely to have difficult children; after all, a child's personality is partly inherited and partly the result of his management. It would make life easier if instead of having a difficult child, difficult parents had a placid easy-going one.

It is salutary to remember that when people criticise others, whether their own children or not, they tend to be particularly critical of faults which they have themselves.

When your child's behaviour is really difficult and you are at your wit's end, it is a good thing to sit down and think about the underlying reasons for the conflict — even including your own health and your need for help in the home or a break away from the child. We suggest that you jot down on paper for a day or two the cause of every little fight you have with him — and see if you think that your stands were really justified and made over matters of real importance. Usually they are not.

The remedy which works more often than any other is love. Unfortunately, no parents are perfect and it is extremely difficult to be really loving all the time, when one's children are troublesome, especially when one is overworked and tired. All one can do is to try one's best and if one succeeds the response in the child will be obvious. *When your child is being really difficult, and you are at your wits' end, try loving him more, showing him your love more, and reprimanding less. Children appreciate love most when they are being really horrid.* It is a good thing to ask oneself repeatedly the following questions:

Do you really love him when he is at his worst?

Do you ever hurt his feelings by describing his misbehaviour to others in his presence?

Would he ever be justified in concluding, by the way you speak to him, that you do not love him all the time?

Would you love him more if he showed as much love to you as he does to his father?

When did you last tell him that you love him? Remember that it is one thing to love a child and another thing to show it.

Has he any reason to feel that you disapprove of him?

Do you make a fuss and reprimand him about things which are of no importance, trivial things which do not matter?

Would it be a gross exaggeration to say that your most frequent conversation with your child consists of criticism, scoldings, admonitions not to do this, that or the other, and threats of retribution?

Do you ever, in anger, say 'When will you learn?' When he says 'Why?' do you ever say 'Because I said so?' 'How many times have I told you?' 'Can't you hear me?' 'What on earth has got into you?'

Or is your conversation nearly always kindly, loving, helpful, constructive and always polite?

22

Some school problems

The young child at school

The majority of children pass through their school days without any special problems. It is a happy time for them. They look forward to their holidays, but they are glad to get back to school at the end — to rejoin their friends and to return to those parts of the curriculum which they enjoy. Some subjects they do not like, but they take them in their stride.

Other children are not so fortunate. A variety of problems arise, and some of them may be serious. The factors involved are many. The include the child's personality, physical health, the nature of the school and the character and methods of the teachers, and above all things the management of the child at home, for the more happy and secure he is at home, the less likely he is to have difficulties at school.

Below are some of the difficulties which we have seen.

Fear of going to school

It is common for the young child, particularly the boy, to be worried about the first day or days at school, and to shed a few tears. His courage fails him at the last minute as he approaches the school. Much can be done to pave the way by a suitable 'build-up' — telling him how much he will enjoy himself, and describing some of the things he will meet there. It is a help if it can be arranged for the uncertain child to go along with a friend on the first day — as long as the friend is a little more certain than he is!

A few children take some time to settle down, and refuse to co-operate with the teacher. This is largely due to shyness, and the parents should not feel that they have made some mistake in his management. A wise kindergarten teacher will know not to push him too hard. The majority thaw out in a few days, but some remain difficult for a few weeks. They are afraid of taking a note to the teacher, or of talking to him unless the teacher talks to them. The vital thing in the home management is to encourage him, to give him love and security, never to ridicule him for his behaviour, and on no account to let him miss school because of his fears.

The problem of the older child who refuses to go to school is a much more serious one. Research has shown that in the great majority of cases the cause lies not in the school, as one would think, but in the home. The problem is liable to occur after an illness, or after some difficulty with a teacher or a bully at school. The child may be timid, burst into tears readily, and be unable to stand up for himself — perhaps because he experienced overindulgence or overprotection at home, with inadequate discipline. The usual cause is basically the dislike of leaving home rather than the fear of going to school. The child gives the impression that he dislikes school, or a particular teacher or subject, whereas in fact his real reason for refusing to go to school is that he does not want to leave his mother. His mother may unwittingly encourage him to stay by letting it be seen how much she likes to have him at home. This applies particularly in the case of an only child, or the last of the family. It is undoubtedly a strain on the mother when the last of her children starts school and leaves her alone in the house. The child must be left in no doubt whatsoever that he is going to school whether he likes it or not. There must be no wavering or sign of indetermination. If he really refuses, then action must be taken immediately. The family doctor should be consulted, and he should get in touch immediately with the school authorities. The longer the child is absent from school, the more difficult it is to get him back.

A more common problem is that of the child who develops symptoms such as abdominal pain, headache or vomiting when about to get ready for school. If these symptoms occur regularly, the diagnosis is easy. If they are only occasional, the parents are in a difficult position, because on the one hand they do not want a child to discover that he can miss school by feigning some symptoms or other, while on the other hand they are afraid of allowing him to go to school and to become poorly there. The best advice which we can offer for the child with only occasional symptoms is to give him the benefit of the doubt, keeping him off school for half a day in order to see how he is. It would be wise to take his temperature, because if that is raised, there can be no further doubt that he should stay at home. If the symptoms occur regularly, the parents should consult the teacher in order to determine whether there are difficulties which can be attended to.

Apparent dislike of school and slacking may be due to the departure of a particular friend from the school.

The fear of failure

The fear of failure is a common symptom in children. One factor is the child's innate sensitive personality. Other important factors are over-ambition in the parents, leading to excessive demands on the child with a resultant fear of criticism by the parents or fear of disappointing them. There is something wrong when a child is afraid of criticism or unkind comments by the parents when the term's report reaches them. Comments, other than praise, should be guarded. Encouragement and praise will always achieve more than discouragement and criticism.

It is difficult to strike the balance between giving too little stimulation to work hard and overdoing it. The one allows the child to be lazy. The other causes insecurity and perhaps rebellion and the opposite of the effect desired. If a child has the requisite intelligence and his performance is not as good as it should be, he may need stimulating to work, though other possible causes should be looked for: but if he lacks the necessary level of intelligence, determined efforts to make him concentrate and work harder will do nothing but harm, adding a psychological handicap of insecurity to his intellectual handicap.

Fear of the teacher or of bullying

A child may become afraid of a particular teacher. This may be because of unkindness, excessive strictness or, more often, because of ridicule or sarcasm. Often the teacher seems to be blameless, and the child's fear is difficult to explain. Sometimes the fear has been implanted in the child by foolish gossip before he or she had even seen the teacher. The matter can usually be sorted out by an interview with the teacher.

Other behaviour problems at school

Bullied. Children are liable to be teased or bullied if they are unable to stand up for themselves, if they readily subside into tears, if they are poor at sport, if they are tall for their age and yet immature. They may be teased on account of their accent, clothes, obesity, social class, mannerisms, clumsiness, short temper, tale-telling, showing off, attempts to boss others, prudishness, or courting favour with the teacher. The parents may step into every dispute instead of letting the children settle their own troubles. The teased or bullied child is often an only child who has not learnt give and take at home.

Whenever possible it is better to help the child at school to find his own answer to the problem rather than to make a direct approach to the head teacher. We suggest that a good way to deal with the problem is to build up his self-confidence and ability to stand up for himself by taking judo, karate or boxing lessons.

Bullying. When a child bullies others, it is essential not to attack the problem directly, by punishing him for it, but to try to discover the cause. The cause lies in insecurity, and the commonest cause of this is the fact that he is himself being bullied either at school or at home — or at least that there is some unkindness or unhappiness at home or school. A child who is being bullied at school, or who is finding difficulty with some subject or teacher at school, is likely to vent his spleen on his brother or sister when he gets home. The approach must be a sympathetic one, to find the cause, rather than a censorious one, for that would merely increase the insecurity.

Petty larceny. One feels that this problem, like that of bullying, is sometimes dealt with at school with insufficient imagination, and with punishment, which anyway is excessive, instead of a genuine attempt to find the cause of the larceny. It is likely to be regarded as a heinous offence at school, demanding really severe punishment. It does not help the child at all.

As with bullying and many other behaviour problems, one should look for the cause, which is usually insecurity. It may be due to the bad influence of friends. It may be due to bravado and a desire to show off. It may be due to the envy of others who have more pocket money. An Australian study of 500 children who had been stealing revealed a background of a family history of theft, of parental lack of concern about honesty, excessive religious strictness, separation of the parents, a mother who was out at work all day, and of poor school performance. The cure lies in giving the child love and security and sympathetic understanding, and he usually responds well to this.

Smoking at school — and other addictions

In one study it was found that 40 per cent of children were smoking by the age of 9. Various factors are responsible for this: they include particularly the example set by parents and to a less extent by teachers, friends and siblings. The habit may start as a 'dare' or because it is regarded as a status symbol, a sign of toughness or of growing up: it may begin from mere curiosity or boredom, or as an attention seeking device because the parents object. Excess of pocket money is also a factor. Various studies have shown that less intelligent children and students are much more likely to smoke than the more intelligent. Children who smoke are more likely to have coughs and to wheeze: and children who do not smoke themselves, but whose parents smoke, suffer more chest complaints than those of non-smoker parents. Once a child (or adult) has started to smoke, it is difficult to stop it. The most important thing is to do everything possible to prevent his starting. Whoever regretted not having started to smoke? It is vital that the parents should not set the example by smoking.

Much the same applies to alcohol, other drug addictions and solvent sniffing. The example set by parents, teachers and friends is vital. As we have written elsewhere (Chapter 23) children should be brought up to be tolerant of the ways and eccentricities of others; but they must be taught to recognise right and wrong, to think for themselves, to know that whatever their friends and others think they have a right to their own views and they must not follow the ways of others just in order to be 'popular'.

Sex play and masturbation

One feels that this problem, too, is sometimes managed with too little imagination. The problem is more likely to arise if the attitudes in the home to sex matters have been undesirable. This has been discussed elsewhere. Around puberty all children go through the homosexual stage, and certainly in boarding schools some sex play is almost inevitable. It is harmless, but troublesome if the teachers are disturbed by it.

The backward intelligent child

In our book *Lessons from Childhood: some Aspects of the Early Life of Unusual Men and Women** we wrote that dozens of children destined for fame were thought to be backward at school. For instance, Oliver Goldsmith was described as 'a stupid heavy blockhead, little better than a fool, whom everybody made fun of'. Sheridan was described as 'by common consent, a most impenetrable dunce'. Leo Tolstoy was said to be 'both unwilling and unable to learn'. Anthony Trollop and the Duke of Wellington had to leave school because of poor work. Auguste Rodin was described as the 'worst pupil in the school'. His father said 'I have an idiot for a son'. Edison was always bottom of his class. Isaac Newton in the early years was bottom of his form. Amongst many others who were in trouble at school for poor work were Ehrlich, Einstein, Charles Darwin and Winston Churchill.

In their book on *Failure in School,* Wall, Schonell and Olson wrote that, 'It is reasonable to conclude that in many, if not most school

*Edinburgh, Churchill Livingstone (1966)

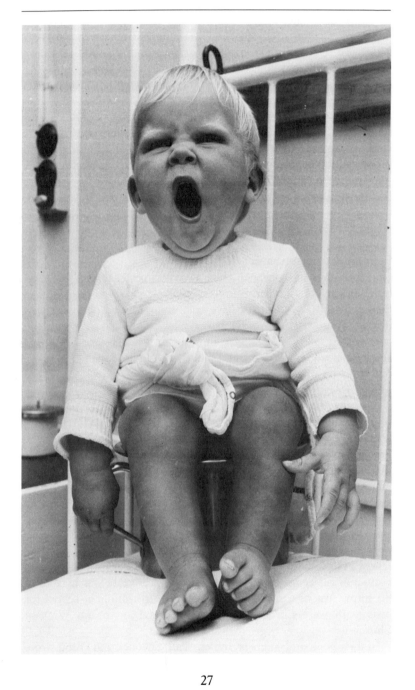

systems, general levels of attainment are lower than they need be, and that in most there is an appreciable degree of underfunctioning'. It was thought that as many as one in every five pupils might be regarded as an 'underachiever'. Others have mentioned similar figures.

One of the most difficult problems facing a parent is deterioration in a child's work. It is most important that the cause of this should be sought with the help of the teachers, and if necessary with the help of a child psychiatrist and a psychologist. The cause may be something quite simple, like excessive devotion to time to sport, or it may be something much deeper, such as insecurity or worry.

Finally, one of us (RSI) wrote elsewhere, 'when children are underachievers, refuse to work, do badly at school, look dreadful or behave abominably, it is a good thing to know that one can never tell what they will achieve in the long run: they may be the world-famous men and women of tomorrow'.

Backwardness at school

The commonest reason for poor performance at school is a low level of intelligence compared with others in that school, but in this section we are concerned only with the child whose poor performance cannot be explained by an inadequate intellectual level — the child who earns the unhelpful comment in his school report 'Could do better if he tried'.

The causes should be sought in the home, the child or the teachers. The home is a more likely cause than the school. In Chapters 13–15 we discussed the most important factors in the home which bring the best out of of child, and we emphasised the importance of love and security at home, a good example — in the parents' interests, choice of books, papers, radio programmes and records. We mentioned steps to promote the child's health and nutrition, the significance of parental ambitions and interest in his child's education, and the vital part which they play in preparing the child for learning. When children start school without having experienced the attributes of a good home, they begin with a grave disadvantage.

Unhappiness at home or school is a major cause for a child's poor performance at school or for deterioration in his school work. The cause may lie in over-strictness or discord at home, bullying at school, self-consciousness about clothes, obesity or appearance, or other factors.

The child may be a *'slow starter'*. Slow maturation undoubtedly occurs, but not as commonly as parent think. It must partly explain the fact that so many world famous eminent men and women apparently did badly at school.

The child's *personality* is of great importance. *Laziness* may be a feature of his personality: it may be due to boredom, lack of interest in subjects in the curriculum, insecurity, the influence of friends, deliberate slacking to avoid going to a boarding school or to avoid criticism from other children. It may be due to an unusually high level of intelligence which makes the work too easy for him.

Unrecognised *defects of hearing or vision* may be responsible. Other physical handicaps may retard a child. Epilepsy, and especially drugs used for its treatment, may impede his progress.

Day dreaming is another problem which may interfere with school work — as it did in the case of many famous people when they were at school: examples were Honoré de Balzac, Gauguin, Hans Christian Andersen and Edouard Manet. It may result from finding the work too easy, lack of interest in the subjects being taught, boredom, insecurity or even unrecognised defects of hearing or vision.

Slow thought was a problem of which Charles Darwin complained. Some bright children have a remarkable way of seeing some explanation other than that which the teachers expect. They see round a problem and need time to think it out. Others experience a complete emotional block when a teacher tries to hurry them to give an answer.

Poor concentration may be due to most of the factors already mentioned, which will not be repeated here. It is often a feature of the child's personality. It is a major factor when the intellectual endowment is below average. It is often a feature of children born very prematurely, or of children with cerebal palsy or hydrocephalus. It is commonly associated with overactivity (Chapter 21), or with fatigue or ill health.

The so-called *'learning disorders'* include especially difficulty in reading, spelling or mathematics. An obvious factor in all these disorders is the level of intelligence, for one expects a mentally retarded child to be late in learning to read; other factors include insecurity, a poor home, visual or hearing defects and poor teaching. Certain factors operating during pregnancy may be relevant — especially maternal smoking, alcohol, or other drug addiction. But there remain the so-called 'specific learning disorders', which almost always run in the family. The best known one is 'specific dyslexia', or difficulty in reading; whereas the commonest causes of dyslexia are those mentioned above, and especially a low level of intelligence or a poor home — and any of the other factors mentioned above, operating equally in boys and girls, the so-called 'specific dyslexia' or 'specific learning disorder' is almost always a familial feature, and much more common in boys. In our book *Lessons from Childhood*, describing the childhood of famous men and women, we noted the many famous people who in their school days had special difficulties with certain subjects. Difficulty in learning to read was the particular problem of Froebel and the famous British physician John Hunter. Spelling baffled Joshua Reyholds, Napoleon, Yeats and Picasso (and many others). Languages baffled Charles Darwin, the Duke of Wellington, Gogol, Carlyle, Thackeray and Winston Churchill (making it impossible for him to go to Oxford or Cambridge). Mathematics were a source of tribulation to Lord Northcliffe, Adler, Jung, Epstein, Picasso, Conan Doyle, Wagner, Schubert and Benjamin Franklin.

'Specific dyslexia' is a very troublesome feature for some bright children. There is a high incidence of mirror-writing (making it necessary to hold the writing up to a mirror to read it), reversal of symbols and words (e.g. interpreting WAS as SAW, ; as ?, reading from right to left, and left-handedness or ambidexterity — lack of preference for one or other hand. It is commonly associated with spelling difficulties. The spelling difficulties may persist, while the reading difficulty may disappear with age. Special methods of teaching are employed to help these children, but it is not certain how much subsequent improvement is the result of these special methods and how much would have occurred anyway with maturation.

Some children do less well than they should because of wrong *choice of subject.*

Deterioration in school work may be due to many of the factors mentioned, or to *rebellion against authority (or parental overambition), drug-taking* or *ill health. Excessive interest in sport* is often a major factor in causing poor performance in school work.

Frequent absences from school are inevitably liable to retard work: it is vital that children should not be kept off school unnecessarily on account of minor illnesses or other factors. This applies particularly to asthma: school absences lead to falling off in school work, which in turn worries the child and aggravates the asthma, setting up a vicious circle.

Frequent changes of school cannot always be avoided, but they may upset a child, who has to face different methods of teaching and the loss of friends.

We deprecate the sending of children to *special schools* (for handicaps) unless it is absolutely necessary: they are liable to add the educational handicap to the physical handicap.

Failure to recognise a child's true ability is a common problem, and must have been the explanation of the poor performance of many children who turned out to be men and women of fame and brilliance.

Bad teaching is a major cause of poor school work. A child may do well with one teacher, who has the knack of getting the best out of her pupils, and who is liked by them, while the child may do miserably badly with other teachers, whom he fears or dislikes. Teaching problems include lack of motivation, the use of discouragement and threats instead of praise and encouragement, and failure to recognise a child's true ability, special interest or special difficulties.

Such are the main causes of backwardness at school. The parents' problem is to decide whether their child's backwardness is due to an inadequate intellectual level or to other causes, such as poor teaching. The teacher will probably know, but not necessarily. If a parent is convinced that the child should be doing better, and he can obtain no satisfaction from the teacher, and certainly if he is dropping back in class, he should obtain an outside opinion concerning his intelligence, by having an intelligence test performed. The family doctor would arrange this through a paediatrician or psychologist.

It would be a mistake to suppose that an outstanding performance at school is a prerequisite for success in later life. Research has shown that outstanding eminence in adult life is not even related strongly to a high level of intelligence. Many other factors are involved, and in particular the personality, opportunity, powers of concentration, determination and willingness to work hard. Some would add that a feeling of inferiority, perhaps because of smallness of stature or because of some handicap, may goad a person on to achieve outstanding success. There is no evidence that the more clever a child is, the nicer he is or the nicer he will be when he grows up. The parents of a child whose performance is poor or mediocre at school should be encouraged by the thought that their child may achieve far more than the habitual prizewinners in his class, and that he may be a very much nicer person.

Keeping children away from school

In our opinion far too many children are kept away from school for no good reason at all. They are kept away because of a trivial cold, or a residual cough following a cold, or even because the weather is bad. It is difficult to understand why it should be thought wise to keep a child away from school on account of a cough or a slight wheeze, and yet to take him shopping or to a baby clinic with his young brother. They are kept off for longer than necessary after one of the infectious diseases. Older girls are kept at home merely to look after a younger child. A mother is likely to be pleased to have one of her children at home for company, and does not need a good excuse for letting him stay at home. Work suffers as a result of school absence, and children may worry as a result of dropping behind their fellows. We feel that a child should be kept away from school only for a good reason and that he should return to school as soon as possible.

Pocket money

We do not propose to suggest how much pocket money children should receive. We know that children in the lower social classes on the average receive more than those from upper classes, but in less good homes there may be no pocket money or else it is given at irregular intervals or only when the child asks for it.

We feel that it should be given as a right, and that it should not be withheld or reduced as a punishment — though a child may well be expected to make retribution if he has deliberately damaged another child's property or has stolen. We do not think that it should be given as a bribe.

Older children, by seven or eight or so, should be discouraged from spending all the money on sweets, but should be encouraged to save some and to budget for their particular wants. Some extras could well be given for membership of a book club or other some useful purchase.

23

On trying to do one's best for one's child

Nearly all parents want to do their best for their child, but what they want to know is how to do it. If they seek advice, it is apt to be conflicting. The fact is that no one really knows the answer. It is therefore with some temerity that we have tried to put our views in writing, with the help of the latest research.

We all want to know what talents our children have, but what we want to know more is how to help them to use their talents to the full.

Intellectual aspects

The child's intelligence quotient (I.Q.) can be raised or lowered to a considerable degree by the home environment. A good parent would like to know how to raise the child's I.Q. — and certainly how to avoid lowering it.

It is vital that children should be given the opportunity to learn, from the earliest age. We do not mean that a child should be subjected to such intensive teaching as that meted out to John Stuart Mill, Lord Kelvin, Carl Witte and others described in our book *Lessons from Childhood* — though how much of their remarkable genius and eminence was due to that early teaching is a matter of conjecture. We do mean that parents should not have the idea that children learn nothing until they start school. In fact some educational psychologists consider that the pattern of learning is established long before the child starts school. Dr Kellmer Pringle, in an address before the Royal Society of Medicine (1967) said that 'learning to learn does not mean beginning to learn arithmetic or reading at the earliest possible time. It is far more basic and subtle, and includes motivating the child to find pleasure in learning to develop his ability to pay attention to others, to engage in purposeful activity, to delay gratification of his wishes, and to work for more distant rather than immediate rewards and goals. It also includes developing the child's view of adults as sources of information and ideas as well as of approval and rewards. Through such learning the child develops his self-image, the standards he sets for himself for achievement, and his attitudes towards others, be they his contemporaries or adults. Evidence is accumulating to show that early failure to stimulate a child's desire to learn may result in a permanent impairment of learning ability or intelligence. The child should "learn to learn", and decide whether learning is a pleasurable challenge or a disagreeable effort to be resisted as far as possible.' The child must find very early that learning is pleasant. His mother plays with him, shows him how things work, shows him how to do things, and reads to him.

A famous Swiss psychologist wrote 'the more a child has seen and heard, the more he wants to hear and see'. An ancient Chinese proverb is:

'I hear and I forget.
I see and I remember.
I do and I understand'.

Much recent interest has been shown in the sensitive and critical period of development. By sensitive period one means the best stage of development at which to apply a stimulus to evoke a particular response. By the term critical period one denotes that period of development at which a particular stimulus must be applied to evoke a particular response, while if the stimulus is applied later, the response will not be evoked: it is too late. There are numerous examples of the sensitive or critical period in animals — in birds, dogs, cats, rats, monkeys, squirrels and others. We have stated elsewhere that if the human baby is not given solids to chew shortly after he has become able to chew (usually 6 or 7 months), but only given solids for the first time later (e.g. a year), it will be extremely difficult to get him to take solids; he will refuse them and vomit. Madame Montessori based her system of primary education on the sensitive period — claiming that children should be taught certain skills as soon as they are ready for them, and not later. It is well known that if an adult tries to learn a foreign language, it may be difficult or impossible for him to acquire a good accent, whereas a child could do so easily. It may be important that children should be taught skills as soon as they are ready to learn. Unfortunately, it is not easy to be sure just when that is. But some parents are afraid that they will 'overstrain' a child. That will not occur, if the child wants to learn, and he is taught without coercion. It is wrong to hold a 3 or 4 year-old back from learning to read, if he has shown that he is ready for it. Parents should never try to keep a child back, because it is thought that he is learning too fast. An occasional child is ready and anxious to learn to read long before he starts school at 5. Let him — as long as it does not interfere with outdoor games and play with other children. On the other hand, do not 'push' him and consciously try to teach him when he shows no desire to learn. It is far better in the first five years only to teach him those things which he wants to learn — apart from necessary discipline and manners. Parental anxiety about teaching him is really harmful. If he is clever and advanced, the urge to show him off to friends must be avoided: friends will not like it and it is bad for the child, tending to make him boastful, priggish and unpopular.

Parents who are ambitious for their children are interested in their work and their school. Parents of the lower social classes tend to have less contact with the school than do parents of the middle and upper classes who more frequently discuss their children's problems and progress with the teachers. Parents who regard the teachers as friends and helpers are likely to help their children more than parents who take up a critical and antagonistic attitude to the school, blaming their children's failure entirely on the school.

Ambition can do harm if it is excessive; understimulation is harmful, but overambition, leading to the child being pushed too hard, forced to work against his will, and being afraid of criticism and loss of affection if he fails to live up to expectations, is disastrous. Many parents implant examination fear in their children, and cause excessive anxiety, often leading to an unduly poor result. No child should ever be afraid of his examination results or of what his parents will think and say about his report. There is something seriously wrong if he is afraid of this.

Suggestions — summarized

Because this is such an important subject, and because each point which we are going to make is of such relevance, we felt that we would make it easier for our readers if we arranged the points in tabulated form. For this purpose we have deliberately repeated some matters already discussed when dealing with the psychological management of children: and we have repeated a few points made elsewhere in the book. The following seem to us to be the most important matters regarding the child's optimum emotional and intellectual development.

In the first year

Answer the baby's basic needs for love, security and comfort.
Provide proper nutrition, avoiding overweight.
Talk to him, play with him.

Let him see and observe: prop him up so that he can see the
activities of the house. Avoid leaving him outside all day with
nothing but a brick wall to see; provide play material.

As soon as he is ready allow him to practice new skills: chewing,
holding a bottle, cup or spoon, feeding himself, managing a
cup.

At the end of the first year read to him, tell him nursery
rhymes, show him pictures.

After the first year

Give him love and security; as he gets older avoid criticism,
ridicule, sarcasm, belittling him, disparagement, derogation.

Avoid talking in front of him about his crimes and faults.

Make constant and determined efforts to avoid favouritism.

Never make threats of deserting him, of not loving him.

Avoid constant nagging.

Be sure that he does not feel that you disapprove of him or are
disappointed in him.

Accept him always for what he is and do not expect the impossible, namely perfection. This is particularly important in
adolescence, when parents are apt to be disappointed with
their child's imperfections.

Avoid prolonged separation from the child in his first 3 years of
so: if he must be left by day leave him only in charge of
someone whom he loves.

If possible the father should avoid prolonged separation from
the child after 3 or 4 years of age.

Provide proper nutrition, but prevent overweight. Attend to his
physical appearance as he gets older, dealing with malocclu-
sion, donkey ears, etc. Take the usual steps to prevent infection, illness and accidents.

Encourage him to practise his new skills as soon as he is ready:
to feed himself, dress himself, attend to his toilet needs, play
and make a mess on playing.

Encourage the development of independence of thought and
action, as soon as he is ready.

Avoid overprotection: take calculated risks, as distinct from
carelessness and thoughtlessness. Enable him to acquire self
confidence. Do not treat him as a baby when he is no longer a
baby.

Exhibit firm loving discipline, with a minimum of punishment.

Avoid constant scoldings and reprimands.

Teach behaviour acceptable to others.

Praise him for good behaviour.

Teach discipline by encouragement, praise and reward, rather than by discouragement and derogation.

Teach him to accept a 'no': teach him that he cannot have all his own way,

Be firm, but not rigid: show the ability to reason, to discuss, to change your mind, to be persuaded without giving way to secure his approval or to avoid a temper tantrum designed by him to get his own way.

Teach him that if he disobeys, something to his disadvantage will inevitably result.

Set a good example in everything which he sees you do or hears you say.

Set the example in love, honesty, good manners, unselfishness, kindness to others, going to help others when they need it: show calmness in emergency.

Apologise for loss of temper or unfairness.

Set the example in trying to find the cause of things.

Set the example in taking the lead when necessary.

Set the example in avoiding criticism of others, but rather in excusing them and looking for the good in them. Never let him see you knowingly unkind to anyone — and encourage him never to be knowingly unkind.

Instil a sensible attitude to illness: avoid talking and complaining about symptoms in front of the child. Avoid giving medicine for every symptom, putting the child to bed for every symptom, exaggerating symptoms or fussing about them, or keeping the child off school for every symptom.

Instil sensible attitudes to sex. Bath the children of different sex together until they want to be separate. Answer questions honestly. Explain what they need to know.

Aim at having a happy home and giving the children a happy childhood.

Show tolerance and understanding of his developing mind, recognizing the normal negativeness and aggressiveness of the 1 to 3 year-old, and the recurrence of negativism at puberty. Remember that the adolescent appreciates tolerance and kindess most when he is feeling bad-tempered, tired or irritable.

Teach a tolerant attitude to others: but try to get the child to appreciate right and wrong. Show and teach tolerance for non-conformity, unusual dress, thought, action, eccentricities and foibles, as long as they are harmless to others. Teach him to be tolerant to those not as clever as he is, and never to gloat over their deficiencies. Encourage him to mix with others and make friends with others, irrespective of class, race, tribe, sex, colour, religion or opinions. Teach him that he has a right to his own opinions, and must not be coerced by others into doing something which he thinks is wrong. Help him to feel free to be different.

Teach respect for the opinion of others; teach him to see that there may be two points of view and one or both may be right.

Teach him thoughtfulness for others, unselfishness and good moral values. Teach him to avoid telling tales or cheating. Teach forgiveness and the folly of bearing malice. Teach the child above all things to put himself into the position of others, to treat others as he would like to be treated: but do not expect unselfishness too soon.

Encourage the child to take the lead, to take responsibility, but not to insist on it.

Discourage boasting, showing off, and avoid showing him off to friends.

Read to him, show him pictures in books.

Talk to him, explain things to him, listen to him, discuss things with him. Do not send him out of the room when adults come to the house. Let him listen to conversation and join in it.

Try to teach the concept of numbers, counting, getting him to count (e.g. the steps as he puts each foot down, numbers on the clock, items in the supermarket, places at the table, conkers). Play snakes and ladders.

Provide suitable play material — to help him to use his hands and eyes, to think, construct, use his imagination, determine how things work. Provide interlocking bricks, bricks of different size and shape, paper and pencils or crayons, bead-threading, picture dominoes, jigsaws (eight piece at first), constructional toys. As soon as he can read, see that he has a constant supply of reading material — *not* 'comics'.

Let him develop his own play and do not plan play for him: play with him but limit it and when he is older, let him play alone, or with siblings or friends.

Give him time to play: do not fill his time with organized pursuits e.g., piano lessons, horse-riding, if he does not like it. Try to teach him to be a good loser — and never a cheat.

Let his play material present more and more difficult problems for him — but do not let him fail and lose self-confidence.

Allow him to make mistakes and learn from them.

Do not lead him into situations for which he is not ready. Success leads to success, and failure to failure.

Never punish him for trying to find out.

Teach him to argue, to ask the reason why, to think round a subject, look for another explanation, to evaluate what he is told, to question statements heard on the radio or T.V. (e.g., advertisements and claims), to seek evidence — and show him how to get it. Teach him to learn similarities, dissimilarities. Teach him to question, but not to be nihilistic or unpleasant in questioning.

Encourage him when asked to say 'it all depends' — seeing other possible explanations.

Instruct him, when old enough, in the use of the library.

Teach him to try to see what is important, what matters, and what is unimportant.

Teach him to think of eventualities and not to be foolhardy.

Encourage accuracy, thoroughness, observation, originality, imagination, creativity.

Encourage him to develop his special interests and show him how to develop them (e.g. by play material, or by reading, when old enough).

Teach accuracy and clarity of speech.

Avoid baby language in the case of the young child.

Encourage friendly leg-pulling when someone in the family is vague or imprecise in his speech.

Give him experiences outside the home — in the country, factory, museum.

Get him to enjoy learning, to want to learn: never let him feel that it is a chore.

Have ambition, but not overambition: do not expect more of him than his endowment will permit. Expect success up to the limit of his ability, and good behaviour, but never perfection.

Always accept him, however meagre his performance.

Give praise for his achievement, however small, and never criticize for failure.

Avoid comments about his weaknesses; don't let him think that you expect him to fail; give him the impression that you expect him to succeed. But don't expect too much of him.

Do not try to make him a genius.

Accept the value of education. Do not let him miss school unnecessarily. Expect him to do his homework without question or persuasion: and do not do it for him. Provide him, if possible with a comfortable place in which to work. Beware of choosing a third rate school outside the state education system for snob reasons. Relate his education to his ability, personality, desires, as far as possible. Guide him with regard to choice of subject, but do not go against his special interests, which should always be encouraged. Keep contact with the school and where necessary discuss any difficulties with his teachers.

Provide him with the material for learning — books, magazines.

You may think that our list refers only to helping the unusually bright child. For the most part, this is not so: but you must adapt our advice to the understanding, personality and interests of your particular child.

Helping the gifted child

Many parents think that their child is a genius, when he is just a delightful average child. But many parents and many teachers fail to recognise the unusual gifts which a child possesses.

Psychologists are likely to say that it is impossible to predict superior intelligence in infancy. It is true that there is no good statistical proof that one can detect mental superiority — but there is no doubt that one can detect the opposite in infancy — mental subnormality. But some of us think that there are good indications of superior intelligence or qualities, but that they are difficult to quantify. Knowing that mentally subnormal infants, such as mongols, are late in almost all aspects of development — e.g. late in beginning to respond to the mother by smiling and, in a further week or two, 'vocalising' by cooing and gurgling, one might guess that a mentally very bright child would achieve various milestones earlier than usual. We would certainly feel that a baby who begins to smile in response to the mother in the first week, and to 'vocalise' with smiles a week later, would be an unusually bright child. Other features which one would observe would be the unusual interest in surroundings, the alertness, the degree of eye following when the mother moves around the room. A difficult feature to quantify (except by certain recent electronic devices) is the quality of the vocalisations (e.g. at six months onwards); these precede the development of speech. A child who learns to speak unusually early is of high intelligence — but many children of superior intelligence learn to speak much later than average, as did Albert Einstein and Alessandro Volta (of voltage fame) and many other famous people. Early speech development in the way of sentence formation, and later maturity of vocabulary, expression and questioning, are undoubtedly good indices of advanced intelligence. A really bright child may be speaking well in sentences long before the average age of 21 to 24 months. Early reading, long before school age, is always an indication of superior intelligence.

Early sitting and walking are of little importance. Much more important are the infant's alertness, determination, concentration, rapid thought and responsiveness: after infancy one notes particularly the degree of concentration, the good memory, and the reasoning, the power of observation.

Children may be gifted, and show early signs of their gifts, in any of numerous subjects — such as the use of their hands, obsessional thoroughness, appreciation of music, imaginative drawing, unusual imagination and fantasy thinking, curiosity, the perception of differences and analogies, their interest in classifying and collecting. They may be gifted in music, drama, art, writing, conversation, humour, finance, mechanics, science, arithmetic, personality, leadership, sport and any of many other fields. Giftedness is by no means a matter of just of intelligence: far more important are creativity and personality.

Parents tend to overestimate the intelligence of their children. It is normal and natural for a parent to be constantly impressed by the baby's or toddler's understanding. But if the parent allows himself to become really convinced that his child is endowed with superior intelligence, much serious harm may result if he is wrong, for he expects too much of the child, may try to push him too hard and teach him things before he is ready, and then be seriously disappointed later when he finds that the child has not lived up to expectations. All this has a harmful effect on the child. It will lead to insecurity, temper tantrums, and various other behaviour problems which will be discussed in another section.

Our advice to you is that you do not attempt to predict your child's intelligence, particularly when he is a baby. It is far better just to accept him as he is, to love him as he is, to make every effort to bring him up wisely and sensibly, and then to wait and see how he develops. You will do nothing but harm by thinking that he is mentally backward if he is not, or mentally superior if he is merely average. But it is important that if he has special interests and abilities they should be recognised and encouraged: one wants to prevent him becoming bored or lazy; one wants to stimulate his special skills and aptitudes, without exerting too much pressure and depriving him of time for play and his own pursuits. When he is at school it would be unwise to demand special privileges for him.

There are numerous books about gifted children. A particularly sensible one is that by Ogilvie (*Gifted Children in Primary Schools.* London, MacMillan 1973). Another is *Gifted Children* by J. Gibson and P. Chennells, 1976, published for the National Association for Gifted Children, 27 John Adam Street, London, WC2.

Many gifted children learn to read long before they start school — many of them at about three years of age. Ability to read opens a completely new world to an intelligent child and gives enormous pleasure. Pre-reading materials include picture dominoes, different shapes and forms, formboards, and jigsaws. A useful book is that by J. Bennett, *Learning to read with picture books.* Thimble Press. 1980.

Helping the backward child

It is sometimes difficult to give a backward child adequate nourishment. In the newborn period, he may suck badly and show no desire for feeds. He is backward in all aspects of development, so that amongst other things he is later than others in learning to chew, and therefore to take solids. If you give him solids before he can chew, he is likely to be sick. You will have to do your best after the normal weaning period, to give him nourishing food which he can manage, and to be sure that he has the additional vitamins given to other babies.

We do not propose to attempt to give a full account of the upbringing of a backward child. That would be impossible in a short space. We propose, however, to mention some general principles of importance.

Firstly, if you think that your child is backward, you should consult your doctor. He may ask a child specialist to see him if there is any doubt. Your fears may be unfounded. You should remember that there are slow starters, who are a little backward at first and do well later on. But there is another important reason for consulting your doctor. There is one form of backwardness, that due to deficiency of the thyroid gland, which responds extremely well to treatment — and the earlier treatment is given, the better. Your doctor will diagnose this. There are other causes of backwardness (such as a visual or hearing defect) which your doctor can eliminate.

Secondly, you must try not to allow yourself to feel shame or guilt that your child is backward in comparsion with other children. It is not your fault or anyone else's fault. You have to accept the fact that he is backward. It is no use trying constantly to make yourself believe that he is normal when you know that in fact he is retarded.

Thirdly, the child needs to be accepted as a member of the family and loved just as much as other children of higher intelligence. A retarded child needs love just as much as anyone else. It is normal for a child of 2, 3 or even 4 to cling to his mother and to be reluctant to be left by her, but by the time he reaches school age he has matured sufficiently to be able to tolerate being separated from her. A backward child is likely to be later in reaching the stage of being willing to be separated from her: he clings to her and demands her love longer than normal children. On no account should the child acquire the feeling that his parents are disappointed in him. Any sort of ridicule for his failings, however trivial that ridicule seems, must be absolutely avoided. On no account should the child's backwardness be mentioned or hinted at in his presence. He should never be compared with his brothers and sisters. His position is a difficult one if he is a first child, and a second one comes along and learns things before he does. His position is particularly difficult if he has a normal or bright twin brother or sister. You should be particularly careful not to show favouritism to his more intelligent brother or sister. Backward children, like any other children, thrive on encouragement, and achieve less than their true ability permits if discouraged and thwarted.

Fourthly, do not feel that there is nothing to be done for the child, even if your doctor assures you that he is not suffering from thyroid deficiency and that therefore no medical treatment will help him. You can help him by loving him, by giving him the right toys and by not expecting too much of him. He will take your time, but you must not allow your other children to suffer on his account. He has to learn one thing at a time, and he has to have plenty of time to learn. He must not be pushed. Attempts to make him stick at his lessons and to learn things before he is ready to learn will do nothing but harm. It must be remembered that backward children are unable to concentrate as long as others, and efforts to make them concentrate will simply lead to insecurity, unhappiness, and an unnecessarily poor performance. It is wrong to consider that he is just 'lazy'. He must be allowed to develop at his own pace, but given all possible help, in the ways of toys of educational value, in order that he can be helped to concentrate, to think, to use his imagination, and to develop and practise new skills. Try to look for his assets, and encourage his skills and interests.

If he is severely backward, you will need guidance in trying to help him to learn. We suggest that you should seek advice from the National Society for Mentally Handicapped Children, 86 Newman Street, London W1P 4AR.

Fifthly, he must not be spoiled and over-protected. He has to learn discipline, obedience and good habits, like any other child, but he will take longer than others to learn, and due allowance for this must always be made. It is a natural reaction of parents to over-protect a retarded child, and to do everything for him istead of allowing him to learn to be independent. He must be allowed to grow up, to dress himself, to attend to his own toilet needs, and to look after himself, if at all possible. Many backward children are caused to be more backward than they need be by over-protection. It is vital that he should acquire independance.

It is easy to show favouritism for the backward child at the cost of the normal ones. Everything possible must be done to prevent the normal ones suffering in any way because of the backwardness of a brother or sister. Remember that he may with reason be jealous of his normal brother or sister.

A troublesome feature of many slightly backward children is persistence of the normal overactivity which a bright child usually grows out of; it persists longer in the backward child, whose maturation is slow.

He is helped to learn control of the bladder, by being taught to hold the water longer and longer during the day — just as any other child is taught, when late in learning control. He should not last out so long that he has a mishap. A good special school will work wonders with a backward child by teaching him to look after himself, to do things for himself which his parents had always done for him while he was at home.

It is easy to retard a backward child. It is easy not to give the retarded child a chance to learn. He shows less interest than the normal child in his surroundings, and so he may be left far too long in the pram outside the house with nothing to see. When he is a little older, it is a temptation just to leave him in the play-pen convenient-ly out of the way, but not learning anything. As soon as you see him show interest in his surroundings, let him see what is going on, take him out in his pram, and prop him up as soon as he wants to be propped up. Show him pictures in books as soon as he shows any interest. Read to him if he is interested. Give him toys which teach him to use his hands. But do not do nothing. Give him every possible chance to learn. It takes time and a great deal of patience to teach him, but it is well worth while. Only by wise management will his true ability and aptitude be discovered — and once discovered they should be encouraged to the utmost. If he is particularly good with his hands, concentrate on that and help him to use them. If he is good at music, encourage it. Do not neglect other things entirely, but do concentrate on the skills which he enjoys, so that he may achieve the maximum proficiency in them.

The time may come when a difficult decision has to be made about the choice of school for him. His teachers will advise. It is particularly difficult when a child's intellectual capacity is on the borderline for a normal school or for a school for slightly backward children. The question is whether it is better for him always to be bottom in a normal school or top in a special school. It is psychologically harmful for any child always to be bottom.

Conclusion

We have tried to set out on paper those aspects of parental management which we think are important for helping a child to be happy, to use his talents and to develop his potential to the utmost. Many parents will think of points which we have failed to mention, or will disagree with points which we have made. It would not be surprising, for none of us know all the answers. More important than anything, however, is this. The child should be accepted for what he is. We have to make the best of his intellectual level, his personality, his health. He will not be perfect — neither will his parents. We must not expect too much of a child, and on no account must we let him feel that we are disappointed in him. It should always be remembered that there is a great difference between being a nice child or adult, and being a clever one. Not all clever children are nice children. The nice but no so clever child may achieve a great deal more in the long run than the very clever child who is not so nice.

24

Accidents and their prevention

We do not want to alarm you, but we do want to make you careful, and we think that you should know that more children lose their lives every year from accidents than from all the infectious diseases combined, and that in children over one year of age accidents are the commonest cause of death. In England and Wales around 4.5 million children are taken to hospital Accident and Emergency Departments each year. About 30,000 children under the age of five are admitted to hospitals in England and Wales each year due to poisoning. In one British city, it is calculated that about one in every five children is taken to the Casualty Department of a hospital every year. About 65,000 children are hurt each year in Britain in road accidents, and 120 are killed. In the United States, 700,000 children are injured each year by defective or dangerous toys. About 260 children under 10 drown each year in Britain.

In Britain there are more firework accidents than in any other country: in one year 260 children received serious injuries from them; and apart from fireworks, around 140,000 children received burns or scalds.

The management of the child

Accidents are more common in early childhood when someone other than the mother is looking after the child. They are more common at the time of the mother's menstrual period. The parents become, or should become, sensitive to possible dangers to the child and prevent accidents occurring. Others, particularly those without children, often have no idea of the capabilities of a small child, and accidents are therefore more likely.

The difficulty in the management of the child lies in the fact that whereas in the first few months he is totally unable to look after himself and therefore to avoid accidents, he has to learn to look after himself as he gets older. The mother has to learn when to begin to relax her supervision and take calculated risks, in order that the child can gradually become completely independent and look after himself. This is by no means easy, and much inevitably depends on the child's personality, on the number of other children, and on the character of the house and other social circumstances.

In the first year it is the parents' responsibility to give absolute protection against accidents, for the baby is unable to tell what is dangerous to him and how he may be hurt. Even at this age the baby is beginning to learn the unpleasant consequences of certain acts. A 6 months old baby remembers very well if he has been given something to drink which was too hot, for he may refuse anything out of the cup concerned for two or three weeks. A bad bump will stop many children trying to walk for three or four weeks. Nevertheless, every possible step has to be taken to prevent children of this age having accidents.

The important point is that if this absolute protection continues (and we call this 'overprotection'), then the child will not learn to fend for himself, and will remain dependent on his parents. He is likely to grow up to be timid and unreliable, and to have difficulties at school. Experience has shown that children who have been overprotected in their early years become 'accident-prone', meaning that they are more likely to become involved in accidents than other children. They seem to rebel against their overprotection as soon as they acquire some freedom, and go too far the other way. They have not learnt caution, their personality has been warped by being excessively dependent on their mother, and they are liable to be involved in accidents. It follows that some time after the first year the child must begin to look after himself, to learn what hurts and to profit from mistakes. The age at which the child begins to learn will depend on his intelligence and personality. The latter is important, for some children do not care at all if they receive quite bad bumps. Others are very upset and are unlikely to repeat the act which caused the discomfort.

In the first half of the second year the child is still almost completely incapable of avoiding danger. Protection still has to be absolute. Nevertheless, the child is beginning to learn the meaning of 'no', and the mother has to begin to use that word on appropriate occasions. Constant warnings are almost inevitably ignored. We all know mothers who say scores of times a day 'Mind the step', 'Mind the fire', 'Don't touch', 'Be careful you don't fall'. The child is so used to hearing her say these things that he does not take the slightest notice, and she does not seem to care, for she takes no steps to see that her orders are obeyed. This question is more fully discussed in the section on discipline (Chapter 14).

In the latter half of the second year (18 months to 2 years) the child is beginning to understand quite a lot of what his parents say, and his memory is improving. He is beginning to realize that certain acts lead to certain consequences. It is wise deliberately to allow the child at this age to have certain mildly uncomfortable experiences in order that he will learn what is meant by 'hot', 'it will hurt'. For instance, when he has been warned on several occasions that the teapot is hot, on one occasion he should not be prevented from touching it, so that in future he will not need to be warned. When he has been warned repeatedly that the water from the hot tap is hot and will hurt, he should be allowed to turn the hot tap, as long as it is known that the water will not scald him, in order that he will remember in future what 'hot' means. Minor falls serve a useful purpose in teaching a child to be cautious. A child who is showing a tendency to sample the contents of bottles in the pantry may be taught his lesson if a tempting bottle is left in a conveniently accessible place for him — containing vinegar.

The difficulty lies in striking a balance between carelessness and overprotection. Every child, at least up to the age of about 10, has to be protected from scalds and burns. But over-protection must be avoided, for this will prevent the child learning independence, it will make it impossible for him to learn from his own experience, and it will lead to insecurity and timidity, temper tantrums and thwarting. It will involve constant remonstrances, warnings, threats and punishment, which do nothing but harm. Parents have to take calculated risks when they allow children, as they must do, to acquire independence.

It is difficult to avoid implanting fear. On the one hand the small child has to learn caution in crossing the road, and on the other hand he must not be caused to become afraid of traffic. He must not go up and pat every dog in the street, for some dogs would not welcome him. On the other hand, he must not be warned in such a way that he becomes afraid of all dogs.

Parents must be careful to set a good example to their children in order to prevent accidents. If the father climbs on to a rocking chair in order to adjust a curtain, leans dangerously out of a window in order to wash it, or does anything else which is dangerous, he must expect his child to copy him.

At all times the parent has to be sensitive to possible dangers, to notice the upturned carpet which will trip even the older child, to move the teapot away from the edge of the table, or to have a broken step mended. The parent of a toddler must notice that certain ornaments are invitingly within his reach — and move them. One must remember that even a well-behaved older child may fall at times, and even older children must be prevented from having unnecessary accidents. A mother must never be too busy to notice possible dangers to her child.

Some children are more likely to become involved in accidents than others. There is a much higher incidence of accidents in the lower social classes, perhaps largely due to overcrowding and lack of play space. Psychiatrists have ascribed frequent involvement in accidents to indiscipline or excessive discipline in the home, attention seeking, unconscious self injury because of guilt feelings, psychiatric or physical illness in the family, domestic discord, personality features, rebellion against restraint, a desire for independence, the avoidance of unpleasant tasks, revenge, parental alcoholism, a punitive or rejecting parent, or a submissive or overprotective mother. When parents take tranquillising drugs they may be less able to supervise their children and to prevent accidents.

Specific measures to prevent accidents
Burns, scalds, electrocution. All gas fires, coal fires and electric radiators must be adequately protected by a fireguard. All new gas and electric fires sold in England must by law be fitted with fireguards. Children's clothes are often highly flammable, and every effort must be made to prevent their clothes coming into contact with the fire. For this reason there is much to be said for pyjamas instead of a nightdress. Flame resistant material is specially treated to resist burning. Portable stoves, whether gas, electric or oil, are a danger, unless kept strictly in the fireplace. A child may trip over the

gaspipe or flex and hurt himself, or worse still upset the stove and cause a fire. A portable oil stove should never be used in a house containing a small child. No heating device should include a hot pipe or other hot place on which a child can burn his hand or leg. Electric wringers are a frequent cause of serious accidents: an entire book has been written about 'wringer injuries' involving small children. It is foolish to have an electric wringer in the house if there is also a small child.

Do not make the mistake of thinking that the danger of burns and scalds only applies to the young child. The older child must be protected from burns and scalds too.

You should see that all flex to lamps and radiators is in good condition, and unable to give electric shocks.

All electric points must be of the safety variety, so that a child cannot push a pencil in and receive a shock.

See that the clothes-horse cannot be knocked over into the fire, and do not put clothes on the fireguard.

There should not be an electric fire in the bathroom, unless it is at the top of a wall and operated by a long flex. Many fatal accidents have occurred as a result of electric installations in bathrooms.

The absurd practice of placing hot water in a potty before the child sits on it should be stopped.

In the kitchen be sure that you always turn pan handles inwards, so that the child cannot knock them or reach them.

Never leave a bucket full of water on the floor in the kitchen (or elsewhere), especially if it is hot. He may fall into it and drown, or scald himself. This is a frequent cause of severe scalds.

Beware of leaving a child in his high chair so near a fire or cooking stove that he can either fall into the fire, or reach over and pull a pan from the stove.

A fire extinguisher is a useful thing to have in the house.

Never leave your children in the house alone even for five minutes. Hundreds of fatal accidents, mostly by burning, have resulted from this. There is absolutely no excuse for it. Be sure that you know just a little about the reliability of your baby sitters. They are not all safe to leave in charge of your children. In a university city girl students are usually pleased to undertake the work.

Electric blankets must never be folded. They should be serviced regularly. No child (or adult) should ever sleep on an electric blanket which is plugged in and switched on. Innumerable serious accidents have occurred as a result of wetting the blanket.

All electric equipment should be unplugged when out of use.

Only an expert should wire up the lights on a Christmas tree.

Many serious accidents have resulted from neglect of this precaution.

Never let a child play with fire or matches.

Never let him climb into the fireplace to recover a toy. It is unwise to have a mirror above the fire, for it may tempt the child to climb up to look at himself — with the result that his clothes catch fire.

Fireworks should be let off only under the strictest supervision. They should never be held in the hand. They must on no account be thrown. They must never be placed in the pocket. No one should bend over a firework to light it. A firework should never be placed in a milk bottle.

The danger of electric mixers must be known. Many serious accidents have resulted from their use when there are small children in the house.

At the tea table, be sure that the teapot, or other vessel containing a hot substance, is in the centre of the table. Many serious scalds have resulted from babies and toddlers pulling the table cover and so upsetting the teapot on themselves. Beware of holding the baby in your arms when you are having tea. A sudden quick movement on his part may causes a serious scald. When your child is learning to set or clear the table, never let him carry the hot teapot or coffee pot. Be careful not to pass a hot cup of tea in such a way that he may suddenly catch your arm and make you spill it.

In the bathroom, it is safer to run the cold water before the hot. A child of 2 can climb into the bath when you are looking the other way. Avoid holding the baby in your arms when filling the bath. Never leave a small child in the bath to answer the telephone or door bell. He may drown or turn the hot tap on.

Except for an older child who has no younger brothers and sisters, a gas fire in the child's bedroom, or a gas water-heating apparatus, should be avoided, in case by accident the gas tap is turned on without the stove or heater being lighted.

In all rooms the connection between the gas tube to the radiator and the gas tap should be of the safety variety, which will not allow gas to escape if the tube becomes disconnected.

All drugs, cleaning materials and other dangerous substances must be kept out of reach of the small child. This is difficult, especially with the child who 'climbs' and can reach the highest shelf of a cupboard by means of a stool. Thousands of children are admitted to hospital every year on account of accidental poisoning. The green ferrous sulphate (iron) tablets, so often taken by women, are one of the commonest causes of death from poisoning in children, for they look like pleasant sweets. Kerosene and similar compounds are important causes of deaths by poisoning. Other common poisons are barbiturates, paracetamol, strychnine, insecticides, pesticides and weedkillers. Camphor balls, matches, aspirins and oil of Wintergreen are all frequent causes of serious poisoning in children. Toy fuel cubes and wax crayons are dangerous. Do not leave your medicine about. It may be highly dangerous for your child. Never put poisonous substances, such as cleaning materials, into an empty orange juice or similar bottle. Never leave drugs on food shelves. Always destroy discarded medicines. Always refer to medicine as medicine, and not as sweeties. Do not let him see you take medicine: he may imitate you. Do not let him see you hid it: he may deliberately look for it when your back is turned. Do not leave medicine in the room of an ill child. Do not think that the outhouse shelf is a safe place for an insecticide. Remember that there are many hundreds of poisons which children may get hold of — with disastrous results.

See that you have no flowering shrubs which have pretty berries. Laburnum and many other shrubs are dangerous to small children. It is a good idea to go out of your way to make a child understand that berries are intended for birds only, and that berries hurt boys and girls if they eat them.

If you see fungi growing in the garden, you should immediately dig them out. You should warn your children not to touch fungi when you see them in the woods or elsewhere.

Before you give medicine to your child, be sure that you have read the label on the bottle. A surprising number of serious poisoning cases are due to neglect of this simple precaution.

In the garden keep the child well away from motor lawn mowers. Rotary mowers may project stones at high speed into a child's eyes or cut off his fingers.

Always remember the possibility of small objects being taken into the mouth and then accidently inhaled. Peanuts are the main offenders, and should never be given to young children. They are particularly dangerous if they are thrown into the mouth with the head back.

Certain dangerous practices should always be stopped. These are throwing objects about the room, hitting other children on the head, pushing children under stress of anger, especially near the stairs, removing a chair or stool in fun just before a child or adult sits down, stepping into the fireplace to rescue a toy, climbing on the window sill, running about with sharp objects in the mouth, such as a pencil, or with an object such as a plastic 'flute' which would seriously injure the roof of the mouth if the child fell, getting off a stool to pick something up from the floor while holding a fork in the hand, playing on the stairs, and putting a cord round the neck. The door banging game should be stopped immediately: it is only a matter of time before it leads to a finger being trapped.

Be careful not to leave other objects of potential danger within reach of your child. Razor blades, needles, pins, hairpins, buttons, opened tins, knives, scissors (especially sharp-pointed ones), should all be out of reach. For your own peace of mind see that fragile ornaments are not liable to be pulled over by him. No child should ever be left with a dummy in the mouth. He may swallow it. Rusty nails should not be left in pieces of wood, and broken bottles must not be left about.

Do not polish a floor on which rugs are to be placed. If you must, you should fix non-skid devices to the rugs so that they do not slip. See that there are no holes or loose loops of thread in the carpet which may trip a child; and if you see a corner of a carpet turned up, attend to it immediately. If you drop grease on the floor, remove it.

All upstairs windows should be safe. Unfortunately, there are difficulties about this. On the one hand, the child must be prevented from falling out of the window, and many fatalities have resulted from such falls. On the other hand, if all upstairs windows are rendered safe for the child, by means of bars or other devices, then in the case of an emergency (a fire) it will be impossible to escape. Our feeling is that the windows of the child's bedroom and playroom must be safe, so that the child cannot get out even by climbing, but that other windows should be available for use in case of emergency. If window bars are used, they should not be more than six inches apart. No chairs, drawers, or radiators should enable the child to climb out of his cot then out of the window.

The stairs should be as safe as possible. They should be well lighted. Always attend to a loose stair-rod. If possible use a stair-carpet clip, instead of a stair-rod, because it is more secure.

Many advocate a gate at the top of the stairs. We think that it is inadvisable. A child may climb over the gate, and the fall will then be more serious than a simple fall down the stairs. He may push against it when it is not properly fastened, and fall down the stairs, or he may unfasten the catch and fall down when the gate suddenly opens. It gives a false sense of security. There is something to be said for a gate at the foot of the stairs, to prevent a child creeping up.

Never ask a child, who is still not secure on his feet, to carry an object down the stairs. It may make him fall. You should see that his dressing gown is not so long that he can trip over it.

The age at which a child should be allowed to come downstairs without help cannot be stated exactly. It depends on his steadiness on his feet. He should be taught always to hold on to the banisters with both hands, until he is old enough to do without that support. It is easy to postpone the age at which he is able to manage alone by always carrying him (to save time). He should not be able to crawl under the banisters. He must not be able to get his head between vertical bars or climb up horizontal bars over the banisters.

Many accidents are due to overloading the pram by parcels or by another child, especially at the handle end. It is dangerous to use a single pram for two children. See that the safety strap is safe and fits round the child's waist and shoulders. The safety strap should be fixed 9 to 11 inches from the interior back of the pram, according to its size. This should bring the strap fastening to a position from which a vertical line will come within the wheelbase. Do not allow too much play in the strap, for if you do the child may climb over the side. See that the brake of the push-chair is not within reach of the toddler in it.

Some people advocate a net over the pram to keep cats away.

You should try to get into the habit of opening doors gently, so that if your child is at the older side he will not be sent flying, and of closing doors gently, so that you will not trap his fingers if he puts them in the door as you are going out. Always stop the door banging game.

Be sure that the pram is safe when you leave it in the garden. An active child of 10 months or so can upset a pram by bouncing movements.

Remember the ever-present dangers of swings and roundabouts. The young child can run into the way of a swing and receive a serious head injury. Do not forget that although horse riding is a pleasant occupation, many children have received serious concussion from falls from horses.

Beware of glass in doors and windows accessible to young children. All glass in doors should be safety-glazed. Safety-glazing material is advised for all glass below 800 mm from the floor. Existing glass can be boarded up with plywood, or covered with plastic-covered wire guards or plastic film. Do not allow a small child to walk about carrying a glass object.

Lily-ponds should never be allowed in the garden if there are small children. Many deaths from drowning have resulted from them. All children should be taught to swim as soon as they are old enough. Children should never be allowed on to a canoe, small boat or sailing boat without a life-jacket on. Remember the danger of an inflated lilo floating out to sea; and the danger of airwings becoming deflated, or inverting the child with his head under water. At the seaside remember the danger of the undertow. We do not know the youngest age at which children learn water-skiing, but you should know that a girl should wear rubber pants or a rubber wet suit, for otherwise water may be forced into the vagina under pressure.

Deliberate overbreathing before underwater swimming is dangerous.

In the bedroom, never take a child into your own bed because he will not sleep. Many cases of suffocation have resulted from this practice. Be sure that if you put a hot bottle into his bed you take it out before he gets in. The older child may unscrew the top and scald himself. Put him into a bed as soon as there is a danger that he will climb over the side of the cot.

A child must never be allowed to play with a cord round the neck, or to play with a plastic bag (which he may put over his head). Elastic or string across the pram, with rattles or other objects on it, may strangulate the baby, as may a safety harness in bed or a dummy on a string. A harness must be firmly attached to both sides of the bed under the mattress: if fixed on the bars of the cot it may slide up and strangulate the child. If fixed on one side only, the child may climb over the side of the cot and remain hanging on the strap or get his head caught on a loop or strap. The straps should fit closely on the child's chest so that they are taut on either side: if they are slack he may slip underneath them and get strangled. There should not be over one inch between the mattress and the side or end of a cot. The cot side should be properly fixed. There should not be more than two and a half inches between vertical bars of the cot side — or the baby may get his head caught in it. Toddlers have been strangled by buttons getting caught in netting over a cot or playpen. Older children have been strangled by a long-flowing scarf getting caught in machinery, or a merry-go-round. Others have been strangled by cord on the neck of a cardigan.

Never play with a child who has food in the mouth. He may inhale it.

The danger of a child shutting himself or another child into a large refrigerator must be remembered.

Do not enable a child to lock himself into a room — and lock you out of the room: he can suffer serious injury — and be unable to reopen the door.

Avoid giving your child dangerous toys. Bows and arrows, airguns and catapults should on no account be given to a child. They may cause the loss of an eye. The parent who supplies his child with an airgun is guilty of criminal negligence. Beware of letting your child play with a ballpoint pen or other sharp object which may penetrate the eye.

If the older child has a tricycle or bicycle, be sure that he does not get his clothes caught in the wheel. Many cycle accidents are due to a dangerous drain hole in the drive. Other cycle accidents are due to losing control on a hill or corner, skidding on gravel on a corner, hitting a pothole, the road edge or an animal, riding with a friend on the cycle, riding on one wheel or without hands on the handlebars.

Do not let the child run out into the street for a ball. Remember the danger of the car backing out of the garage and running over the child.

You should begin to teach him when to cross the road, to cross at a safe place, and set a good example yourself. You should avoid running across the road and dodging fast moving traffic. You can make it a pleasant game, allowing your child to tell you when it is safe and unsafe to cross the road. You should teach him that he must never run across the road after a ball, and you can show him dangerous practices as you see them in the streets. You should also teach him not to rush suddenly to the edge of the road, as if he is going to run on to the road, for he may cause a serious accident by making a motorist swerve to avoid him.

If you take your child in a car, you will need to see that the doors are safely secured. In some cars the handle is so badly designed that pressure downwards by the child in the car will open the door. You may be able to remedy this by reversing the handles, so that the pressure has to be in an upward direction to open the door. You should try to prevent your child leaning on the door at any time. A child is far safer in the back of the car than in the front, if an accident occurs. *Do not have him standing up, especially in the front of the car:* if you stop suddenly he may be seriously injured. Do not let him sit on your lap in the front seat: in an accident he may be squashed between you and the front of the car. The car should be equipped with safety belts. If he is in the back of the car, a suitable restraint is desirable. In an American study of 27,000 childhood car accidents, 30 per cent would not have occurred if the child had been in the back seat without a restraint and 35 per cent if he had been in the back with a restraint. There are various designs of car seats for babies and toddlers. They hook over the ordinary seat, and keep the child out of harm's way. Avoid flimsy seats hooked over the front seat: a seat or belt should be approved by the British Standards Institute. Avoid baby seats with attached toys. Never have one safety belt around both you and your child.

If you want to have a child on your knee, it would be safer at the back. In Austria all children under 12 must by law sit in the back:

there is much to be said for this.

We have tried to make this section comprehensive, and we hope that you will read it over and over again. You may think that some of the precautions are excessive. They are not. Remember that every Children's Hospital, and every Casualty Department, treats injured children every day of every week of every year. We have ourselves treated many hundreds of such children.

However careful parents are accidents will happen — perhaps because of an unfortunate combination of circumstances. One cannot absolutely prevent them, and if parents have taken all reasonable precautions, they must not feel guilty if an accident does happen.

A useful booklet to keep in the home is *Accident Prevention and First Aid in the Home*, produced by the Edinburgh Royal Infirmary.*

First aid

Suggested materials for a first-aid box include a roll of zinc oxide strapping, a box of 'Elastoplast' dressings, a small roll of cotton wool, and half-a-dozen assorted bandages: Melolin non-stick dressing; Ethistrip or Steristrip to bring small cut surfaces together, a bottle of proflavine, which is a useful antiseptic, in that it does not hurt like iodine when applied to an injured part: a sling, a clinical thermometer, an eyedropper, a fine-pointed pair of tweezers for removing splinters from the finger, and a pair of scissors.

Below is an outline of first-aid treatment for the mishaps which may occur in the home.

Abrasions and grazes

The part should be washed in soap and water, dried by patting it with a clean towel, and covered up by a dry dressing and left. The dressing should not be removed daily, for this will pull the healing tissue off and greatly delay healing. It should be left untouched for at least 4 days and perhaps a week. If necessary it is then redressed. Antibiotics are not required.

Iodine is never used, because it causes so much pain.

Cuts

You should let your doctor treat a large or deep cut. If the cut is dirty, do not give your child anything to drink or eat, for that would make an anaesthetic dangerous. An anaesthetic may have to be given by the doctor in order to remove dirt from the cut. Small cuts are treated like abrasions. The cut edges can be brought together well by an adherent dressing or in an emergency by Sellotape.

Bleeding is stopped by applying pressure on the bleeding part with a finger, not lifting the finger up for at least five minutes to see if bleeding has stopped. You should not try to apply a tourniquet, for in inexperienced hands it may be dangerous.

A puncture wound anywhere, or a cut of the mouth or tongue, should be treated by your doctor.

For a more serious injury, your doctor may give a booster dose of tetanus toxoid, to prevent tetanus (lockjaw), provided that the child has been previously immunised (e.g. with the triple vaccine).

Bites and stings

An animal or human bite should be treated by your doctor. There is no special treatment for stings. A cold application may give some relief.

If a severe allergic reaction to a sting occurs, your doctor may provide you with a mini-jet 'syringe' with adrenaline for injection in a future emergency.

Splinters

These should be removed as soon as possible by fine tweezers. If you cannot do it, your doctor should be asked to help.

Burns and scalds

When a child's clothes are on fire, the flames should be smothered by rolling him tightly into a blanket or rug.

A small burn or scald is treated by immediately inserting the affected part into ice cold water, and then cleaning the skin with soap and water, patting it dry, and covering it up with a dry dressing (e.g. the Elastoplast dressing). Do not apply jelly or other dressing to a burn or scald. Never apply ointment. Never put a burnt or scalded child into a cold bath. Do not give anything to drink in case an anaesthetic has to be given. Anything but the most trivial burn should be seen by your doctor. Do not disturb burnt clothing, unless it is smouldering.

A child with a bad burn or scald should be wrapped in a clean sheet and blanket and rushed to hospital immediately, without waiting for your doctor to come and without waiting to telephone to the hospital. If there is saturated clothing, remove it. If clothes are heavily contaminated by a chemical, remove them and wash the skin. If the face is burnt, leave it exposed. Do not apply jellies, creams, wet dressings or ointment. Keep him warm, but do not make the mistake of making him too warm. The danger of a bad burn or scald is that it causes severe shock, which does not develop until some time after the injury, so that what appears to you to be a trivial burn may lead to serious shock. If in doubt you should always take the child to hospital immediately.

A fracture or suspected fracture

If you suspect a fracture, move the affected part as little as possible and immediately take him to the doctor or hospital. Keep him warm, but do not make him too warm. Do not give him anything to drink, in case an anaesthetic has to be given.

Trapped fingers

The modern treatment is to avoid all suturing and plastic surgery. The hospital doctor will clean the fingers, reposition separated parts and hold them in place by Ethistrip or Steristrip, leaving the nail in position. Non-adherent Melolin is applied and left in place for 7–10 days.

If the finger tip has been amputated, provided that it is distal to the distal joint, the finger and nail will regrow *provided that no stitching or plastic surgery is done.*

Pulled elbow

In this condition, commonly caused by a sudden pull on the child's arm, as when swinging him in play, or dragging him reluctantly forward, the head of the radius bone of the lower arm is slightly dislocated. The child will refuse to use the arm, and there is pain in the elbow *or* only in the wrist or shoulder (though the wrist and shoulder have not been damaged). A doctor in the nearest Children's Accident and Emergency Department of a hospital can correct the position in a second without an anaesthetic.

A head injury

When a child has had a bad knock on the head, he is treated by being put to bed. Your doctor must then be called. If in doubt, and you are unable to find your doctor, you should take him to hospital. You should take him to the hospital immediately if he becomes unconscious, vomits or has bleeding from the nose or ears. If you are uncertain whether he is conscious, you should not hesitate to try to waken him. Do not give him anything to drink until he has been seen by a doctor. Do not give him a sedative before he is seen by the doctor.

Swallowed objects

When a child swallows a solid object, such as a toy, you should consult your doctor, but as long as the object is not something sharp,

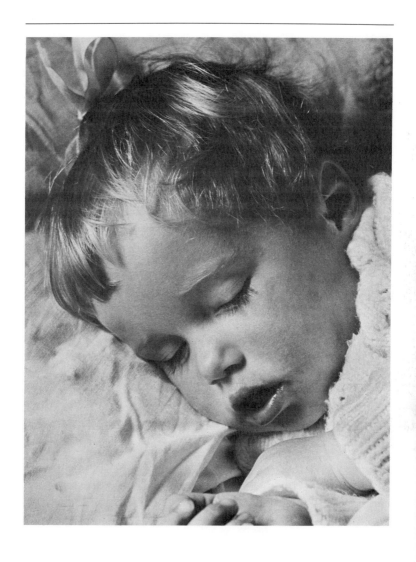

like an open safety pin or hair-clip and as long as it does not seem to have become impacted, causing salivation and retching, the matter is not urgent. Eighty to 90% of swallowed objects are passed without trouble, on average in five or six days. There is no purpose in withholding fluids, giving nothing but solid foods, or administering a purgative. If the child vomits, has pain or develops a temperature, take him to the hospital immediately.

Inhaled objects

If you think that your child may have inhaled an object into the windpipe, take him to the hospital immediately.

If he chokes as a result of swallowed food or something stuck in the throat, hold him upside down and firmly pat his back. Do not try to remove the object with your finger, for you may push it further down.

If a fishbone becomes stuck in the throat, you should ask your doctor or hospital to remove it.

Poisoning

If your child has taken any poison or possible poison, never fail to take it seriously. If you cannot get your doctor immediately, take him direct to the hospital. Do not give him salt water to make him sick: it may be dangerous. Transport him to hospital in the prone position (on his abdomen), so that if he is sick, he will not inhale the vomit. Do not waste time waiting to see if the child shows any ill effects from the poison. That is dangerous, because the effects often do not show themselves for some hours after the poison has been swallowed, and if your doctor had treated the child immediately, the effects might never have developed. Poisonous substances which are likely to cause serious trouble only after a latent period in which the child appears to be well include iron preparations, Lomotil (given by some for diarrhoea), salicylates, paracetamol and fungi.

Do not destroy the poison or throw it away. Keep the poison in the container. You will be asked exactly when he took the poison and how much you think he has taken. You should take it to the hospital, for it will help the doctors to give the correct treatment.

Particles in the eye

Much unnecessary damage is done to the eyes by clumsy efforts to remove particles from them.

A particle can be safely removed from the lower eyelid by the corner of a clean handkerchief, but it is dangerous to use this for particles on the surface of the eye. You should bathe the eye with water by means of the eye dropper, and try to wash the particle away. If you cannot do this, you should ask your doctor or hospital to deal with it. If an object has penetrated the eye, or if the eye has been burnt, you should consult the hospital immediately. For chemical substances in the eye the best thing to do is to wash it out immediately by holding him face upwards under the cold tap for at least five minutes. You may then bathe the eye with a weak salt solution, a teaspoonful in a pint of tepid water. You should try to stop your child rubbing the eye. When a child or adult feels something enter the eye when working with a hammer, he should consult the nearest Casualty Department immediately: a fragment of metal may have entered the eye.

Objects in the nose or ear
Efforts to extract objects from the nose or ear are liable to lead to their being pushed further in. You should consult your doctor. If the object is in the nose, try to get the child to blow the nose, while you occlude the other side; apply pressure *behind* the object so that he will not sniff it in.

Do not attempt to syringe a nose or ear because if the object consists of vegetable matter it is likely to swell by absorbing fluid, making removal more difficult.

Nose bleeding
In most cases nose bleeding can be stopped effectively by simply applying continuous pressure for 5 minutes by nipping the nose along its entire length. You should not keep relaxing the pressure to see if it is still bleeding. If it still bleeds after 5 minutes pressure, you should consult your doctor.

Bleeding after removal of a tooth
If you are worried you should consult your dentist about this. If, as often happens, it is the evening, and his surgery is closed, you will have to consult your doctor.

Particles in the skin
Most small particles work their way out, but you should always consult your doctor. If the cut was caused by broken glass, there may be glass left behind: it shows up in an X-ray.

25

Common infections and their prevention

General principles

Infections are due to small living organisms, some of which are so minute (viruses) that they cannot be seen under the ordinary microscope. Infections pass from one person to another by a variety of means. Colds, coughs, sore throats, measles, mumps and many other infections are spread by 'droplets' — minute particles which are coughed, sneezed, or emitted in speech from the nose and throat of people harbouring the infection. Other infections are spread by contact. Impetigo and other conditions are passed from person to person by infected discharges, mostly by the hands, towels and infected linen. The organisms can survive in dust for several weeks. Bowel infections and certain types of food poisoning are due largely to infection carried from the bowel by hands, and particularly to failure to wash the hands thoroughly after having a motion. Minute particles, each containing millions of organisms, adhere to the hands and finger nails, and are readily transferred to food in the process of cooking or preparing meals. The majority of cases of food poisoning are due to transfer into food of infection from the bowel or from septic places on the skin. Some of these infections are carried by flies from infected material to uncovered food.

It follows that every care must be taken to keep food covered up, so that flies cannot infect it; to wash the hands thoroughly before food is handled; to take especial precautions if one has a septic place anywhere in the skin, and to avoid handling food at all in that case; to avoid handling food if one has diarrhoea, and to take special care to wash the hands thoroughly after every motion; and to keep away from small children as far as one possibly can, and from those in charge of them, when one has a sore throat, cold or other infection. Animals may spread infection, including diarrhoea and worms. It is unwise to allow a dog to lick the child's face or hands.

The newborn baby, particularly if he is born prematurely, has a low resistance to infection, and simple infections such as colds may sometimes cause complications. One must try to prevent him acquiring infections.

We now have to consider how infections can be prevented after the newborn period. The methods available include immunization, the prevention of the development of disease by means of sera or drugs after exposure, isolation of children and others suffering from an infectious disease, the quarantining of contacts, the prevention of exposure to infection, and the prevention of the spread of infection by soiled clothes and linen.

By the term 'quarantine' we mean isolation of children who have been in contact with a case of infectious disease. In the case of school children this would mean keeping them away from school. By the term 'quarantine period' we mean the number of days for which such children are isolated. This depends on the incubation period — the number of days before the development of symptoms after exposure to infection. As for instance, the incubation period of mumps is 12 to 28 days, no child would be 'quarantined' for longer than 28 days, because he would not develop the disease after that time. As mumps is not infectious until one to two days before the swelling of the face occurs, it would be senseless to isolate ('quarantine') contacts for ten days after exposure, because they could not develop it before that time, unless they have been in contact with the original source of infection. It is never right to quarantine a child because of contact with a case of infectious disease if he has already had that disease. If a child is kept away from school because of contact with some infectious disease, it would be impossible to prevent him coming into contact with his school fellows after school hours.

It is now recognized that except in the case of possibly poliomyelitis, the quarantining of contacts is unnecessary and undesirable. In other words a child should not be kept away from school because his brother or sister has an infectious disease. Contacts cannot carry the infections from home to school by the throat or other means, except in the case of poliomyelitis (which can be carried in the throat), and possibly scarlet fever. Whether quarantining is carried out or not, nine out of ten children will acquire measles unless they have been immunized, and the majority will acquire German measles, mumps and chickenpox. There is much to be said for acquiring the common infectious diseases in childhood rather than later. They are often more severe and troublesome in adult life.

Diphtheria, whooping cough, tetanus (lock jaw), poliomyelitis, measles, German measles, mumps, typhoid and certain tropical diseases can largely be prevented by immunization. If they develop after immunization they generally occur in a mild form which does not cause serious illness. Tuberculosis can usually be prevented in children who cannot avoid being exposed to infection, by giving them BCG vaccine. There are means of preventing measles and diphtheria from developing after the child has been exposed to the infection, provided that the treatment is given soon enough after exposure.

Children who contract diphtheria and poliomyelitis have to be isolated and treated in infectious disease hospitals or units, while children with mumps, scarlet fever, German measles, measles, chickenpox and whooping cough should normally be nursed at home. If there is overcrowding at home, or circumstances make it difficult to look after them at home, they can usually be nursed in an infectious disease hospital or unit. If they are nursed at home, and there are other children in the house, the question arises as to whether the other children should be kept away from them. In the first place, it is extremely difficult, if not impossible, to keep one child away from another in an ordinary house. Secondly, most infectious diseases are infectious before the development of the rash or other feature of the disease, and it is inevitable that the child will have been in contact with other children during that time. Thirdly, it is almost inevitable that children will acquire infectious diseases while at school, if they have not already had them, and there is something to be said for getting them over in the family at one time. In the case of measles and whooping cough these diseases are more serious in infancy than in older children, and every effort should be made to prevent them in the young child.

It is a mistake to 'overprotect' one's child, and to be so afraid that he will 'catch' something, that he is not allowed to play with other children, go to the swimming baths (when older), or go to parties. We shall discuss possible exceptions to this in the section to follow.

The incubation period of common infectious diseases of childhood are as follows:

Disease	Incubation period in days	Duration of infectivity
Chicken pox	11–21 (especially 13–17)	1 day before rash appears to 6 days after its appearance
German measles	10–21 (especially 18)	1 day before rash appears to 2 days after its appearance
Glandular fever	10–20	Uncertain
Measles	10–15	6 days before rash appears to 5 days after its appearance if afebrile
Mumps	16–26 (especially 18)	2 days before the swelling begins till the swelling has disappeared
Whooping cough	7–10	2 days before the onset for 5 weeks

All children acquire infections. When your first child gets his first infection, you will be seriously worried — but after he has had a few infections you will take them in your stride.

Chickenpox (Varicella)

This is nearly always a trivial disease in childhood. Unless your child is poorly, there is no need to try to prevent his coming into contact with it, for he will almost certainly get it sooner or later, and there is much to be said for getting it over in childhood. A second attack is exceedingly rare.

About three-quarters of all children exposed to a case in the home acquire the disease, and eight out of 10 children have had it before they leave school. Adult contacts sometimes develop shingles.

Chickenpox commonly begins with spots on the body, which rapidly become vesicles like tear drops. These dry and form scabs. Crops continue to occur for three or four days. There are more spots on the body than on the limbs.

Medicines are of no value, but scratching (with the risk of infection and therefore scabs) should be avoided as far as possible. There is no point in keeping the child in bed or indoors.

There is no vaccine available at present.

Colds

Doctors are not yet able to prevent children acquiring colds, though intensive research on the subject is in progress. The difficulty is that colds are caused by dozens of different viruses, so that a vaccine has not been developed. If a mother acquires a cold while breast-feeding her baby, there is little she can do to prevent his becoming infected. It is doubtful whether it is worth her while wearing a gauze mask while feeding, bathing, dressing or changing him. If the baby's brother or sister acquires a cold, it is futile to try to keep him or her away from the baby. Attempts to do so will only lead to unpleasantness, and will achieve nothing, for close contact can hardly be prevented. Unfortunately, a child is particularly liable to acquire colds frequently in his first few months at school, so that he takes the cold home and infects smaller children. Nothing can be done to prevent it: but one should try to keep a small baby away from a visitor who is unkind enough to come to the house when suffering from a cold. It follows that no adult should visit a house in which there are small children when he is suffering from a cold or sore throat.

Excessive efforts to prevent a small child (except a newborn baby) acquiring a cold should not be made. Refusal to allow the child to go out to play in cold or wet weather will achieve nothing. Provided that he is properly dressed for the occasion and put into dry clothes when he comes in, he is less likely to acquire colds by playing outside in bad weather than he is if he stays indoors.

Children usually develop considerable immunity (resistance) to colds by the age of six or seven, and it may well be that excessive efforts to prevent them catching colds may merely postpone the development of that immunity. The removal of tonsils and adenoids is most unlikely to make any difference. There is nothing in the idea that frequent colds and coughs predispose to tuberculosis.

Vitamins or ultraviolet light are useless for preventing colds.

A cold may slow down a baby's weight gain for a few days. Some small children develop a middle ear infection or wheezing a few days after the onset of a cold. Many toddlers have a discharge down the back of the throat after a cold; it causes little trouble in the day, but may cause a troublesome cough when they lie on their back at night. It may be helped if they sleep on the abdomen.

Medicines, such as antibiotics, are useless in treatment, as colds are a virus infection and are therefore unaffected by antibiotics. We do not advise the use of nose drops: they are of no value and may irritate the nose. If middle ear infection should occur, it should be treated forthwith by an antibiotic, usually penicillin.

Dysentery

Dysentery and certain allied infections (e.g. salmonella) which cause diarrhoea are spread by adults suffering from the disease, by the hands, by flies and by animals (e.g. incompletely defrosted and cooked meat). Hands carry the infection as a result of failure to wash them after a movement of the bowels. In countries abroad, milk, cream cakes and made-up foods which require handling are the chief dangers. It may be nursed at home or in the infectious disease hospital. If a case of dysentery occurs in the home, there is no need to quarantine other children who have been in contact with the case. In Britain dysentery is nearly always a mild infection. It is better not to give antibiotics for it.

It is important that the child (or adult) with dysentery or convalescent from it, or with any other form of diarrhoea, should wash the hands thoroughly after passing a stool, because otherwise the hands may spread the infection.

As dysentery and other diseases are carried by flies, you should always be sure that all food is properly protected from them.

German measles (Rubella)

This is almost invariably a trivial disease in childhood, but its danger is in early pregnancy, when it may damage the fetus by causing deafness, cataract, congenital heart disease or other conditions. Girls are routinely immunised against it at the age of 11-12, unless blood tests show that they are immune. So many conditions cause a german measles-like rash that the story that a girl has had the infection cannot be accepted.

The vaccine occasionally causes mild symptoms around the ninth day, including occasionally a rash, enlargement of glands in the neck, or even joint pains.

When a child develops german measles, there is an approximately equal chance than other children in the house will get it. There is no point in trying to prevent others getting it, but the danger to an unimmunised pregnant woman makes it essential that a child with the infection, or a child who has been in contact with it, should not come into contact with such a woman.

German measles is rare in the first six weeks. Second attacks do not occur.

Commonly the first indication of the disease is a rash, but occasionally the child is off colour for a day before the rash develops. The rash appears on the face, rapidly spreads to the trunk, with little or no fever: the rash usually disappears by the third day. No treatment is necessary; the child should not be kept in bed or indoors.

Glandular fever (infectious mononucleosis)

This is due to a virus, and is only slightly infectious. Only one in about 25 children coming into contact will acquire it. It is rare in the first six months. It is characterised by fever, swollen glands in the neck, a sore throat, and in one in 10 or so, a rash mainly on the body, and other symptoms. Without a special blood test it cannot be distinguished from the common sore throat with enlarged glands in the neck. It is not helped by any medicine, but ampicillin will almost certainly cause a remarkable rash.

Impetigo

Impetigo may spread from one child to another by a common towel. This can be avoided, but apart from this, and apart from cleanliness and prompt treatment of impetigo if it develops, there are no other measures which prevent the infection. Any sore place or abrasion may become infected by it. Contacts of a case should not be quarantined, but a child suffering from the disease should not go to school until all affected areas have healed. With proper treatment a child should not be away from school because of impetigo for longer than a week. It is a mistake to apply a corticosteroid ointment.

Influenza

The incubation period is one to four days.

Jaundice (infective hepatitis)

This occurs in child or adult: it is only slightly infectious. It may be spread by contaminated water or foods, especially shellfish. The early symptoms are loss of appetite, fever, headache, vomiting and sometimes abdominal pain, with the development of jaundice, with dark urine and pale coloured stools. The illness in children is usually mild.

Measles (morbilli)

Measles affects only man and monkeys, but it is closely related to distemper in dogs.

There may be fever for eight or nine days before the rash develops, but more often the child is poorly for five or six days before the rash; there is often a cold, cough and conjunctivitis. The rash begins on the side of the neck and along the hairline, spreading to the face and chest in the first 24 hours. The rash then spreads to the body and limbs, reaching the feet by the second or third day, when the rash on the face is begining to fade. The temperature usually falls when the rash reaches the feet. Second attacks do not occur. Medicines do not affect it, but an antibiotic is given for a complication, such as middle ear infection: but antibiotics do not prevent complications. The organism is spread by the nose and throat.

When a child develops measles, there is a nine out of 10 chance that other children at home will get it unless they have already had it or been immunised. Unless children have been immunised, 90% of them will have had it by the age of fourteen.

Measles can now be prevented by a vaccine. It gives about 96% immunity, and a single dose is required. The main purpose of immunisation against measles is the prevention of encephalitis, but to a lesser extent other complications such as bronchopneumonia. The incidence of encephalitis in measles is one in 500 to one in 1000: this has to be balanced against the risk of encephalitis resulting from the vaccine, namely one in a million. The vaccine is given at around 15 months: it is avoided if the child has an infection or is receiving corticosteroids, and is not given within four weeks of other live vaccines such as poliomyelitis or german measles. At five to 10 days after the injection, the child may have mild symptoms lasting 24 to 48 hours. It is effective in preventing measles for about 10 years.

If a very young child, especially if he is poorly as a result of another illness, is exposed to measles, development of the infection can either be prevented or allowed to develop in a mild form, by giving gamma globulin, as long as it is given within three days of exposure. If there are good reasons for preventing measles, your family doctor may be able to obtain a supply through the Health Authority. Measles is so much more severe in infants that every effort should be made to prevent a baby becoming infected. Measles is rare, however, before the age of six months. The development of a cold or fever during the incubation period probably indicates an attack of measles.

Mumps (infectious parotitis)

Mumps is rare in the first six months; it is spread by droplets. When a child develops it, there is only a one in five chance that other children at home will acquire it. Half of all children have it before they leave school.

There are usually no symptoms before the parotid gland in front of the ear swells, but there is sometimes fever and headache. One or both sides of the face may be involved. The swelling reaches its maximum in one to three days, subsiding in three to seven days. The swelling on one side usually subsides a day or two before the other side begins. In a quarter of all cases only one side is affected. There is often some puffiness of the chest wall for two or three days. The swelling of the parotid gland may be painful.

Second attacks do not occur. As aspirin may be given to relieve pain, but no other medicine helps. There is no point in confining the child to bed.

A vaccine against measles, german measles and mumps is used in America but at the time of writing it is not available in Britain.

Roseola infantum

There is a virus infection affecting children mainly between the ages of six months and three years. It is a trivial infection without complications. There is a high temperature for three or four days, and then a rash appears on the trunk, spreading to the arms and neck, disappearing in 24 hours. As soon as the rash appears the temperature settles.

Scarlet fever

It is now realised that scarlet fever is nothing more than tonsillitis with a rash. It is no more infectious or dangerous than a similar tonsillitis without a rash.

If a child has been exposed to infection, the development of the disease may often be prevented by a medicine (penicillin) given by the doctor.

The infection is spread by droplets and discharges from the nose and throat. The incubation period is two to five days, so that if quarantine is demanded, it should not be for more than seven days. Scarlet fever should normally be nursed at home. It is impractical to prevent other children from coming into contact with a case. The child is infectious until the nose and throat swabs taken by the doctor are negative, meaning that they do not grow the organism. This may be a week or two from the onset. Prolonged isolation (six weeks), such as used to be demanded, is totally unnecessary. It is just possible, though unusual, for a child to transfer the infection to others by discharges from the throat, or from septic places, without suffering from the disease. Every effort should be made to keep an infected child away from a mother who is about to have a baby or who has just had one, for she is particularly liable to acquire the infection.

Tetanus

Tetanus spores are widespread, and occur particularly in soil and dirt, especially if there is contamination by horses. The infection reaches the human by injuries, especially puncture or deep penetration, burns, ear infections and even dental extraction.

Tuberculosis

Tuberculosis is largely a preventable disease. It is not a hereditary disease, and you need not have the slightest fear that your child will develop it merely because some relative of yours had it, as long as he has not been exposed to infection by that relative. We are often asked whether a child might have tuberculosis because his grandfather had it. On enquiring it is found that the grandfather died of it 10 or 20 years before the child in question was born, and therefore contact was impossible. A child only acquires tuberculosis because he has been exposed to infection by an adult suffering from the disease in the lung, or by infected milk. Mothers often fear that their child may develop tuberculosis because he has frequent attacks of bronchitis. The child with such attacks is no more likely to acquire tuberculosis than any other. The only disease which seems to predispose a child to infection, presumably by lowering his resistance, is diabetes.

It is essential to see that every effort is made to prevent a child coming into contact with the infection. The younger the child, the more susceptible to infection he is, and the more dangerous it is for him to acquire the disease. If you or your husband feel unduly tired, lose weight, or have a chronic cough, you should consult your doctor and have an X-ray taken to make sure that you are free from infection yourself. Ordinary physical examination of your chest is not enough to exclude the disease. An X-ray is essential, for it often shows disease which cannot be detected by the stethoscope. Unless your child has been protected against tuberculosis by BCG vaccine, you must on no account allow any relative, friend or other person who is known to be suffering from the disease, to visit your house. Neither must you allow your child to visit the house of any relative, friend or other person who is suffering from tuberculosis of the lungs. One would have thought that this would have been obvious, but we constantly see small children who have become infected with tuberculosis as a result of the most shocking carelessness in exposing them to adults suffering from the disease. We have even known of babies in arms being taken into a tuberculosis ward to visit a relative, of relatives or friends coming out of such a ward at weekends and visiting mothers with babies in their home, and of mothers allowing their children to go and play in a neighbour's house, knowing that he has advanced tuberculosis in the lungs. We have seen scores of tragedies from such carelessness.

It should be noted that tuberculosis in children, unless there is a discharging gland or unless the child has a particularly serious form, has been shown to be non-infectious. If your child has been infected you need not fear that he will infect others, except under the above circumstances, and he will not be infected by playing with a child who is said to have tuberculosis.

Cow's milk must always be boiled or pasteurized before it is given to small children, for some cows in England have tuberculosis, and milk from them may be infected. It is safe if it is boiled or pasteurized. Cream, unless pasteurized, is just as dangerous as milk.

If a parent has tuberculosis, every effort must be made to separate him from the children. If a mother who is suffering from tuberculosis has a baby, the baby must be separated from her immediately after birth, and in this case, and any other case in which contact of the child with the infected adult cannot be avoided, he should be given BCG vaccination. If your child may come into contact with anyone who has had tuberculosis in the past, even though it is confidently stated that the tuberculosis is healed, your child should be protected by BCG before contact. BCG must be given before the child acquires the infection, and if at all possible before exposure to infection. After the BCG has taken, as shown by a special test, the child returns to his parents. BCG protects a child against the severe forms of tuberculosis. It is safe, and has been given to millions of children in various countries of the world. Your family doctor will arrange for this to be given through the chest clinic. You may choose to have your baby immunized against tuberculosis even though you know of no infected person with whom he is likely to come in contact.

An adult suffering from the disease should not cough without properly covering his mouth with his handkerchief. This must never be shaken before or after use. It should be properly boiled. All rooms should be well ventilated, and children should not share the same bedroom as an infected adult.

Whooping cough (pertussis)

Whooping cough commonly begins with a mild cough and often sneezing; the cough is worse at night. After about 10 to 14 days spasms of coughing develop, the cough being worse at night and causing vomiting. In the third or fourth week the cough decreases, but may persist for a further two or three months. When a child gets it, there is an 80 to 90% chance that other children will get it unless they have been immunized. Seven out of 10 unimmunized children get it by the age of fourteen.

Antibiotics and cough medicines have little or no effect on the clinical course.

Immunisation

It is important to realise that *every* drug and every immunisation carries some risk; in the case of immunisation one has to balance the risk of the immunisation against that of the infection which could have been prevented. Mothers are likely to feel guilty if they have refused immunisation (e.g. for whooping cough) and then the child becomes seriously ill or dies; they would certainly feel guilty if they agreed to immunisation (e.g. for poliomyelitis) and the child is the unlucky one out of four million who has trouble with the immunisation. It is easier for parents if immunisation is compulsory (as behind the Iron Curtain and in some States in the U.S.A.).

There are some possible general contraindications to immunisation:

(i) Immunological deficiency — an extremely rare inborn defect — or 'immunosuppressant' drugs (e.g. for malignant disease, or corticosteroids).

(ii) Infection. We never give an injection for immunisation when a child is beginning an infection — not that a cold or other infection predisposes to brain damage, but because if the child develops some complication of the infection (such as middle ear disease if he has a cold), the parents would (wrongly) blame the immunisation. One never gives drops of poliomyelitis vaccine to a child with diarrhoea — not because the diarrhoea increases the risk of an untoward reaction, but because the vaccine would not 'take' when there is diarrhoea.

(iii) Allergy. Allergy is *not* a contraindication to immunisation against diphtheria, whooping cough, tetanus, poliomyelitis, measles, german measles or mumps. It is used to be thought that allergy to egg is a contraindication to measles immunisation, but we now know that idea was incorrect. One is advised not to give BCG immunisation to a child with eczema. We are not sure how valid that prohibition is. One should avoid immunising a child against yellow fever or flu if he is sensitive to egg.

(iv) History of convulsions in child or parents or of 'birth injury'. This applies to whooping cough immunisation and partly to measles. The whooping cough vaccine frequently causes a rise of temperature in the 24–48 hours after the injection — as may measles vaccine six to ten days after the injection. Fever may precipitate a fit in a child liable to convulsions because of epilepsy, cerebral palsy or mental subnormality, but this does not cause 'brain damage'. The immunisation, however, is likely to be blamed for causing a fit — even though he would be just as likely to have a fit with any infection. If a parent has epilepsy, there is a 4% risk that the child will have epilepsy — and the doctor would be just unfortunate if the injection which he gave to the child was followed by a fit when there had been no previous fits. If more distant relatives had a fit, it is totally irrelevant to the matter of immunising the child.

A history of asphyxia at birth is irrelevant. But it is true that children with mental subnormality or cerebral palsy are far more likely than others to have epileptic fits — whether immunised or not, and fever, whether caused by an infection such as tonsillitis or by immunisation, *may* cause a fit. Many normal children aged six months to five years have a 'benign febrile convulsion' when they have a sudden rise of temperature, whatever the cause, and whooping cough or other vaccine *could* cause a febrile fit because of a rise of temperature. But in all the above examples, *the fit does not cause brain damage or encephalitis.* Just over 7% of *all* children have a convulsion or convulsions by the age of five years. It is this frequency of fits in young children which has led to so much confusion with regard to the risks of immunisation

The fact is that we do not know what factors predispose to 'brain damage' (encephalitis) with immunisation.

We will now discuss immunisation for individual diseases.

Diphtheria, whooping cough (pertussis), tetanus (DPT)

Every child should be immunised against diphtheria, tetanus and poliomyelitis. Diphtheria is now exceedingly rare in Britain, thanks to immunisation. If a child, who has received an injury, has not been immunised against tetanus, he is given an injection of humotet; that will provide temporary immunity, but he should then have a full course of tetanus toxoid immunisation to prevent the infection in future.

When a child has been fully immunised against tetanus (i.e. has had his three injections) he will be given a booster (diphtheria, tetanus, poliomyelitis) before he starts school; but if he receives an injury there is no need to give a booster if less than three or four years have elapsed after the completion of the immunisation or a previous booster. There is a danger of allergic reactions if tetanus boosters are given too frequently.

The poliomyelitis drops are given at the same time as the diphtheria, tetanus (and whooping cough) injections or the pre-school booster.

The publicity given by the media to possible brain damage from whooping cough immunisation is thought to have caused in England 100 000 cases of whooping cough, which could have been prevented. (4 000 of them had convulsions). In 1974 and 1975 there were 170 deaths from whooping cough in England and Wales, with 13 500 admissions of children to hospital for the infection. In the 1977–1979 epidemic there were 28 deaths from whooping cough, and 5 000 children were admitted to hospital. It is tragic, when this could have been prevented, for the vaccine is around 90–95% effective, and those who do get the infection despite full immunisation usually have a mild attack. We stress full immunisation, because the child is not immune until he has had the three injections.

Immunisation against whooping cough is not given after the age of about three or four.

If for some reason there is a bigger interval between injections than that recommended, there is no need to start the course again. For example, if the first injection was at three months and the next at 10 months instead of five months, the third would be six months after the second, i.e. 16 months, but the child would not be immune till after the 16 months' injection.

A mother may have refused immunisation against whooping cough, so that the child was immunised only against diphtheria, tetanus and poliomyelitis, and she may then regret her refusal: in that case whooping cough vaccine can be given alone, three doses at monthly intervals. Any one of the three can be combined with diphtheria-tetanus injection (therefore DPT).

The only significant reactions to the whooping cough component of the vaccine (or whooping cough immunisation alone) is in the first 24 hours — *possibly* in the first 48 hours. A third of all children get a rise of temperature within a few hours of the injection — subsiding in a few hours. One out of eight children has a rise of temperature after the DT injection without the whooping cough. In a Welsh study one out of 101 children immunised with DPT had a fit (usually a 'benign febrile convulsion') within 48 hours, while 12% of 116 unimmunised children had a fit with whooping cough.

Severe permanent brain damage can be caused either by whooping cough in an unimmunised child, or as the apparent result of the immunisation. It is impossible to give precise figures for the risk, because the 'brain damage' or 'encephalitis' following immunisation is in all respects exactly the same as that which occurs in unimmunised children, whether they get whooping cough or not, and there is no laboratory test which can show that the encephalitis was due to the injection. It is *probable* that the risk after the injection is one in 110 000 or less.

A common sequel of immunisation, whether DPT or DT (diphtheria tetanus alone) is a small lump at the site of the injection. It is totally harmless, and it is not painful. It is due to a reaction to one of the constituents of the injection (aluminium hydroxide).

When a child in the family develops whooping cough, it is *possible* that other unimmunised children in the family may be partially protected by erythromycin given for one week only.

If a fit should occur within 48 hours, or if there is the very rare uncontrollable high pitched crying (different from the ordinary crying which occurs just with a rise of temperature), on no account should a further injection of DPT be given. But the injection for diphtheria and tetanus should be given in the usual way but without the whooping cough component.

If a *severe* local reaction follows the immunisation, let your doctor see it and advise about further DPT injections: the same applies to a *severe* febrile reaction. The doctor may decide to omit the whooping cough next time, giving DT polio only.

Measles

The immunisation is about 95% effective in preventing measles. It is given in a single injection at 15 months: it is not as effective if given before that age. In America it is combined with mumps and german measles.

A rise of temperature occurs in about 10% of children six to 10 days after the injection: very rarely there is a rash. There is full recovery in about 24 hours. The risk of encephalitis is somewhere between one in 100 000 and one in a million: but the risk of encephalitis when an unimmunised child gets measles is one in 500. A benign febrile convulsion follows the injection in about one in 500, but follows measles in the unimmunised in one in 150.

German measles

The immunisation is about 95% effective. It is given as a single injection at 11–12 years. Complications, which include short-lasting joint pains or fever, rarely follow the immunisation. Encephalitis follows in about one in 500 000 injected, but in one in 6 000 unimmunised children developing German measles.

All girls should be immunised unless they are proved by blood tests to have had the infection.

Typhoid fever

Immunisation is about 75% effective. It is strongly advised for those visiting Africa, including the North African Coast, Spain and the islands and other parts of South Europe. For holiday purposes a single dose is given; for prolonged stay a further injection is given four to six weeks later and if necessary a booster in three years. The immunity lasts about three years. A preparation taken by mouth is now being tried.

Cholera

Immunisation should be given for those visiting any part of Asia or Africa — in a single dose for holiday, or repeated four to six weeks later for a prolonged stay. It gives immunity for about six months and is about 60% effective.

Poliomyelitis

All children should be immunised. See the table at the end of the chapter.

Yellow fever

The infection is spread by mosquitos. Immunisation is essential for those visiting central Africa. It has few side-effects.

Tuberculosis

BCG immunisation is at least 80% effective. It is given to any newborn baby if there is any possibility of infection by someone who has had tuberculosis even though it is said to have healed. Children are given a tuberculin test at the age of 11–13, and if the skin test is negative, they are given BCG to protect them from future exposure. In some countries abroad (e.g. Asia, Africa) tuberculosis is likely to be very prevalent and one can never be sure that one's child will not come into contact with it (e.g. in a bus). It is not given if the child has eczema or a general skin rash.

One in 200 develop a shallow ulcer which discharges, with enlargement of the gland in the armpit; it heals without treatment in four to six months.

Infective hepatitis (jaundice)

This is common in Asia and Africa. An injection of gamma globulin provides protection for up to six months.

Meningitis

When a child in the family develops meningococcal or influenzal meningitis, there is a small risk that other children will get the infection. Your doctor may prescribe an antibiotic for two days to prevent the infection.

In epidemics a vaccine is now available, and is effective against two of the three types of meningococcus.

Standard immunisation scheme

Age	Immunisation
Newborn	BCG (for tuberculosis) for possible contact.
3 months	DPT (diphtheria, pertussis (whooping cough), tetanus) Poliomyelitis.
5 months	DPT (diphtheria, pertussis (whooping cough), tetanus) Poliomyelitis.
11 months	DPT (diphtheria, pertussis (whooping cough), tetanus) Poliomyelitis.
15 months	Measles.
4–5 years	DTPoliomyelitis (Not whooping cough) — booster.
10–13 years	German measles for girls.
	BCG for those with negative skin test.
15–19 years	Tetanus, poliomyelitis booster.

26

Some common and important symptoms

In this section we propose to discuss some common and important symptoms in children, with special emphasis on those which should cause you to consult your doctor. It is not intended to be a complete discussion of those symptoms, or to give a complete list of their causes, or in any way to usurp the position of the family doctor. You cannot consult your doctor about every little variation from the normal which you observe in your children, and it was felt that guidance could be given on some common symptoms which you can treat yourself. There are certain symptoms and signs which should make you seek expert help immediately, symptoms and signs which we have all too often seen ignored by parents, and ascribed to teething or other trivial conditions, with disastrous results to the child. Some trivial symptoms are mentioned in other parts of this book. Others will be described below. One of us (RSI) has written a comprehensive review of all the common symptoms of childhood (*Common Symptoms of Disease in Children.* 8th edn Oxford, Blackwell. 1984). This was intended primarily for doctors.

When we advise you to seek expert medical advice, we do not mean that you should seek help from your neighbour, mother or chemist. The chemist is not qualified to give medical advice, and you should not seek it from him. We mean that you should consult your doctor.

Sometimes a mother feels intuitively that something is wrong with her child. She should then not hesitate to consult her doctor, and no one is more competent to detect slight alterations in the behaviour of a child than a good mother, who is with her child every day, and knows his moods, habits and day to day variations in appetite, energy and behaviour. We do not want to be in any way disloyal to our colleagues, but we pay so much attention to the intuition of a good mother, that we feel that if your doctor does not convince you that you are wrong in your fears, you should seek another opinion, if necessary, by going to the casualty department of a hospital, preferably a children's hospital or a hospital with a large children's unit.

We do not want you in any way to feel that you cannot believe what your doctor says. All we suggest is that no one is infallible, and if, in spite of reassurance by your doctor, you are still seriously afraid that there is something wrong with your child, you should be perfectly honest with your doctor, state your fears, and ask him to arrange for a second opinion to be given. He will then ask a specialist to see the child.

Although we propose to try to draw attention to those symptoms which should make you seek medical advice, the final decision can only rest with you, and that decision will be arrived at with the use of your own common sense and intuition. We do not want to alarm you by mentioning these symptoms which you should not pass off lightly. We are only drawing attention to them because we have seen so much unnecessary suffering as a result of ignoring them. When we advise you to seek a doctor's help immediately, we do so in all cases because early medical or surgical treatment may give rapid and complete cure, whereas delay in treatment may prolong the illness, or even make the outcome uncertain.

You will be foolish to go to your chemist's shop and buy medicines or so-called 'tonics' which your doctor has not prescribed. You can take it that your doctor would give you a prescription for any medicine which is necessary for your child's health or recovery. Some medicines, bought in this way without medical advice, are not only useless and a waste of money, but actually harmful.

Before we discuss some of the symptoms which worry mothers, we will mention the principle symptoms of any general infection.

Symptoms of general infection
An acute infection usually presents with the child going off colour, losing his appetite, crying, usually with fever, and commonly with vomiting. A shivering attack, common in adults, is unusual in children. There may be non-specific 'flu like' pains in the limbs. Occasionally there may be a febrile convulsion (see p. 312).

The commonest causes are a throat or ear infection, the onset of an infectious disease such as measles, gastroenteritis, and in girls a urinary tract infection.

A chronic infection is usually indicated by vague loss of energy and appetite with reluctance to go out to play. In a girl a urinary tract infection is a common cause.

Common worrying symptoms

A large abdomen
When a child begins to walk, the abdomen often seems to be large

when he is standing up (but not when he is lying down). This is common in toddlers, but more in some than others. If he is well, it should be ignored.

Abdominal pain

Abdominal pain is such a common symptom in children that you cannot consult your doctor every time your child has a trivial discomfort in the stomach. But you must consult your doctor immediately if your child has a bad pain in the abdomen, or if it lasts more than about three hours.

If a child suddenly develops spasms of screaming which come on every few minutes, and he looks pale, appears poorly and vomits, you should consult your doctor immediately. It is particularly important to do so if he passes blood in the stool as well. The condition may be due to a form of obstruction of the bowel (intussusception) which the surgeon will remedy. The usual age for this is five to nine months; it is unusual after two years of age. It is important that this condition should be treated early, so you should not just 'wait and see'. Naturally, we are not suggesting that you should call your doctor every time your child screams. It is the regular spasms of screaming, in a child who is poorly, which are important. The attacks commonly last for two or three minutes, and recur about every 15 to 20 minutes. Rarely there are sudden attacks of pallor and limpness without pain. In all these cases you must ask your doctor to come urgently; he is likely to want a specialist to see him.

If there is tenderness when you gently press the abdomen where it hurts him, it may be acute appendicitis. The pain is usually, but not always, continuous from the onset. It often begins in the mid abdomen, near the umbilicus, and may then settle in the lower part of the right side of the abdomen. There is usually some vomiting and there may be some elevation of temperature: rarely there is diarrhoea instead of the more usual constipation. It can occur at any age from the newborn period onwards.

Do not give a child with abdominal pain a dose of castor oil. Do not give him food or drink until your doctor has seen him.

Some children have pain in the abdomen at the onset of pneumonia.

All mothers know that abdominal pain may be caused by indiscretions of diet. If you are worried, you should consult your doctor.

Severe vomiting or coughing for any reason may cause some abdominal pain. Severe diarrhoea is commonly associated with pain in the abdomen. When a boy or girl has acute abdominal pain, one should examine the groin to make sure that there is not an obvious hernia. If a boy of any age has an acute abdominal pain, one should examine the scrotum, for the testis may have got twisted, and there is then an acute emergency which should be dealt with (and cured) forthwith by a surgeon. Frequent recurrent attacks of abdominal pain occur in about 10% of school children: there may be some vomiting, and in that case it could be a manifestation of migraine. More often there is no sickness, but the pain may be severe. In the majority of cases your doctor will find no sign of disease and in time the child grows out of them. It is advisable to make as little fuss as possible about the attacks, for he may learn to make the most of his complaints. It is often found that the mother or father has abdominal pain at times, and it is unwise to discuss such pain in front of a child.

It is always difficult to assess the severity of someone else's pain, but as a rule a pain which does not stop a child playing or take him off his food or change his colour or make him sick is unlikely to be serious.

Poor appetite

By far the commonest cause of a poor appetite in a well child is food forcing (Chapter 18). It may be a temporary change for no obvious reason — perhaps hot weather or teething. There is a normal slowing down of the speed of weight gain after the first few months, and this is associated with a falling-off of the appetite (Chapter 18).

If the lack of appetite gets worse, or there is loss of weight, you should consult your doctor, for the possible causes are numerous.

Swelling and blueness of an arm

Many a mother has been horrified to find that one arm of her baby is blue, cold and swollen, when she has gone into his bedroom to get him up in the morning. The swelling subsides in an hour or two in most cases, but it may last almost a day in others. It is not due to the child lying on the arm. It occurs in the arm which is not covered by bedclothes, and which has become cold as a result.

Asthma

The common cause of coughing with wheezing is asthma or asthmatic bronchitis. Asthmatic bronchitis consists of breathlessness and wheezing occuring a day or two after a cold, and at no other time, only between the age of about six months and six years.

Asthma is an allergic condition, but virus infections and emotional causes may precipitate attacks. It is characteristic of asthma that exertion often makes a child wheeze. If parents smoke they increase the risk that the child will have attacks of asthma. Antibiotics do not help in attacks of asthma.

A mother can do much to reduce the severity of asthma by trying to reduce the amount of dust in the child's bedroom by daily vacuum cleaning, the avoidance of stuffed toys, of a carpet and of a Venetian blind. The pillow should be of foam rubber, as should the mattress if possible, otherwise it should be sealed in a plastic envelope. There should not be an eiderdown. The bedspread should be of plain cotton or synthetic fibre. Cotton blankets are preferable to wool ones, and should be washed frequently. Curtains should be washed weekly. Wool clothes should be avoided. The walls and ceiling, woodwork and floors should be kept clean, and the walls and woodwork washed weekly. Dust on furniture is removed by a damp cloth, as is dust on the bed itself. There should be no upholstered furniture. It is unwise to have pets in the house. Forced air central heating is harmful.

Attacks are sometimes caused by aspirin or by the yellow tartrazine in various foods, drinks and drugs.

Your doctor will advise you about other treatment to prevent attacks of asthma. Recent advances in treatment have done much to reduce the severity of asthma.

An acute attack of wheezing could be due to the child having inhaled some object such as a peanut.

Bow legs

The legs of a baby, after about six months of age, and especially when he begins to walk, usually give the appearance of being bowed. The separation of the legs by the napkin increases the appearance of bowing. In the majority of children this rights itself without treatment. It will right itself if there are less than two inches between the knees when the ankles are placed together with the child lying down.

Convulsions

A convulsion should be reported to your doctor immediately, though if you know that the child has epilepsy, you will not consult your doctor every time he has a fit. *But any fit lasting more than five to 10 minutes, whatever the cause, is an emergency,* and if you cannot contact your doctor, you should take your child direct to the nearest hospital Accident and Emergency Department without delay.

In Chapter 21 we described 'kinks' — due to the child holding the breath after breathing out. Many small children aged six months to five years (but not later) respond to a rapid rise of temperature by having a fit, but your doctor must be consulted so that he can be sure that there is not a more serious condition in which there is often a fit associated with fever, namely meningitis. *Convulsions are not due to teething: that diagnosis is always wrong.*

When your child is having a fit, do not slap him or put him into a hot bath. Try to prevent him biting his tongue by inserting a pocket handkerchief between his teeth, but that is often impossible. Do not try to force something into the mouth. If he is feverish, sponge him down with tepid water.

Cough

Coughing is due to a wide variety of causes, the commonest of which is a cold, or a discharge down the back of the throat after a cold, making the child cough when he lies on his back in bed. You will not consult your doctor every time your child gets a cold and coughs a little with it, but if he is feverish, breathes quickly and makes a grunting noise on breathing, and you see the side of the nose being drawn in and out as he breathes, or if he has a pain in his chest or abdomen, he may have pneumonia, which calls for prompt treatment. A chronic and persistent cough may be due to a variety of causes, and should be investigated by your doctor. A common cause is adenoids, which lead to a constant discharge down the back of the throat, and so to coughing particularly on lying down at night. The treatment consists of their removal. If the cough is associated with a wheeze, it is likely to be due to asthma or asthmatic bronchitis. *A chronic cough may be due directly to the parents smoking.* Cough is *not* due to teething.

If the cough is much worse in the night, comes in spasms, and frequently causes vomiting, it is almost certainly due to whooping cough — even though you have not heard a 'whoop'. The whoop develops only after a week or two, and treatment, to be effective, must be given before that.

If your child has a sudden spell of severe coughing when eating, and then continues to have a cough, consult your doctor immediately. Something may have entered the trachea and lung.

Croup

Some babies from birth make a noise in the larynx when breathing and especially when crying. It is usually due to a slight abnormality which rights itself in a year or two, but we advise that the baby should be checked by an Ear, Nose and Throat specialist in order to make sure that the condition does not require treatment.

When hoarseness and noisy breathing follows a cold, you should consult your doctor immediately. The usual cause is laryngotracheitis, which responds well to treatment, but there is a more serious condition termed epiglottitis: this often follows a cold, and there is a rapid onset of fever, difficult breathing, hoarseness, cough, drowsiness, pallor and often salivation. It is vital that the Ear, Nose and Throat specialist sees the child without delay to give appropriate treatment.

Deafness

Deafness may be due merely to wax in the ear, or to the effect of a cold, but you should consult your doctor.

If you suspect that the child cannot hear well, he should be examined by an Ear, Nose and Throat specialist.*

Diarrhoea

The usual cause of diarrhoea is gastroenteritis, and your doctor must be consulted, for the baby may rapidly lose a dangerous amount of fluid by vomiting and by the bowels. The diarrhoea may be due to other infections, notably dysentery or salmonella infection. In both these conditions there is diarrhoea, often with vomiting, abdominal pain, and blood in the stool. Your doctor must be consulted. It is normal for the baby to be taken off milk and other food for not more than 24 hours, and the fluid requirement is made up with a special preparation Dioralyte or Electrosol.

There are many less serious causes of diarrhoea. Some toddlers have mild diarrhoea from the age of about 10 months to three or four years, yet thrive, are well and gain weight.

Diarrhoea is *not* due to teething.

Drowsiness and other indications of illness

Some parents find it difficult to decide when their child is ill. Persistent vomiting, diarrhoea or abdominal pain obviously demand urgent medical attention. A high temperature is one indication of illness, but the child can be seriously ill with a temperature which is only slightly raised, or normal or even subnormal. A severe headache, not previously experienced by the child, certainly demands attention. If a child becomes drowsy with any illness, the doctor should be consulted forthwith.

Noises in the ear (tinnitus)

This may be due to drugs, especially aspirin.

Pain in the ear

Pain in the ear, particularly when it follows a cold or is associated

*We advise you to discourage your child from exposure to much loud noise, as in a Disco; it may lead to deafness.

with fever, may be due to middle ear disease (otitis media), and should be investigated by your doctor immediately, for it responds rapidly to early treatment with penicillin. Do not waste time putting drops into the ear or applying fomentations before calling him in.

Pain in the ear may be due to the eruption of a molar tooth (Chapter 10), to a cavity in a molar tooth, or to a boil in the ear.

Ears

Protruding ears usually look less obvious as the child grows older. Only in exceptional cases, in which the ears look really ugly, is it necessary to do anything about it. A plastic surgeon can then help to improve the appearance. He is unlikely to operate before the child is five years old.

All children and adults have wax in the ears, but in the majority it gradually works out. If it did not, it would eventually accumulate so much that it would cause deafness and have to be removed by syringing. Many mothers, seeing wax coming out of the ear, think that the ear is 'discharging'. Wax looks different from the yellow and much thinner pus or 'matter' which comes out if there has been an abscess in the ear.

Loss of energy

Loss of energy, with lassitude and a disinclination to play, is often a symptom of disease, but it may be due merely to worry at home or school. If your child has been previously full of energy and then begins to become easily tired and disinclined to play, you should consult your doctor. It may be due to an infection, such as a urinary tract infection in a girl, or to anaemia, diabetes or other causes. You should consult your doctor.

Chronic fatigue is most likely to be due to insufficient sleep. The tiredness may be due to the child going to bed too late, lying awake for a long time, or awakening early. It may be due to the child not having a midday nap when he is not able to do without it. These problems are discussed in Chapter 17.

Even when the duration of sleep is adequate, some children seem to be always tired. Some children are naturally more energetic than others. Some do not want to play out of doors. They prefer to sit in the house reading, or to play alone. This may be due to worry, shyness, or fear of other children. It is partly a matter of personality.

Eyes

Most babies do not begin to shed tears until they are three weeks or so of age. Thereafter it is common for eyes to 'water'. This is due to the fact that the duct or passage which conveys tears from the eyes to the nose (the tear duct) has not completely opened. Often, as a result, the eye becomes a little 'sticky' and in the morning there is a yellowish crusted material at the inner corner of the eye. (See normal babies do not shed tears for several months).

Our advice is that you should have nothing done about the watering of the eyes, for if you leave them alone the duct will open up in time — nearly always by six months of age, but sometimes a little later. Some doctors pass a probe down the duct under an anaesthetic to widen it, but we think that that is rarely necessary, and never necessary in the first nine months for simple 'watering'. Even if there is a little infection in the eyes as a result of the obstruction, we still think that it is better to treat the infection by drops or ointment, according to your doctor's advice.

When a baby has a severe infection of the eye as a result of failure of the duct to open, it may be necessary for an eye specialist to pass a probe down the duct in order to open it up. He will advise you on the matter.

Mild redness of the eye is treated by bathing the eye with a lotion which your chemist will supply, but for anything more than this you should consult your doctor. A collection of blood vessels showing in the white of the eye round the pupil may mean a deeper inflammation in the eye, which should be treated immediately by your doctor.

In the hay fever season there may be an alarming looking swelling of the eyes (oedema of the conjunctiva) which is due to rubbing the eyes. The swelling is due to the intense itching which may occur in hay fever. Appropriate eye drops (Eppy, Simplene or Otrivin) in a Casualty Department of a hospital will immediately remove the swelling. If you can see a 'foreign body', such as an eyelash or a particle of dust, you can remove it with a pocket hanky if it is on the lower lid: otherwise you may be able to remove it by irrigating the eye with water through a pipette. If you have difficulty, consult your doctor.

A mild and occasional squint is normal in the first six months, but if it persists after that you should ask your doctor for an appointment to see an eye specialist. It is important that a squint after the age of six months should be treated. If it is not, within two or three years the child may lose his vision in the squinting eye. If you suspect a squint, you *must* have your child seen by an eye specialist. You may notice a squint only now and then, especially when the child is tired. You should consult your doctor forthwith if a squint suddenly develops in an ill child.

Feet turning in or out (toeing in or out)
If the foot of the newborn baby turns in, your doctor should be consulted.

It is very common for the toddler and young child to turn the tip of the foot inwards (so that the knee caps turn towards each other). In the vast majority the condition cures itself without treatment. It may be wise, however, if only one foot turns in, to ask your doctor.

Rather less common is 'toeing out' — in which the knee caps turn away from each other. It almost always cures itself, and one only considers treatment if it persists to about seven years of age.

Fever
If your child is feverish, and there is no obvious simple cause for it, such as a cold, which you will treat without medical advice, it is as well to ask your doctor to see him. The most likely cause is a sore throat, an ear or urinary tract infection, or an infectious disease. It may be due to something more serious. If, in addition to fever, he has some pain in the back on bending the neck forward (not on turning it from side to side), or there is stiffness of the neck in bending it forwards, you should consult your doctor immediately, in case of meningitis. If, in addition to fever, he is usually drowsy, you should consult your doctor for the same reason. In general, unless the cause of a raised temperature is obviously merely a trivial infection, you should consult your doctor, in order that prompt treatment can be instituted if necessary. If you have recently come back from a holiday abroad, you must tell your doctor, because the cause may be an infection acquired on holiday.

Flat foot
Most infants and toddlers appear to have a flat foot, because the arch is filled with a fatty pad. It is exceedingly unlikely that the child will have any discomfort from this normal condition. It is only if there is pain or a weak or spastic ankle that you need consult your doctor.

Sometimes there is a round painless lump of fat in the sole of the foot. No treatment is required.

Enlarged glands in the neck
The commonest cause of enlarged glands in the neck is an infection in the mouth or throat (especially tonsillitis), or any infection in the skin of the face, scalp or neck. Any septic place or patch of eczema may cause enlargement of the glands. We are mentioning this be-

cause you should not think that your child has tuberculosis merely because his glands are enlarged. Your doctor can readily eliminate tuberculosis by doing a simple skin test.

Other causes of enlarged glands include German measles, in which the usual glands involved are those at the back of the neck, and glandular fever — an infectious disease which often causes many glands to become enlarged.

As there are many possible causes of this symptom, you should consult your doctor about it.

Glands in the axilla (armpit) are usually due to an infection some-where in the arm, or to BCG immunisation.

Glands in the groin can almost always be felt in child or adult. Enlarged glands are usually due to an infection anywhere on the leg or around the buttocks.

Growing pains

Many children, aged usually between six and 12 years or so, experi-ence pains in the calf muscles, mainly at night when in bed. They are well in all other respects. We do not understand why some children experience these, but we do know that they are not associated with any disease and have nothing to do with rheumatic fever. They disappear in time without treatment.

Headaches

Headaches are common in children, occurring in about 20% of school children. Apart from their occurrence with infections, such as tonsillitis or other infectious diseases, they may be due to several causes, but usually no particular cause is found. If your previously well child becomes poorly and has a headache, you should consult your doctor straight away.

A headache may be due to staying indoors too much, with lack of outdoor exercise, and it may be due to fatigue or worry. Some experience a headache in thundery weather, or when hungry. Unless there is obvious short-sightedness — the child having to hold a book extremely close to the eyes — eyestrain is not a cause of headache. Antrum infection is also a most unlikely cause.

Migraine is probably the commonest cause of headaches in chil-dren. There is nearly always another sufferer from it in the family. It may be precipitated by fatigue, worry, excitement, hunger, a loud noise, a long car journey, menstruation, or infection. Migraine in child or adult is sometimes brought on by certain foodstuffs, especial-ly chocolate or cheese. Others have an attack of migraine if they eat citrus fruits, drink certain wines, eat fried foods, onions, fish, broad

beans, cucumber, Bovril, Marmite, nuts, tomatoes, game or raspberries. Others have a headache if they eat prepared meats containing a nitrite preservative. Of all these items, cheese and chocolate are
the chief offenders. Symptoms usually occur 12 to 24 hours after
eating them. You should watch carefully in order to determine
whether your child's migraine attacks follow any of these foodstuffs.

Sometimes the headache is feigned in an attempt to avoid certain
unpleasant or undesired occupations, such as walking to the shops.
Certain drugs may cause headaches. You should consult your doctor
about the cause, especially if the headaches are of recent onset and
becoming worse, and especially if they are associated with sickness
or with pain at the back of the head.

Hernia or rupture
An umbilical hernia — a rupture at the navel — is extremely
common in babies. It will protrude when the baby cries, but it does
no harm. It may become a little larger in the first few weeks. The
hernia will almost certainly cure itself if left alone. On rare occasions
it may be desirable to have a simple operation done to cure it if it is
still there when the child is four or five years old. Research has
shown that it is unnecessary to apply strapping, and that it may delay
its cure rather than hasten it. It may irritate the skin and make it
sore. We advise you to leave the hernia alone. It is safe and does no
harm. It virtually never becomes obstructed.

If the child has a hernia in the groin or scrotum, you should
consult your doctor about it, in order that he can arrange to have it
operated upon. It must not be left to cure itself. Trusses are of no
value. It is important that it should be operated on without delay,
especially in the case of the younger baby or child, because if it is left
it may strangulate (i.e. become obstructed), and in that case the
child will rapidly become ill.

If a boy of *any age* suddenly develops a painful swelling in the
scrotum, tell your doctor immediately; it could be torsion of the
testis, requiring urgent operation.

Hydrocele
Your doctor has to distinguish this from a hernia. It is a collection of
fluid around the testis. It is a self-curing condition.

Knock-knee
Knock-knees frequently cause anxiety when the child is around two
years old. In the great majority of cases it is a self-curing condition.
When lying down with the knees together, three out of four children

have a gap of 2.5 cm or more between the ankles, and one in five has a gap of over 5 cm. Only if there is a gap of over 10 cm at the age of three or four is investigation needed.

Labial adhesions

The labia may appear to be stuck together, so that there is no evident opening into the vagina. The doctor may apply a special ointment, which will lead to the separation, or separate them with a probe and apply Vaseline. In either case the cure is complete. The application of an oestrogen ointment will cause separation of the labia in three or four weeks without the use of a probe.

Limp

It is by no means always possible to determine why a small child has developed a limp — often in the last few hours or for a day or two. There may be an obvious cause such as a painful heel, or a nail protruding from the shoe, or an enlarged painful gland in the groin.

Sometimes a limp is due to an unsuspected slight fracture of a bone in the leg, or to disease of the hips. You should try to prevent the child weight-bearing and consult your doctor.

Mouth breathing

If this merely occurs in the night when the child is asleep, it is unlikely to be of importance. If it occurs during the day, it may be due to adenoids, which block the back of the nose, or occasionally to an obstruction in the nose. You should consult your doctor about this, and he may ask you to see an Ear, Nose and Throat specialist, who will use special instruments in order to determine the cause of the trouble. Some children keep the mouth open as a habit, and gentle reminders may suffice to stop it; but the presence of adenoids should be excluded before you conclude that it is merely a habit.

Ulcers in the mouth
See Chapter 10.

Nose bleeding

Nose bleeding may be due to the child picking the nose, inserting something up the nose, or to an infection or injury: it sometimes occurs with a cold or measles, but more often there is no obvious cause.

The bleeding is usually from the lower part of the septum dividing the nostrils, and we suggest that you nip the nose in such a way that you apply pressure to as much of the septum as possible: you keep up *constant* pressure for at least five minutes, resisting the temptation to release the pressure to see if the bleeding has stopped. If you do that, it is likely to start bleeding again. If you fail, you will have to consult your doctor.

Discharge from the nose

Some babies, without having a cold, seem to have a constant clear nasal discharge. It is often termed 'snuffles'. It is of no importance and clears up as the baby gets older.

Other children, apart from the ordinary colds, have a persistent watery discharge from the nose with frequent sneezing. A common cause of this is 'allergy'. In the hay fever season, from May to July, it is due to sensitivity to certain pollens present in the atmosphere. At other times of the year it is due to sensitivity to certain substances in dust. A persistent yellow discharge is usually due to an infection of the antrum. (The antra are cavities in the bone, which communicate with the nose). A discharge which is always confined to one nostril may be due to some object such as a bead which has been pushed up the nose. Your doctor should be consulted about the cause of the trouble and its treatment.

If your baby's nose is blocked, it should be gently cleaned with pledgets of cotton wool. Some doctors supply nose drops for such babies, but some specialists think that these drops may damage the delicate lining of the nose. We never prescribe nose drops ourselves.

Pallor

Many children are pale faced. Your doctor will tell you whether it is due to anaemia. Usually it is not.

Paleness of complexion often runs in the family, and this familial trait is probably the commonest cause of pallor. Examination of the blood shows that it is not due to anaemia. Pallor is often due to fatigue. A child who has insufficient sleep and is tired is likely to be pale. Another common cause lies in lack of outdoor exercise. A child who stays indoors all day is unlikely to have a good colour.

Erection of the penis

This is common in babies and children of any age, without apparent reason. It is often noticed when the boy is lifted out of bed in the morning, or when the nappy is being changed. It is of no significance.

Ulcer at the end of the penis (meatal ulcer)

Sometimes a circumcised boy develops an ulcer at the end of the

penis. It causes great discomfort when urine is being passed, and it
may be necessary to allow him to pass urine only in the bath. It is
usually associated with a nappy rash, and this should be treated. The
doctor may prescribe an anaesthetic ointment (Lignocaine), or a
protective covering of 'tulle gras', or zinc and castor oil ointment. It
soon responds to the above treatment.

It only occurs in uncircumcised boys if the foreskin fails to cover
the tip of the glans of the penis.

Personality change

A change in personality should always be investigated. When a child
who has previously been of a happy personality becomes different,
bad tempered, irritable or weeps easily, you should consult your
doctor. It may be due to a worry at home or school, to illness, or to
the effect of drugs.

Pigeon chest

Some angulation of the sternum (the front of the chest) is a normal
variation. Sometimes it is more marked, and often it is a familial
feature. It usually disappears as the child grows older. No treatment
is required, as it does not cause symptoms.

The opposite condition is a 'funnel chest' — a hollowing in the
middle of the chest: it is of no importance unless it is marked, when
your doctor should be consulted. Only for severe cases is operative
treatment advised (in later years) for cosmetic reasons.

Skin Conditions

Abrasions. They should be cleaned and left uncovered, without
occlusive dressings, ointment or cream.

Birthmarks. Naevi or birthmarks should be seen by your doctor.
The staining of the skin on the inner end of the upper eyelid, on the
forehead above the nose, and on the back of the neck, will disappear
in a few months and no treatment is required.

The so-called strawberry naevi, bright red raised birthmarks,
appear a few days after birth. They grow somewhat up to the age of
six months, then stop growing, become grey in the middle, and
gradually disappear, so that in five to 10 years there is not a mark
left. No treatment is required except for the rare one which begins to
grow rapidly.

The so-called 'port-wine stain' is a purplish birthmark, mainly on
one side of the face. It is of no significance, apart from looking ugly,
unless it involves the upper part of the face, above the eye. The
port-wine stain can be completely concealed by a 'make up' such as

Boots' Covermark or Elizabeth Arden's Cover Cream. You can get professional advice on suitable make-up.

Boils. They should be left untreated unless they become tense and painful, when the doctor may make an incision. It is unwise to cover the boil with a dressing and harmful to apply a hot fomentation — which would be likely to spread the infection. The skin around should be cleaned several times a day by surgical spirit.

Cold sore (herpes). No treatment is required. The affected part should be kept clean by soap and water. It is wrong to apply antibiotics or steroid creams or ointments.

Colour changes on the trunk in the new baby. Doctors call this the harlequin colour change. It is a remarkable sight, for the baby, in his first five or six weeks, may be found to be white down one side of the body and pink down the other side. Sometimes, if he is turned over, that which was white becomes pink, and vice versa. The episode only lasts for a few minutes. It is of no importance and is not associated with disease.

Scurfy scalp (cradle cap). Scurfiness of the scalp is so common in young babies that it is almost usual. Regular washing of the scalp with soap and water, as already recommended, may prevent it, but scurfiness often develops in spite of it. It usually responds well to washing the scalp every night with one per cent Cetavlon instead of soap. Others recommend the application of olive oil to the scalp every night.

Cracks behind the ears. It is important to see that the baby is properly dried after a bath. Sometimes despite all care sore cracks develop behind the ears. They clear with 1% hydrocortisone cream.

Impetigo. This is an infection, commonly on the face, but often on any other part of the body, often superimposed on an abrasion, cold sore (herpes), scabies, pediculosis (nits) or eczema. It is spread by hands or infected towels.

It is unwise to apply an antibiotic cream, because it may cause a sensitivity reaction, and steroid creams or ointments should never be used, for they may spread the infection. Chlorhexidine cream can be used for a small area. Your doctor will treat it; usually an antibiotic has to be given, which should clear it up in a few days.

Infections of the skin. Infections of the skin, except the most trivial ones, should be treated by your doctor, because they clear up so quickly with proper treatment. If ever you see red streaks on a limb, arising from a septic place, you should consult your doctor immediately, so that prompt treatment can be given, for they mean that the infection is spreading. They are due to 'lymphangitis' — an inflammation of the vessels which pass to the lymph glands.

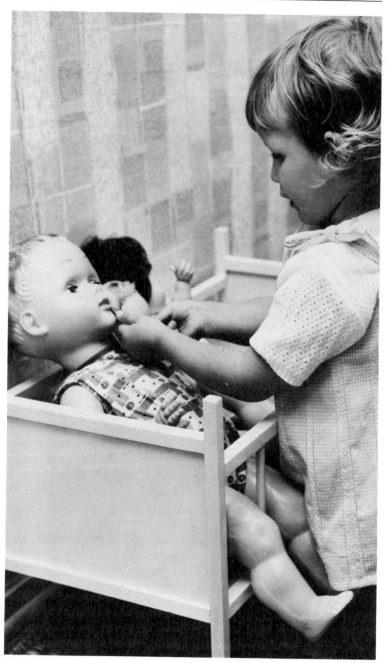

It is particularly important that skin infections in young babies should be treated promptly, because they may lead to serious disease if neglected.

Never apply fomentations to any infected abrasion, or to any infection in which the skin is broken, or in which there are separate spots, for fomentations are likely to cause a rapid spread of the infection.

Itching. The commonest causes of intense itching are urticaria, scabies or eczema. Sensitivity to wool clothes may cause it. Nits, ringworm, chilblains, psoriasis and chickenpox are other causes.

Scabies causes spots on the sides of the fingers, wrist, armpit folds and buttocks: in infants it may affect the scalp or the soles of the feet. Other members of the family are commonly infected, and your doctor will arrange treatment.

Ingrowing toe nails. This is fairly often seen in older babies. It may sometimes be due to compression by elasticated socks or tight shoes, but more often there is no discoverable cause. Treatment is virtually never required: it would certainly be wrong to operate on the nail or nail bed.

Nappy rash. Soreness of the buttocks around the anus is common in the newborn period, and at other times if the stools become unusually loose. It is by no means always possible to prevent it. It seems that the skin is so delicate that contact with the stools irritates it and makes it inflamed. You will increase the risk of soreness developing by neglecting to change the nappy frequently, thus leaving the soiled napkin in contact with the skin.

When soreness occurs around the anus, in spite of all possible care, it can best be treated by the liberal application of a baby cream five or six times a day. In warm weather it can be treated successfully by letting the baby lie in his cot without a napkin on at all. That is easy in a hospital, where there is no difficulty about the amount of dirty linen which has to be washed, but it is difficult in a private house.

Most babies, sooner or later, develop some redness over the napkin area and if this is not promptly treated the skin becomes rough and corrugated. If it is still not properly treated it may become spotty, due to an infection of the sore skin, or even wet and oozing. The skin between the buttocks and the groin is usually unaffected, because it has not been in contact with the nappy. Doctors used to call this 'Ammonia dermatitis', on the grounds that it was due to ammonia which was broken down from the urine by organisms from the stools: when the nappy which has been wet for an hour or more is changed there is often a strong smell of ammonia. We now know that it is not the ammonia which irritates the skin but the prolonged contact of the skin with a wet nappy. It has nothing to do with the diet, and it is useless to give medicine for it, and it does not mean that there is anything wrong with the urine. It is not 'too strong' or 'hot'. It only scalds the child when it is being passed if the skin is sore. It follows that the longer a wet nappy is left in contact with the skin, the more likely it is that a nappy rash will develop. At night the 'Marathon' or similar 'one way' nappy allows the fluid to pass through (e.g. to a Turkish towel type of nappy), the special nappy next to the skin remaining dry.

It is unwise to have tightly fitting rubber pants on the baby, for they keep the warm moisture in and predispose to a nappy rash.

The mildest forms respond rapidly to the liberal use of a baby cream or silicone barrier cream over the affected areas five or six times a day.

You can cause a rash similar to a nappy rash by failing to rinse the soap or detergent out of the nappies after washing them. Make sure that they are thoroughly rinsed.

Investigations have shown that if a nappy rash persists for over about a fortnight, it is very likely to become infected by the 'thrush' or 'monilia' organism. There is often a thrush infection in the mouth. We suggest that if your baby has a persistent nappy rash, you should ask your doctor. A preparation which we find successful in these refractory cases, dealing with the thrush infection, is the Nystaform H.C. ointment.

No baby with a nappy rash should be circumcised, for he would be likely to develop a painful ulcer on the tip of the penis.

Nettle rash or urticaria. Any mother knows that 'nettle rash' or 'heat bumps', called urticaria by doctors, is extremely common in small children. It itches severely, and causes severe discomfort.

Much nonsense has been talked about urticaria. It has been ascribed to acidosis, acid fruits, too hot food, too rich food, and all manner of other things. Mothers have been advised to avoid giving this, that, and the other foodstuff, often much to the annoyance of their children.

Exceptionally, a child may be 'sensitive' to particular foods such as shellfish, eggs or certain fruits, and every time he takes any of that food, even in the smallest amount, he develops urticaria or other sensitivity reactions. In that case the mother should avoid giving her child the offending food. Unless she has clear evidence that one particular food causes the rash, it is unnecessary and wrong to withhold it. Our advice to you is that you should give him a normal diet, except when you know that a definite food upsets him.

The idea of 'acidosis' is a myth, except when it is due to vomiting or some other serious disease. Foods do not 'overheat the blood'. The blood is never 'heated'. There is no evidence that rich food causes urticaria, and lots of evidence that it does not cause it. Acid fruits do not, in fact, produce acid after they have been eaten. On the contrary, they tend to neutralize it.

What then is the cause of urticaria? The answer is that there is no one cause. It is a sensitivity reaction, indicating that the child is sensitive to something. Certain foods which may cause it have been mentioned. It may be caused by yellow colouring matter in foods and drinks, or by preservatives in foodstuffs. Many medicines, such as aspirin or penicillin, may cause it. But it is becoming more and more recognised that the commonest cause of urticaria is sensitivity to insect bites, such as those of fleas or bed bugs. Domestic pets are an important source of fleas. Cats should be dusted with Rotenone or pyrethrum powder. In the past dogs were treated with DDT, but that is no longer available. You should consult your local pet shop about disinfecting your dog, his bedding and kennel. Bed bugs must also be dealt with. The treatment cannot be expected to help in all cases, because not all cases of itching are due to bites.

Non specific rashes. Many refer to 'milk rashes', but in fact there is no such thing. Soreness around the mouth is usually due to slobbering. Spottiness on the baby's face is often due to his lying on one side against a pillow, often slobbering, sometimes possetting, so that the face becomes sore. A baby cream may be enough to protect the skin.

Sweat rashes or rashes due to sensitivity to wool or nylon are commonly found on the baby's body.

Sprain
Ask your doctor.

Sweating
Excessive sweating is rarely due to disease, unless there is an elevated temperature. It is not a feature of childhood tuberculosis. It may be due to over-clothing.

Sweating around the head at night is sometimes profuse; it is of no importance and not due to disease.

Incomplete descent of the testes
In some boys the testes are slow in descending into the scrotum. In most cases they descend spontaneously, but if they have not descended by two years of age the boy should be referred to a paediatric surgeon, who will bring them down by operation.

Threadworms

Mothers are usually horrified to see threadworms in a child's stool. They may ascribe all manner of symptoms to the infection. Symptoms commonly blamed on threadworm infections include poor appetite, excessive appetite, dirt-eating, nose picking and pain in the abdomen. There is no justification for ascribing any of these symptoms to threadworms. The only symptom which they sometimes cause is itching around the anus, mainly in the evenings. The itching is mainly in the evenings because the female worms, which only measure an average of an eighth of an inch long, emerge from the bowel at that time, lay their eggs and then die. Each worm lays about 10 000 eggs: they adhere to the skin and clothes, and eventually get into the dust of the room, where they survive for long periods. The child is infected by eggs entering the mouth on his fingers or in food. The eggs hatch out in the bowel.

Studies have shown that most schoolchildren have threadworms at some time or other. Fortunately the worms are so small that they are rarely seen by the mother, and it is exceptional for them to cause itching. As this infection is so prevalent, and as it is nearly always harmless, there is no need for you to feel anxious if you discover that your child has it.

Provided that there is no itching, we recommend that no treatment be given. It is likely to die out on its own, and certainly will do if you can be really certain that your child always washes his hands before putting his fingers into his mouth or handling anything which he is going to eat or suck. Unfortunately it is almost impossible to ensure this. The reason why the infection would die out if handwashing was adequate lies in the fact that the worms do not multiply in the bowel. They only multiply by passing eggs outside the bowel, and the child can only continue to have threadworms if he constantly re-infects himself by taking eggs into the mouth. It has been shown that eggs are found in large numbers in the dust of schools, and there is therefore every chance that re-infections will occur. If one child in a house has threadworms, it is almost certain that the other members of the family, including the mother and father, will also have them.

If the child has symptoms from the infection, treatment must be given. This consists of Piperazine. Enemas should not be administered. It is probable that if one member of the family is treated, all the other members should also be treated, because they almost certainly have the infection too.

If your child requires treatment, you must consult your doctor who will prescribe the necessary drug.

Sore throat

You cannot consult your doctor every time your child has a sore throat. More often than not it is merely the beginning of a cold. We feel that if there is a rise of temperature with a sore throat your doctor should be consulted in order that special treatment can be given if he thinks it necessary.

Toe walking

Some toddlers get into the habit of walking on their toes. You can see that they are able to put the sole of the foot flat on the floor if they want. Toe walking can be due to other causes, such as congenital shortening of the tendo achilles (behind the heel), and your doctor should be consulted.

Curly toes

When a toe lies under or over its neighbour, it does not usually cause trouble in childhood, but may do in adult life, causing pain, corn formation or difficulty in shoe fitting. Strapping during childhood is useless. A minor surgical procedure, best carried out between the age of three and five years, is often advisable, unless the condition appears to be righting itself.

Tonsils and adenoids

Adenoids consist of tissue behind the nose which sometimes grow excessively and block the airway if the child is born with a rather narrow space behind the nose. The result may be mouth breathing, nasal speech, snoring and sometimes (possibly) recurrent middle ear infection and deafness. They are not related to frequent colds.

If the Ear, Nose and Throat specialist thinks that the above symptoms are due to enlarged adenoids, they should be removed.

Tonsils are much maligned and more often than not are not the cause of symptoms ascribed to them. They are much more frequently removed from children of well-to-do parents than from other children. Child specialists think that tonsils should be removed before the age of five only in the most exceptional circumstances. The trouble is that children commonly develop frequent sore throats and tonsillitis when they start school and it is normal for tonsils to become fairly large at this age. But if nothing is done about them nearly all children acquire much immunity to the infection in two or three years. It is wrong to remove tonsils unnecessarily. They should not be removed because they are 'enlarged' except only when they are so large that they are obstructing the airway and interfering with breathing, causing noisy breathing especially on lying down. That is very exceptional. They should not be removed because they are said to be unhealthy, scarred, or showing exudate or crypts; careful studies have shown that those findings on inspection are all totally irrelevant. They should not be removed because of frequent colds, for asthma or any general disease. It may be right to remove them if the child is having frequent attacks of acute tonsillitis with fever (say four or more attacks a year), when the attacks cannot be prevented by continuous prophylactic penicillin.

Smoking by the parents increases the likelihood that the child will need an operation for removal of tonsils and adenoids.

Urinary tract infection

Infection in the urine is usually due to an infection in the kidney. It is common in girls, but sometimes occurs in boys. The symptoms vary with the age. When a baby has a urinary tract infection, the most common symptoms are vague unwellness and unsatisfactory weight gain, but in more acute infections there may be vomiting, fever or diarrhoea. Frequency or scalding is unusual. Older children are more likely to have fever, frequency or scalding, bed-wetting, abdominal discomfort, vomiting and sometimes blood in the urine.

The doctor makes the diagnosis by having the urine cultured in the laboratory.

Frequency of urination

If your child begins to pass urine unduly frequently, it may be due to nervous factors (Chapter 20). In a 15–18 month child it is normal. But it is necessary to make sure that the urine is normal and that the kidney is functioning properly, and you should, therefore, ask your doctor about it. He should be consulted if your child passes blood in the urine, for that may be due to nephritis (inflammation of the kidneys).

Colour of urine

The urine is a dark colour if it is concentrated, as in fevers. It is a dark yellow colour is the child has infective hepatitis (jaundice). The urine is red if there is blood in it: but it is much more likely that the red is due to blackcurrant juice, blackberry juice, rose hip syrup, or to dye from sweets or foods. Some children and adults pass red urine after eating beetroot (Beeturia).

Numerous drugs produce striking colour changes in the urine.

Crying or scalding on passing urine

Many babies cry as they pass urine, for no apparent reason. There is nothing wrong on examination of the urine.

Sometimes there is some soreness around the genital area in boys or girls, due to a nappy rash, and it hurts when urine is passed. Mothers describe the urine as being 'hot' for that reason. In fact the urine is never 'hot', for the temperature of the urine is constant. There is nothing wrong with the urine. If in doubt, however, ask your doctor to test it.

Thick urine

Urine passed by any child or adult may have a white or coloured deposit when it is passed or when it has cooled down. It is normal, and does not suggest disease. It is due to a chemical compound (phosphates or urates).

Strongly smelling urine

This is of no significance. It may be due to the fact that it is more concentrated than usual, as in hot weather. Urine in the nappy will soon smell of ammonia, because urea in urine breaks down to form ammonia.

Posseting and vomiting

The distinction between posseting and vomiting is not clear cut, one merging into the other. All babies bring some milk up, whether you call it posseting or vomiting. They bring it up either when they are lying down, a little milk welling up into the mouth, or else it comes up with a belch of wind — in which case it may shoot out and frighten you. In either case it is harmless and normal. It is largely confined to the young baby, disappearing as he gets older. Some babies posset more than others. It is particularly the active, thin baby who possets a lot. Such babies nearly always gain weight well in spite of what appears to be a big milk loss.

Clumsy handling of the baby after a feed may lead to some milk being brought up. If, in order to bring his wind up, you sit him on your right knee, and lean him over your left knee, his stomach will be pressed on so much that the milk comes up. If you tilt him upwards too far in atempting to clean his buttocks when you are changing his nappy after a feed, the milk will come up. If you bounce him about after a feed, he may be sick.

Excessive wind causes vomiting. Some babies vomit if they are left crying for a long time. The crying causes the swallowing of air, and the stomach may become so distended by wind that the baby is sick.

The majority of cases of 'vomiting' are due to the above causes. But there are other causes. Sometimes vomiting may be due to congenital pyloric stenosis. This is an obstruction at the lower end of the stomach. It is commoner in boys, but can occur in girls. The usual story is that the child, usually four to six weeks old, sometimes younger, and sometimes a little older (but hardly ever older than three months), having been previously perfectly well, suddenly vomits during or immediately after a feed, and the whole feed shoots out. This may be repeated at the next feed, or at the next but one, or even only in the next day, but it soon occurs during or after every feed. It is important to note that the milk is brought up in one big vomit. Frequent small vomits are not at all likely to be due to congenital pyloric stenosis. If you suspect this, you should consult your doctor immediately. He is likely to ask a specialist to see the baby, in order to make sure of the diagnosis. A simple operation, done by a surgeon accustomed to operating on babies, cures the condition immediately, and the baby has no further trouble. In good hands the operation is a safe one. By far the commonest condition with which it is confused is vomiting due to excessive wind.

Excessive posseting or vomiting by the breast-fed baby may be due to any of the causes of wind, and particularly to keeping the baby too long on the breast in a feed. It is not due to the breast milk not suiting the baby or the breast milk being too strong or rich. It is not due to overfeeding. The only thing you can do is see that the various causes of excessive wind are eliminated.

Excessive posseting or vomiting in the bottle-fed baby is likely to be due to wind. The causes of excessive wind in the bottle-fed baby have been described in Chapter 4, and they should be eliminated. It is not due to the particular brand of dried milk not suiting the baby.

An occasional baby, from two or three months onwards, discovers a way of making milk come into the mouth, a condition which is called 'rumination'. Observation will show that the baby pushes his abdomen in and out, often arches his back, seems to undergo contortions, and then brings milk up. It is an annoying habit, and may lead to a big loss of milk. Some think that it is an indication that the baby wants more loving and cuddling, but this does not always apply. It would be wise to get your family doctor to refer you to a child specialist who may decide to have an X-ray taken, for sometimes rumination is associated with a lax sphincter between the oesophagus and stomach which makes it easier for the baby to bring the milk up. It is a condition which cures itself in time — by 12–18 months. Try to distract the baby when ruminating. If a breast-fed baby does it excessively, he may have to be weaned and given thickened feeds. If he is fed on the bottle, it is easy to add a cereal such as Farex to the milk in order to thicken it. A dessert-spoonful of Farex to each 4 oz of milk makes a mixture which is less easy for the baby to bring up: you must see that it will come easily through the teat, or else you will have to give it by cup or spoon. In some children, from birth onwards, milk passes back unusually easily from the stomach to the oesophagus. As this has to be treated in a special way it is always as well to consult your doctor about excessive posseting.

Do not be alarmed because the material which he brings up is curdled. It is bound to be, for the acid normally present in the stomach forms curds when it comes into contact with the milk. The curds produced from cow's milk are bigger than those from breast milk, and therefore more obvious. If ever there is blood in the vomited material, it should be reported to the doctor. This could be due to a lax sphincter between the oesophagus and stomach, allowing the stomach contents to regurgitate too readily into the oesophagus, or to a small hernia at the bottom end of the oesophagus. You should consult your doctor about it.

You can treat the excessive posseting, if you have not found any other cause, by thickening the feeds, as for rumination.

Vomiting in the weaning period is likely to be due to forcing him to take food against his will, or to giving him solids before he can chew.

Numerous infections may cause vomiting. When a baby who has been previously well suddenly becomes poorly and vomits, the most likely cause is a middle ear infection, gastroenteritis (before the diarrhoea becomes manifest), or in the case of a girl, a urinary tract infection. A common virus infection is the 'winter vomiting disease', in which the baby or young child, having been perfectly well, suddenly vomits, without fever or diarrhoea. It is a very infectious condition with an incubation period of two or three days: recovery is rapid. Many other infections can cause vomiting, and you must consult your doctor, for other conditions, such as appendicitis, intus-susception or strangulated hernia, have to be eliminated. Particularly important symptoms which demand a prompt medical opinion are persistent vomiting, vomiting of green material, drowsiness and abdominal distension.

Vomiting in older children

The remarks above concerning the numerous infections which cause vomiting in babies apply to older children too. Similar infections are the common cause of vomiting. It is possible that vomiting in association with tonsillitis is sometimes due to the young child trying to scratch or rub his sore throat with his fingers.

Vomiting in older children may be due to excitement. Some children are so excited when about to go out to a party that they are sick. Vomiting at a party may be due simply to overeating, but no doubt excitement predisposes to it. It may also be due to imitation of another child, or to a desire to attract attention. Some todlers, like babies, may make themselves sick by prolonged crying.

Excitement also plays a part, but often only a small part, in 'motion' or 'travel' sickness. Travel sickness is extremely common in children, and may commence as early as six months of age. No one knows exactly why some people are sick when travelling by car, bus, boat or aeroplane. It is not entirely psychological in origin, though psychological factors, such as excitement or suggestion, play a part. It is easy to suggest sickness to a child by talking about it, and to make him sick as a result. The less said about sickness before a journey the better. If a great deal of fuss is made when sickness does occur, the child may repeat it as an attention-seeking device. The main cause of travel sickness lies in the body's balancing mechanism in the internal ear, but the cause is not fully understood. It is prevented, usually effectively, by certain medicines which will be prescribed by your doctor. The best drug for the purpose is hyoscine, or mixtures containing it, such as Kwells.

A common cause of vomiting in children is the periodic syndrome, formerly termed 'cyclical vomiting' or 'acidosis attacks'. The latter term is a bad one, for the acidosis is the result of the vomiting and not the cause of it. The condition is almost certainly a form of migraine. There is nearly always a family history of migraine. These attacks are more common in active intelligent children. They may be precipitated by any excitement or infection, such as a cold. They are not due to fatty foods. The child, having being previously perfectly well, becomes pale, listless, wants to sit about, and then after an hour or two he vomits. The temperature may or may not be raised. The vomiting may be followed by vague abdominal pain. The attack may last half a day or two days. The stools may be pale in the attacks. Recovery is rapid, and the child is perfectly well until the next attack occurs, perhaps a month or two later.

Vomiting of blood

This must always be reported to the doctor. The usual cause in a newborn baby is swallowed blood during delivery, or later from the mother's nipple. Be sure to keep the specimen because the doctor by a simple test can determine whether the blood was the mother's blood which was swallowed, or the baby's blood: in the latter case an injection of vitamin K may stop the bleeding.

If a baby who is posseting excessively brings up material with blood in it, your doctor should be consulted: it is likely to be due to regurgitation of food from the stomach into the oesophagus.

Older children may vomit blood after a nose bleed and sometimes in connection with acute tonsillitis. Aspirin tablets and other drugs may cause ulceration of the stomach and bleeding.

There are other causes, and it is important that you should consult your doctor.

Vulvovaginitis: vaginal discharge

A clear vaginal discharge in the first few days after birth is normal: there is sometimes some blood in the discharge (Chapter 2): it is normal and of no importance. After infancy a clear discharge should be ignored: it is particularly common around puberty.

Whenever a girl has an offensive or white (purulent) discharge, it should be investigated by your doctor. It is most likely to be due merely to lack of cleanliness; sometimes it is due to itching from a threadworm infection.

Sometimes the discharge is due to foreign material which has been introduced into the vagina: material which may be found there includes sand, safety pins, coins, nuts, paper, sorbo rubber, crayons and many other objects.

27

The treatment of the ill child

At no time does anyone feel the need of love and sympathy more than when he feels poorly. Children are no different in this respect. They constantly ask for the company of the parent to whom they are most attached, wanting to be held, loved, and cuddled. No one wants to have his own way more than when he is feeling tired and poorly. Children are the same.

General management
It is difficult to decide how much one should 'spoil' a child when he is ill, how much time to give him, and how much to pander to his wishes. We are sure that it is wrong, on the one hand, to be so afraid of spoiling the child that he is denied that love and attention which a reasonably sympathetic person would give. On the other hand, one has to remember that habits are produced quickly, and that an intelligent child will rapidly learn to exaggerate his symptoms or develop new ones, and make himself appear more ill than he really is, if he finds that he can get all his own way. It is easy to suggest symptoms. If you ask him whether he feels sick, particularly if he has already vomited, the mere suggestion may be enough to make him vomit again. If he has had a genuine pain, unwise conversation about it will prolong and worsen it. Children are highly suggestible especially if they are in bed and separated from their usual occupations. One must aim at a happy mean. We feel that you should be prepared to 'spoil' a child a little when he is poorly, but that you should not overdo it. You should allow him to choose, more than usual, what he would like to eat. You should be with him more than usual. You should read to him and play with him more than usual. If he wants a light at night, he should have it. If there is any special reason for it, you should let him sleep in your bedroom or you should fix up a bed in his. This may be advisable if a child is liable to have, say, bad spasms of coughing when suffering from whooping cough. But you should be fully aware of the probable consequences of what you do, and return to normal routine as soon as you can, for

he will want you to continue giving him extra attention, and letting him have his own way, long after he has recovered. He will object strongly to sleeping alone, to not having a light or to having less time given to him. He will continue to expect you to go into his room and give him a drink in the middle of the night whenever he calls out. You should therefore be firm as soon as he is better and stop bad habits which have been formed and which you expected to be formed.

Adults have learnt much of their attitude to illness or to symptoms in childhood. It is easy to make a child a hypochondriac for life by displaying overanxiety about his symptoms and his illnesses. If an excessive fuss is made over the child's grazed knee, or complaint of abdominal discomfort, or his headache, he will learn to exaggerate his symptoms. If he is put to bed as soon as he develops a cold in the nose, or a sore throat, or any other symptom, is given medicines and is kept off school unnecessarily, the child suffers severely as a result. When a child has asthma, and great anxiety is shown over his slightest wheeze, so that his is put to bed, given medicines and kept off school, his asthma is made far worse, because of the strong psychological component in that condition. Parents have to strike the happy mean between overcasualness and apparent lack of sympathy, and excessive sympathy, fussing and overanxiety. It is important that parents should not discuss their own real or imaginary symptoms in front of their children. Parents who are constantly showing anxiety about their own health and persist in talking about their symptoms, are asking their children to be neurotics or hypochondriacs.

Food and fluid needs

When a poorly child refuses to eat, parents have to decide whether to adopt mild persuasion, or to ignore his appetite altogether. Food-forcing must be avoided, for it is bound to lead to food refusal. It will do him no harm to eat next to nothing for two or three days: when he is convalescent he will make up for it by eating even more than usual.

The feverish child should be encouraged to drink plenty of fluid. Small children often do not demand as much fluid as they need, and may become more ill as a result. Appetizing fruit drinks, and perhaps the provision of a drinking straw, may encourage him to take more.

The sick child who has recently learnt control of the bladder and bowel may wet or soil himself again. As in the case of any other relapse of control, you will have to be tolerant and not show anxiety about it. He may be difficult about sleeping at night; this is natural if he has been in bed all day. If he is sweating a lot, you should see that he is kept comfortable by frequent tepid sponging, and if possible by a daily bath. Do not let him lie in clothes which have beecome damp through perspiration. See that his clothes are changed as frequently as necessary. You will see that his bed is straightened several times a day and remade morning and evening. Your doctor may advise you to give him aspirin to keep the temperature down, and he will advise you about the dose: overdosage can be highly dangerous. You will see that his room is warmed by means of a suitably protected radiator or fire, and yet well ventilated, with windows open, as long as he is protected from a draught. A bed table, which stretches right across the bed, is a great help for the child, not only for his meals, but for play as well.

Medicines

In 1762 Rousseau, in 'Emile' wrote 'Medicine is all the fashion these days. It is the amusement of the idle and the unemployed, who do not know what to do with their time, and so spend it on taking care of themselves.' If there was wastage of money on drugs then, there is vastly more waste of money today. Two Australian studies independently showed that more than half of the hundreds of babies studied aged three to six months had been given medicines in the previous two weeks — and only a small minority had been in any way poorly. In England and Wales in one year enough of just three kinds of nose drops were prescribed to supply 75 drops for every child in the country, and enough children's cough linctus to supply 40 doses to every child in the country. Yet nose drops, in our opinion, are of no value (and may do harm), while it is exceedingly doubtful whether cough medicines are of any value to children.

Children are given antibiotics (especially penicillin), nose drops and other medicines for colds — when none of them do the slightest good: babies are given medicines for wind, when it could not possibly help. They are given so-called tonics for poor appetite or other reasons, when they are completely uselss. They are given medicine for flu or chickenpox and antibiotics for uncomplicated measles, and antibiotics for attacks of asthma when they are useless for the purpose.

All medicines and tablets have possible untoward side-effects, some of them dangerous. In the book *Common Symptoms of Disease in Children* by one of us (RSI), of 150 common symptoms in children, at least 135 could be the result of a medicine. It is said that in the United States adverse reactions to drugs cost 3000 million dollars a year. In a major American hospital 17% of 1114 consecutive admissions were due to the side-effects of drugs.

Antibiotics such as penicillin are by no means free from side-effects. Penicillin by mouth frequently causes diarrhoea; the child may become sensitive to it, so that when he takes it rashes or more serious reactions occur and very commonly organisms become resistant to the drug, so that when it is really wanted for a serious infection it can no longer be given or it is ineffective. Side-effects of antibiotics can affect virtually every tissue in the body.

When antibiotics are given for the treatment of diarrhoea (including dysentery) they merely prolong the duration of the infection, and drugs taken to stop the diarrhoea may delay the body's process of getting rid of the organisms and toxins. *All syrupy medicines are liable to cause dental decay.*

For many reasons we strongly advise you to give medicines to your child only when they are absolutely necessary. Apart from all the possible side-effects they may start your child on the drug-taking pill-taking habit.

When you do give medicine, make sure that you have read the label: scores of children are poisoned by carelessness in this. Note the expiry date, if it is on the bottle: many medicines become ineffective or dangerous if kept too long. Always shake the bottle before use, otherwise later doses may be too concentrated and dangerous. Do not dilute ready-made medicines: dilution may make the medicine unstable. Never give more than the dose recommended. Do not buy unprescribed medicines at the chemist's shop: the chemist is not trained to treat children (or adults).

It is not easy to give medicine to a small child. You should do your best not to have a fight with him about it. You should try your utmost, in other words, to get him to take the medicine willingly, rather than to give it to him by force. If you force him to take it, you can be certain that he will refuse it every time, not only in his present illness, but in the future as well. If you can persuade him by tact to take it voluntarily, he is less likely to be awkward subsequently. You may use the subterfuge of telling him a story about a boy taking medicine. You may pretend to take it yourself and race him. You will try to make a game of it. A bribe may be justified — an offer of a nice sweet after it. It is dangerous to force medicine down a child's throat when he is crying, for he may inhale it. This danger is particularly important in the case of an oily medicine, like cod liver oil, for if this is inhaled into the lungs it may cause a troublesome chronic pneumonia.

Few children are able to take tablets before the age of 5 or so.

Before that age tablets should be crushed and given in a teaspoonful of milk or jam. Some children prefer it this way as many of them dislike the syrupy mixtures so often offered. It is unwise to give him medicine which has not been prescribed by the doctor. It is the height of folly to ask the chemist to prescribe medicine for the child, because he is not trained to do that. The danger of giving unprescribed medicine lies in the fact that almost all medicines, including aspirins, have dangerous side effects, and some may counteract or interfere with medicine prescribed by the doctor.

On keeping him in bed

In our opinion children are kept in bed far too long — and put there for no good reason at all. Even if a child is feverish, with a raised temperature due to a sore throat, influenza or measles, there is no point in making him stay in bed if he wants to sit up in front of the fire reading a book or playing a game. Many feel that a child should be kept in bed on account of jaundice (infective hepatitis) until the jaundice has gone. Apart from this, there are few conditions indeed which should keep a child in bed when he feels well enough to get up. Even if he has a raised temperature, it is difficult to see why he should be thought to be better sitting up restlessly in bed, than sitting in a chair in front of the fire playing a game or reading. In the case of the common infectious diseases, like chickenpox, German measles, a cold or sore throat, we see no reason why a child should be put to bed if he wants to be up. If you try to keep a child in bed against his will when he feels well, not only will you meet with resistance and make him unhappy, but he is likely to be so active in bed that he will have more exercise in bed than he would do if he were sitting in an armchair downstairs.

Your doctor will advise you on how soon to let your child go out of doors. It will depend on the illness and the weather at the time.

Keeping the child occupied in bed

If it is difficult to keep an active child occupied and free from boredom when he is well, it is still more difficult to do so when he is in bed, particularly if he has to be in bed in the convalescent stage of an illness. A wise mother has anticipated the problem of illness by putting aside a box of play material which is strictly inaccessible to the child when he is well. The box may contain Christmas cards for pasting and cutting out, discarded Christmas decorations, pictures from magazines for cutting out and making into a scrapbook, discarded *National Geographical Magazines*, bobbins, spools, acorns, fir cones, sea shells, toy catalogues, mail order catalogues, empty toilet paper rolls, pegs and pipe cleaners, scrap paper and pencils, scraps of wool, leather, sandpaper and fur. Other suggestions include cardboard boxes for making a bed or a doll's house, a magnet with suitable metal objects, gummed paper for sticking into scrapbooks, crayons for adorning newspaper advertisements, mounting paste and brush, and a doctor or nurse kit. Musical instruments and gramophone records will be useful. The child can help to prepare the Christmas decorations, and make his own Christmas cards for his friends with crayons or coloured paper. It is important not to give all the Bed Box at the same time. It would simply confuse the child. The treasures should be strictly rationed, day by day.

A child who has learnt to draw likes to be able to lie or sit and admire his artistry. His favourite drawings can be temporarily stuck on the wall. A balloon or two can be tied to the bed.

A child in bed loves to have postcards through the post. You can arrange this through friends, or post them yourself.

It is essential to make the bed comfortable. The older child will need a back rest with pillows. He may be prevented from sliding down the bed by a pillow, fastened in place by a piece of clothes-line, for his feet to rest against. A bed table is almost a necessity for a child. Care should be taken to ensure that he is not facing the light.

Admission to hospital

Many children's hospitals now have beds for mothers other then those breast-feeding their babies, so that they can come into hospital with their small children, to be at their side when they are ill, to help to nurse them through the illness and to look after them under supervision. It is not always possible, however, for a mother to leave the rest of the family.

If your child has to be admitted to hospital without you, you should do everything you can to help him to accept it with as little difficulty as possible. This is important, for it is a big shock for a small child who is ill to be separated from his mother and to be placed in strange surroundings with strange people, just when he needs her love and support. The older child will usually accept it without difficulty, but it is not always possible to explain to the younger child what is happening, and it is therefore more difficult for him to adapt himself to the new situation. It is particularly difficult for the younger child because of his greater attachment to his parents, and the difficulty which he experiences in changing his routine. Everything is different — his mealtimes, his food, his toys, the people he sees, his bed, his bath. The hospital staff will do everything possible to make him happy. They will love him and give him toys, talk to him, pick him up and play with him, but it is still difficult for him. If he is admitted to a children's hospital or a large children's unit is will help you to remember that the doctors and nurses have specialized in children's work because they love children. Much depends on the child's personality and age. Some are more affectionate than others. Some are more able to adapt themselves to strange surroundings than others. Some are shy, others are not. The majority of children settle down well and rapidly in hospital, but this does not mean that you should not do your best to help them to do so.

Do not make the mistake of thinking that you are doing him a kindness by paying for him to enter a nursing home or a private block of a hospital. He will be far happier in a children's ward, where there are other children to talk to and play with. If you can explain to the child what is going to happen to him, you should do so; at least you can do your best. If you are good at drawing, you may draw him a sketch of the ward, with nurses in white uniforms. We have seen the most painful scenes in hospital when a child has been brought for admission without being told in advance, with the result that he received a severe shock when separated from his mother. Never tell him lies at this stage or any later stage. It is wrong to tell him that you will come to visit him tomorrow, if you will not be allowed to do so, or to say that he will come home next day, if you known perfectly well that he will not. We remember a small boy saying, pitifully, 'Doctor, when will it be tomorrow?' It is wrong to say that you will sleep downstairs when you will do no such thing. The child will only be confused by these promises which are never fulfilled, and he will come to distrust your promises in future. It is our practice to teach medical students never to tell any child that it will not hurt when his finger is going to be pricked for a blood test. It will hurt, and he should be told so, but told that it will only be a prick. A doctor who is used to dealing with children never tells them lies, and always tries to explain to them what is going to happen.

Never, on any account, threaten to leave a child if he does not do what you ask him to do, or if he is 'naughty'. Some mothers are stupid enough to threaten to leave a child in hospital if he does not obey. These threats will not only cause fear and insecurity at the time, but they will cause grave emotional disturbance if at a later date he has to be left by his mother.

You can help him when about to bring him to hospital, by suitable suggestion. You can make the rather older child so look forward to hospital life that he leaves you without difficulty. You can tell him how there will be other children to play with, and how he will be given new toys. You will make it clear to him that he will be able to take some of his own favourite toys in with him, for you must let him take his favourite teddy, or the piece of rag or blanket which he always demands at night when put to bed. We regard this as important.

We hope that the hospital to which you take your child will allow you to visit him every day. Practices vary in this respect, some hospitals feeling that parents who live some distance away will not be able to visit, and so their children would be at a disadvantage compared with others. We feel that the majority should not suffer because of the few, and we firmly advocate daily visiting. It is usual to allow parents to visit at any time of the day convenient to them. It is something for the child to look forward to every day, and it helps to reduce the strain of separation from the parents. Do not be upset if he cries as soon as he sees you, and appears to reject you for a few minutes. It is true that some small children weep when it is time for the parents to go, but they soon get over it and settle down again. We feel that it is a good thing for the parents to visit in the early evening, when they can give the child his evening meal, read him a story, and tuck him up for the night. When you visit him, do not take him food or sweets. They may interfere with tests which are being carried out to determine the reason for his illness, or with his treatment. He will be well fed in hospital and supplied with plenty of sweets. It is a good idea to bring him some flowers — remembering that he will prefer some from his own garden to any that you buy. Do not take him expensive toys. He will be given toys in the hospital. He would be pleased with some cheap toys which give him something to do in bed, and which remind him that he is remembered by you, and particularly one or two of his own favourite toys from home. Children like to receive postcards — even though they are visited by their mothers every day. Try to send him cards every day or so, at least during a short illness, and less frequently if he is in hospital a long time. You may give him a stamped and addressed envelope with paper, on which he can draw, or a stamped card, so that he can send you a letter. It need hardly be added that your child must not see you shedding tears either when you first take him to hospital or when you leave him at the end of visiting time.

When the time comes for your child to leave hospital, his difficulties are by no means over. You may find that as a result of a disturbance of his routine on admission to hospital he has begun to wet his bed again, to demand to be fed, or to be difficult and negative. It is particularly distressing for a mother to find that the child rejects her: it is temporary only, but very difficult as long as it lasts, demanding the utmost love, tolerance and patience. You will have to be patient with him, give him all your love, avoid scolding him for mishaps, showing no anxiety about them, and he will soon return to normal. Do not spoil him on his return from hospital. When a child has been dangerously ill and comes back home, it is extremely difficult to avoid spoiling him, by letting him have all his own way, and by not teaching him discipline. We have often seen children, who have been at death's door and saved by prompt treatment, returning home well and fit, only to be ruined by indiscipline and spoiling. You should make a deliberate and determined effort to treat him as a normal child, showing him no favouritism, giving him special treats as you always did, but not relaxing at all in loving, tactful discipline.

28

Holidays

Holidays with a child under three years old may be a nightmare. Often all goes smoothly, but the child may be upset by strange surroundings and have sleep disturbances. Efforts are made to force him to go to sleep because it is feared that other visitors will complain of the noise — and the result is the opposite of the effect desired. He goes to bed more than normally tired after an exciting day, and sleeps badly for that reason. He is accustomed to an early breakfast, but breakfast is served two hours or more after his usual time, and to make matters worse he awakens an hour or more earlier than usual and demands company. He is afraid of the dark, because he has not his accustomed light at his bedside. On a wet day he is surrounded by restrictions, whereas at home he is allowed considerable freedom. He is constantly warned not to touch things, and this, with the mother's efforts to show him off and to make him show

'good manners', causes him to behave abominably. His meals are at unaccustomed times, and he becomes bad-tempered when hungry. These problems occur more in children of some personalities than others. Placid children are easy to manage on holiday, but others can be difficult. Most children after the third birthday are reasonably easy to manage when taken away. Before that, they may be trouble-some. Not only may the child be awkward when on holiday, but he may be difficult on return home. He has had more than the usual attention when away. He has got used to sharing his bedroom with another, and his daily rhythm has been disturbed, but he soon settles down to his original routine.

When arranging a holiday, every effort should be made to ensure that the small child will suffer as few restrictions as possible, and that no unusually 'good' behaviour will be expected of him. If he is going to visit tolerant and understanding relatives, or apartments in which reasonable freedom is allowed, no difficulty will be antici-pated. If he is going to an hotel, there may be a lot of trouble. A farm presents great attractions to a small child, and not much is likely to be expected of him. A rented house, or still better a caravan or a tent, gives the freedom which a small child should have on holiday — but unfortunately it does not allow the mother to get away from cooking and other chores.

If you are considering an hotel which claims that it caters for children, you should find out in detail what exactly it provides — in

the way of cots, prams, facilities for washing and drying, making feeds, and meal times for toddlers.

Holidays abroad

Many parents who are fond of travel wonder when they will have enough courage to take their young children abroad. Perhaps you are one of them. It depends on where you intend to go, how old they are, and how well they travel. Many parents refuse to be daunted by the presence of a 1 year-old, and have a good time abroad. By the time the youngest is 5, there is no difficulty as long as he travels well, perhaps with the aid of Kwells for travel sickness.

There is much to be said for air travel when there are small children, but do read the timing of the arrangements carefully. You may find that you are expected to leave your airport at 2.0 a.m., flying through the night, or that on the outward journey you are due to arrive at the airport of your destination at 11.0 p.m., followed by a long tedious journey in a bus, with the children worn out.

The children will love a holiday abroad, provided that there is water to play in — seaside, lakeside, or streams, provided that travelling is reduced to the minimum to get to and from a place, and provided that the food is good. Food restrictions are irksome, but they are regrettably necessary if you go to a place where sunshine can be guaranteed (e.g. Spain). It is unfortunately true that the more certain the sunshine and heat, the less certain will be the hygiene. Don't think that diarrhoea is due to sunstroke or rich food. It is not. It is due to food poisoning — infection by careless handling, careless storage and flies. If you go to a hot climate, you will have to take considerable precautions if you want to protect the children from

diarrhoea. The following are the chief ones: always avoid using unboiled milk or water — even for brushing teeth; avoid salads, ice creams, cream cakes, cream dishes, ice in drinks, shellfish, prepared meats. See that the fruit is peeled. You are asking for trouble if you let them have these. It is another matter altogether if you go to Scandinavia or the Alps, where the standard of hygiene is high, but the weather less certain. There you can let them eat what comes with as much safety as in Britain. Beware of swimming in polluted water — lakes or sea. In very many places, such as those on the Mediterranean, the water is heavily polluted, with organisms which cause typhoid fever, diarrhoea, ear, eye, nose and throat and other infections.

If going to a hot place, do remember to take enough fluid. There may be long delays at the frontier. A delay of an hour or two at the Franco-Spanish frontier in sweltering heat can be extremely distressing if you have small children. They will need large quantities of fluid if they are unlucky enough to acquire a fever or diarrhoea.

In some countries it is most unwise to drink water from the tap. Water can be rendered safe by boiling, or adding one tablet of halazone to a litre of water, shaking the water and allowing it to stand for 30 minutes before use. When going to Spain or the Islands, or the African coast, some advise that a medicine, preferably streptotriad, should be taken throughout the time abroad to try to reduce the risk of diarrhoea. It may help, but we are not certain. The trouble is that many, probably the majority, of attacks of diarrhoea are due to virus infections, and these cannot be prevented by a medicine. You should certainly take a supply of Dioralyte or Electrosol with you in case anyone gets diarrhoea.

Certain precautions should be taken before you start. You and your husband should have separate passports, with all the children's names on each passport. This would make it easy for a parent to take one child home in case of emergency. The standard of medicine is high in Scandinavia, and probably high in most parts of the Alps. In some countries, however, it is different from ours, and there is a lot to be said for getting an ill child home by the shortest route (e.g. air) if he is unlikely to make a rapid recovery where he is. If on a winter sports holiday, he suffers a fracture — get him home as soon as you possibly can, and have the treatment checked by a specialist immediately on return. See that you have taken out good insurance policies, but choose them carefully, for they differ widely. Take one out for your baggage and see that it includes loss of money. Take another out for sickness when abroad, seeing that it covers premature return home by one parent with a child, or the need to stay on after the others have gone home. Norway, Sweden, Denmark and Yugoslavia have reciprocal health service arrangements with Britain, so that a traveller from Britain will receive free treatment if ill in one of these countries, but in the EEC countries there may be annoying 'red tape' concerning free treatment if you need it. Treatment abroad can be extremely expensive: see that your insurance cover is adequate. The cover provided by Europ Assistance (269, High Street, Croydon) is very good.

The following equipment will be useful:

1. A camping gas heater, for boiling water, or an electric immersion heater, with a variety of plugs.
2. Tins of instant milk.

3. Polythene bags and water containers.
4. A kepcool or Insulate bag for butter, etc. It would be disastrous to carry chocolate or butter in the ordinary picnic basket in hot climates. A wide-mouthed Thermos flask is useful. Ordinary Thermos flasks are useful for keeping water cold.
5. Lemonade powder. Do not carry fizzy lemonade in the boot of your car; interesting explosions will occur if you do.
6. Kleenex tissues and Quickies, and a wet sponge in a polythene bag.
7. A plastic clothes-line and soap flakes. Clothes which do not need ironing.
8. A potty under the front seat of the car in case of unexpected vomiting.
9. A good supply of biscuits —— more than you think you will need.
10. Toys for wet days or evenings.

It is difficult to advise about medical equipment, and we suggest that you should consult your doctor about this. We suggest that a minimum would be:

1. A cream to preven sunburn, e.g., Uvistat
2. Insect repellent
3. Kwells
4. Aspirins or paracetamol for headaches
5. A clinical thermometer

6. Bandages, Elastoplast, Sterrystrips
7. Dioralyte or electrosol for diarrhoea.

Remember that diarrhoea is not the only ailment which can ruin a holiday. Many holidays are ruined by sunburn. Many drugs make the skin unduly sensitive to sunburn. It is particularly important in fair-haired children who do not tan easily to prevent sunburn rather than to wait for it to develop and then treat it. Too much exposure to sun on the first day can ruin a holiday. If there is a full sun at the seaside, half an hour on the first day should be the absolute maximum: it might be too much in some. Prior to that, thoroughly cover the skin with the ointment mentioned above. It prevents much sunburn. It is no use applying it when once the skin is badly burnt and sore. For the rest of the day most of the skin will have to be covered. Remember that troublesome sunburn can occur under the shade of an awning on the beach: the direct rays of the sun are not necessary. Gradually increase the duration of exposure, and in a few days the children will be able to take anything — with the help of a sunburn preventive cream.

If you are visiting certain countries abroad, you must remember the necessary inoculations. Wherever you go abroad, you should be sure that your children's inoculations and *your own* are up to date (see also Chapter 25).

If you go to Spain, or anywhere on the Mediterranean coast, especially North Africa, be sure that the whole family is protected

against typhoid fever and poliomyelitis; if going to exotic places in Asia or Africa protect the family against infective hepatitis (by an injection of gamma globulin, which protects for three to six months). Malaria is comon in Africa and many parts of Asia, and prophylactic drugs will have to be taken. Sandfly infection occurs in Malta and North Africa. In Asia and many parts of Africa immunisation against cholera is important, and in Africa yellow fever inoculation is essential.

On no account allow your children to play with animals, especially dogs, in Southern Europe, or anywhere in Asia or Africa, because of the risk of rabies.

The following book may be useful:

> Department of Health and Social Security: *Notice to Travellers; Health Problems*
>
> Ross Institute, London School of Hygiene and Tropical Medicine, Keppel Street, London, WC1: *Preservation of personal health in warm climates.* 1980
>
> World Health Organization pamphlet: *Vaccination certificate requirements for international travel.* Her Majesty's Stationary Office
>
> O'Quigley, S. *Health and Travel.* Dublin. O'Brien Press. 1979. (Prepared for Air Lingus)
>
> Jopling, W.H. *Good health abroad: a traveller's handbook.* Bristol. John Wright. 1975
>
> British Medical Association Family Doctor Booklet: *Health on holiday and other travels*

Travel is a wonderful education for children. They will love it and learn much which they would not otherwise learn. But we do suggest that a little planning and preparation may make all the difference to your happiness when abroad.

29

Toys and play

Every mother knows how difficult it is to keep a small child occupied, particularly in bad weather, or in overcrowded conditions in which there is no available garden. Yet boredom must be avoided, as far as is reasonably possible, for the bored child soon becomes cross, bad tempered, destructive and quarrelsome. This leads to a vicious circle, for the mother is apt to respond by irritability and shortness of temper, so that the child's behaviour becomes still worse. Apart from all this, play is essential for every child, to keep him happy, to help him to practise his newly-found skills, and to help him to learn new ones. Play with other children is essential to help him to learn to give and take, and to learn to co-operate with others. Play helps him to grow and develop. It increases his powers of concentration, observation and imagination. It is because of the great importance of play in the management of a child, and because of the difficulties in keeping children occupied, that we have discussed the question in some detail. Some cities now have a toy library, where you can borrow toys, and public libraries have a children's section, where there is a wide selection of books for your children to read — and for you to read to your children.

Toys must be safe
All toys given to children, especially to babies, must be safe for them. They must have no sharp corners. They must have no detachable parts which are dangerous because they are sharp, or because they are small enough to be swallowed or inhaled. They should not be flammable. They should not be made of brittle plastic which if broken would leave dangerous sharp edges. Soft toys should not contain cheap and dangerous stuffing, and eyes must not be removable. Some toy makers produce toys which fail on all these counts. They have sharp corners or edges which cut the baby's fingers. They have small detachable objects, like eyes in a teddy bear, which are of great danger to a child. Never buy a soft animal with eyes which are not firmly sewn in, and even if you have tested it before making the

purchase, you should examine it at intervals to ensure that the eyes are not working loose. Many serious accidents, often involving a surgical operation, have resulted from the inhalation of small toys. Furry 'animals' should be made by a reputable firm which uses good clean material in their manufacture. Cheap furry toys are sometimes made from inferior dirty and dangerous materials — and they cannot be properly cleaned and sterilized. Toys must be washable (apart from some furry animals, which must be 'dry cleaned'). They must have fast colours. Every available object is taken to the mouth of the young baby who is old enough to grasp it, and it is most annoying to find that as soon as he licks a new toy the colours come off. Apart from the nuisance occasioned by paint spoiling clothes, many paints contain lead, which is highly dangerous to the child.

Play in the first year

It is not easy to say when babies first begin to play. Even a 2 month-old baby may play in an elementary fashion, by withdrawing from the breast, looking up and smiling at his mother, burying his head in the breast, smiling, and then starting to suck again. This may be repeated over and over again.

The 3 month-old baby likes to have a rattle placed in his hand, but he cannot pick it up if he drops it. By 4 months, he actively waives it and derives a lot of pleasure thereby. It is important to see that a rattle given to a small baby is a light one, for babies are likely to knock their face and even eyes with the rattle in waving it about. Some rattles offered for sale in shops are too heavy and too sharp, with handles which are too broad for the baby's small hands.

When the baby is old enough to grasp objects himself (from 5 months onwards), a wide variety of objects will give him pleasure, and they need not be expensive. In general, they are toys which make a noise and have bright colours. These include rattles, bobbins, wooden curtain rings, coloured wooden beads on a string, plastic cups, spoons, and a firmly sealed tin with a few lentils or pebbles in it. They should be given to him not only in the pram, but when he is lying on a rug on the floor, and when he is propped up in his high chair with the tray in front of him.

In our experience bricks covered with paper with pictures on are not serviceable, for the paper comes off. Plain coloured bricks with fast colours are all that are required.

Other suggestions for the period from six months to a year include a light pan or aluminium measuring jug with a spoon, a basket or box of bricks, which will enable him (from about 10 months onwards) to enjoy the game of putting things in and taking them out again; a ball; and bath toys. When near the first birthday, firm card books are popular.

Play after the first birthday

General principles. There are several important points to consider in the selection of toys for the child after his first year.

A great deal of money can be thrown away on toys which are of no lasting value, in that they provide only temporary interest to the child, chiefly because they give him no scope for the imagination or facilities for practising new skills. The worst offenders in this way are mechanical toys, particularly those of the expensive type. Clockwork toys rarely provide any lasting attraction to children under the age of 6. We all enjoy seeing the fascinating highly expensive mechanical toys on display in toyshops at Christmas time, and are tempted to put our hands deep into our pockets to buy them. We should resist the temptation. The child will look at them two or three times and then discard them, for there is nothing to do with them. They delight the father much more than the child. Clockwork or electric trains are nearly always a waste of money before the age of about six. Before that age children are more likely to take the engine and coaches off the lines and play with them elsewhere but where they

were intended to be played with. This infuriates the father, who does his best to show the child how the train should be played with, much to the child's annoyance, for he has his own ideas, and he rightly feels that he should be left to play with them as he wants. Even cheap mechanical motor cars provide little advantage over engineless cars in the first 4 or 5 years. The keys get lost, and the cars are more likely to be pushed about than to be wound up to go under their own steam.

It follows that when you are buying toys, you should buy those which will enable the child to use his hands, to develop his new skills, to experiment, and to use his imagination. When considering the purchase of a toy, you should ask yourself 'How many ways will he be able to use it?' 'Will it make him think?' He is more likely to enjoy and to play for a long time with toys of educational value than with mere mechanical toys. You must not think that the time for 'education' will come soon enough, when he goes to school. He will learn constantly at home, and properly chosen toys will help him to learn. You are not 'pushing him too hard' by giving him 'educational toys'. He will like them more than anything else, because like all other children, he likes learning new skills and practising them, experimenting, constructing and creating. Mere mechanical toys give little scope for this — and so have only passing interest.

We admit that it is impossible to predict which toy an individual child will most enjoy. Toys which interest one child have little interest to another. It depends largely on his personality, interests and aptitudes. It is wrong to think that more expensive toys will give

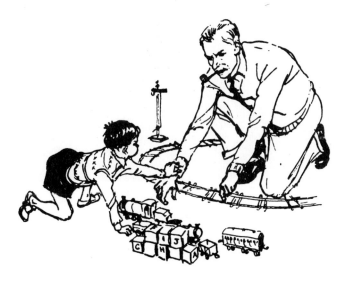

41

the most pleasure. There are large numbers of fantastically expensive dolls on the market. There is nothing to suggest that such dolls
give any more pleasure than others at a fraction of the cost, with
home-made clothes which it is possible for the child to change at
will. Apart from the initial cost, another important drawback of
expensive toys is the parents' fear that they will be damaged, with
resultant unpleasantness and scoldings.

The only toys which need be expensive are out-of-door ones, such
as a tricycle, sand-pit, climbing frame and swing. Money can be
saved by inserting an advertisement for such toys in the local paper,
and obtaining a good secondhand one. With a little touching up and
painting a toy can be made to look like new. Much money can be
saved by the handyman who can make toys himself — and the child
will love to help him.

It is a matter of opinion whether boys should be given guns,
pistols and other weapons. All boys have normal aggressive instincts,
but we cannot see what can be said in favour of trying to encourage
those instincts by giving toy weapons. Some argue that if boys are
allowed to play at hurting people they are less likely to want to hurt
people later. It seems a doubtful argument. It is better for a child to
be given the means of giving vent to his normal aggressive instincts
in as harmless a way as possible, rather then trying to make him
bottle them up. We feel, however, that there is little to be said for
toy guns and other aggressive weapons. A child is liable to break toys
which bore him, because he can do little with them. A useful toy is
one which can be taken apart and put together again, such as wooden
lorries and engines.

It is not necessary to think that a child should have a large number
of toys. Many children have so many toys that half of them are
hardly ever played with and not appreciated. Toys tend to accumulate, and it is better to remove a large proportion of them entirely
and bring some of them out on a wet day, when they will be
welcomed and enjoyed. They can be put away again after they have
been used for a few days. It is better to do this than to let the child
have all the toys at once. He only gets bored with them, and so is
more likely to break or damage them. He will enjoy toys more if they
are put away for a while and replaced by others from the stock.

A common mistake is to give children toys for which they are not
old enough. On the one hand it is wrong to give a child toys which
are more suitable for a younger one. On the other hand, it is a pity to
give a child toys which he is not old enough to enjoy. Such toys are
liable to be damaged from improper use, and this leads to scoldings
and punishment.

As in the first year, it is essential to see that toys are well made, contain no sharp edges, have no small detachable pieces which can be inhaled, have fast colours, and are unlikely to harm the child. Bows and arrows are best avoided, for they have caused many serious accidents. Beware of giving your child sharp pointed pencils and especially indelible ones, for they have caused many accidents, especially to the eye.

A toy cupboard or toy box should be provided, so that the child knows where his toys are and learns where they have to be put when he has finished with them. It helps him to learn the meaning of property.

Finally, if it can be provided, a playroom, however small, is a great help. It takes the child and his toys away from his mother, and enables her to get on with her housework more easily and it is a good thing for the child to feel that he has a place of his own in which there will be a minimum of interference. We do not suggest that the child should always be allowed to have the playroom untidy, or that he should be allowed to damage the room, by drawing on the wall or carving or scratching the paintwork. He has to learn to help to tidy up, and he has to learn not to be destructive even in his own room. But a playroom gives more freedom than any other room possibly can, because it is designed and equipped for the purpose, with furnishings which are liable to as little damage as possible. The lighting in the playroom should be good and the heating adequate and safe.

The child appreciates bright colours. The only furnishing necessary, apart from cupboards, consists of a low table and chairs.

The child from 1 to 2 may be reluctant to be separated from his parents, preferring to play in the room in which his mother is working. Children vary in this. Older children will play in a playroom for long periods.

Suggested toys and play material
In this section we shall divide the periods up into ages 1 to 2, 2 to 3, and 3 to 5, knowing that toys enjoyed at one age are also enjoyed at other ages, even though they may be used differently. Nevertheless, one would not buy for a 5 year-old toys which are suitable for a 1 year-old, or vice versa; hence some degree of subdivision is necessary.

One to two
Bobbins, bricks, plastic cups and spoons, empty tins, bath toys and dolls such as teddy bears from earlier months, will continue to be used in the 1 to 2 year-old period. Children at this age continue to enjoy the repetitive casting game — placing bricks or other objects in and out of containers — baskets, boxes, and so on. The simpler Kiddicraft toys, which do not involve a screwing motion (usually learnt about 2), are useful. These include coloured beakers of various kinds, coloured bricks, round discs which fit on to a vertical piece of wood, and 'pyramids'.

A most useful present, which will be used and enjoyed for several years, is a sackful of bricks of different sizes and shapes. These can

be obtained from any of the manufacturers of eductional toys listed at the end of this section. The 1 to 2 year-old will merely place one or two on top of another, and put them into and out of containers, but as he grows older he will use them more and more for imaginative play, building houses, garages, engines and ships, according to where his interests are and according to what he sees on excursions from home. In our experience there is no better present to buy for a child at this age, and no present which will be used more — especially after his second birthday.

The child of this age enjoys push and pull toys. Many of the larger toys are well made. It is important to see that they are stable, and will not 'throw' the child, whose balance is as yet imperfect. A three-wheel cart, for instance, is unstable, and may cause a small child to fall. The type of toy which holds objects, such as bricks, is better than, say, an engine with no available space for them.

A scrapbook is useful at this age period. Parents enjoy collecting brightly coloured and not too complicated pictures from magazines and sticking them into a cheap scrapbook. Children enjoy looking through such books, and if common objects are pointed out in the pictures, they learn a great deal and are helped in learning speech. There are many simple picture books on the market, only a few of which, however, are suitable for children. The pictures should be simple, unlike many pictures in such books. Pictures with letters of the alphabet are of little value. Though children enjoy looking at the pictures, they often tend to show objects other than common simple ones. We have in mind some books which show 'U for Ulex', 'U for Ukelele', 'E for Evening Primrose', 'G for Gamester', 'X for Expensive', 'Z for Zany' — hardly words which are of importance to the

toddler. The *Colour Photo Books,* included in the list at the end of this section, are particularly good in this respect. They show simple objects, with not enough in the pictures to confuse children.

Picture books with simple stories are appreciated by children of this age. They also enjoy the rhythm of nursery rhymes and learn a surprising number by the end of the second year, even though their articulation is imperfect. There are several good nursery rhyme books on the market.

Towards the latter part of the second year children learn to copy their mother in her housework. Materials for cleaning, washing and cooking will be popular. In this same period children learn to thread large beads. Care must be taken that the beads are large, especially when the child still shows a tendency to put things into the mouth. Musical instruments and anything making a noise will be appreciated by the child.

Out of doors the child will enjoy a ball, plastic paddling pool and sand pit. The latter can be made or purchased. It should be kept clean, for the sand may be contaminated by animals if it is not covered up. 'Washed' sand or silver sand is suitable for it. A bowl of water with cups, funnel, rubber tubing and jug from which water can be poured, will keep children happily occupied for an hour or more.

Two to three

At about the second birthday children learn to rotate the wrist sufficiently to enable them to open doors and unscrew lids. There are barrels of different sizes which unscrew, bricks which screw on to a piece of wood, and interlocking bricks. There is a coloured posting box, with seven holes of different shapes into which seven plastic bricks can be 'posted' — each one fitting one hole only. There are simple formboards, which help to teach appreciation of size and shape, and pegboards, with round and square holes into which appropriately shaped pegs can be inserted. Boys seem to obtain considerable relief from their pent-up aggressive instincts by the hammer and 'piledriving' toy, available in most good toyshops. Other toys include a gyroscope, picture lotto, a magnet, magnetic shapes and construction kits. The reader should consult the catalogues of makers of educational toys listed at the end of this section.

The child of this age is beginning to want to fashion objects, to draw and to paint. A blackboard and easel with chalks, drawing books, and waste paper from the office will be appreciated. Coloured pencils, with a pencil sharpener which the child can use himself, are useful. There is a danger that wax crayons will be eaten by the child.

They are dangerous, and should only be given to the older child (of 4 or 5) who can be trusted not to put them into his mouth. If you can find a place where a mess can be made and you feel that you can face it, modelling clay, plasticine, a painting easel, powder colours and poster paints will be popular. We advise you to be sure that the child is suitably clothed for the purpose, so that there will be no friction when some of the materials are found on the clothes.

A garage, shop, doll's pram, doll's cot, or doll's house, which we suggest should be obtained secondhand by advertisement, provides many children with scope for imaginative play. We say 'many children', for not all children will play with a doll's house. One can obtain doll's houses made up of simple rooms which fit together in a variety of ways, and which can be used to make other types of buildings. Such toys should be of sufficient size and contain sufficient rooms and equipment, such as cars or furniture, according to the toy, to allow imaginative play. Better still, if space permits, a Wendy House, consisting of three appropriately hinged sides with a window and door, fitting into one end of a room, will allow hours of imaginative play. This can be constructed readily by a handymand or by a joiner, or obtained secondhand (e.g. by an advertisement in a nursery journal). A temporary affair can be made from a clotheshorse or from a frame covered with hessian or other suitable material. The equipment may include scales and weights.

Children will enjoy a discarded play-pen, with two or three up-rights removed to make a door, or a table with a rug thrown over the top, and hanging down to make walls.

A doll, with home-made clothes which can be changed at will, and fastened with large buttons, gives the child considerable scope. A mother who does her own dressmaking should not discard the bits and scraps of material which are normally put into the fire. An imaginative girl can make dresses, blankets for the doll's cot, nurse's uniform, and other items out of them. The mother may herself make a dress for the doll from them, and can sometimes supplement the girl's 'wardrobe' by brightly coloured pieces of ribbon. It should not be thought that there is anything abnormal about a boy playing with dolls. In the same way children like to play with discarded clothes for dressing up.

Towards the third birthday the child is old enough to be given blunt-ended scissors with which to cut paper and cut out pictures in magazines, animal templates, and pictures to colour with crayons. Children at this age begin to enjoy mosaic pictures, colour matching (with wools) and picture matching. Sets of pictures of common objects have to be matched with corresponding pictures on a board. Sets of five each of 12 or more pictures have to be put together.

Cut-out numerals can also be used. A plastic tea set, with other materials for a doll's tea party, may be enjoyed. They should be 'washed up' by the child. This may keep him quiet for an hour or two. Simple jigsaw puzzles, with six to ten pieces, may give much pleasure.

Books and stories are enjoyed more and more as the child grows older. The Beatrix Potter stories are enjoyed and understood at this age, and will continue to be enjoyed by older children. The rhythm of nursery rhymes, such as some of those in *The March of Rhyme* will be much appreciated. Some otherwise excellent books are ruined by the shocking doggerel 'poetry' with which the stories are told, and by the use of such words as 'quackies', meaning ducks.

Out of doors suitable toys include a tricycle (which can be worked by about three), a sandpit and garden tools, and disused crates and packing cases (free from nails and splinters), and a plank. These can be used to make 'trains' and 'houses', and other things.

From three to five
Bricks, drawing and painting material, equipment for imaginative play, and out-of-door equipment continue to be used. A climbing frame is a useful piece of garden equipment which provides hours of valuable play in the fresh air. If purchased ready made it will be extremely expensive. It can be made by a handyman or a joiner from a ladder, by carving it into four parts, so that there are two vertical ladders, preferably embedded in concrete on a lawn, one horizontal ladder joining the two vertical ones, and an oblique one. The concrete should be covered by turf, so that falls will not be serious. A motor car tyre, suspended from the horizontal ladder, is a useful addition. Another popular addition is a slide, which will hook on to a rung of one of the vertical ladders.

Stencils provide useful play material for the child. Children can make a wide variety of patterns and designs from coloured gummed paper, cut by manufacturers into various shapes. Cardboard coins are used in connection with the shop. Jigsaws are enjoyed by many children. Children vary considerably in their ability to do them: most children at the age of 5 can manage 20-piece jigsaws. The toy sewing machines which we have seen are well nigh useless, because of the tangles which are produced, even when the child is skilful with his hands. Boys enjoy the 'Nail Mosaic' toy, in which mosaic pieces in various shapes are hammered on to a board with nails, to make designs. They can begin to play simple games with picture dominoes or 'Snap' cards. For other toys which help a child to learn to read, see the booklet *Getting Ready to Read* published by the Educational Supply Association.

A particularly useful toy is a beechwood 'Multibuilder', from which a variety of engines, lorries, motor cars and trucks can be constructed by means of splitpins. The plastic toy 'Lego' is a useful educational toy from the age of 4 onwards even though help is needed at first.

Children between 3 and 5, and perhaps especially girls, like to learn elementary dancing. They may also enjoy suitable music and children's gramophone records.

Finally, domestic pets, such as dogs, cats, goldfish, or even a tortoise, help a child to learn kindness to animals, give him a feeling of responsibility, and provide tremendous and lasting pleasure. Unfortunately, the parents have to take the major part of the responsibility in looking after them — until the child is 9 years old or so.

You should also know that numerous unpleasant diseases, such as worm infections, may be acquired by children from domestic animals.

They include rabies, toxoplasmosis, toxocara, tapeworms, various virus infections, and organisms causing diarrhoea. It is most unwise to allow a dog to lick a child's face, especially his mouth.

Remember that animal bites have their dangers — the worst of which is rabies. Animal bites account for around three per cent of all attendances in a Children's Hospital Accident and Emergency Department: at the Children's Hospital, Sheffield, this amounts to around 700 to 800 new attendances per year on account of bites. The majority are bites by dogs and in buying a dog as a pet it is sensible to choose a small dog rather than a big one; by far the commonest breed responsible for bites is the Alsatian. It is probably wise to delay the purchase of a dog until the child is old enough to look after it and old enough not to provoke it excessively by rough play.

Firms which specialize in educational toys include:

E. J. Arnold & Son Ltd., Butterley Street, Leeds, 10.

Early Learning Centre, Hawksworth, Swindon.

Educational Supply Association, Pinnacles, Harlow, Essex.

James Galt, 30 Great Marlborough Street, London, W. 1.

Philip and Tracey, Northway, Walworth Industrial Estate, Andover.

Wilkane Ltd., Eastbourne, Sussex.

Firms who specialize in children's books include:

E. J. Arnold and Son Ltd., Leeds.

A. Wheaton and Co., Exeter.

The Children's Book Shop, The Broad, Oxford.

Heffer's Children's bookshop, Cambridge.

Epilogue

A word about the future

Have you considered taking out an education policy for your child? The sooner you do it the better. There are several types of policy, and you should consult a good insurance company for particulars. A good type is one in which for a small annual premium (which, for a small sum extra can be paid monthly if you wish), you receive an annual income for five years after your boy reaches the age of 12 or 13. With the Educational Endowment policy, if you die before your child reaches that age, your wife will receive the money yearly from the date of your death until the child is 16 or 17 years old. A similar policy can be taken out to mature at the age at which your child reaches the university — say, 18 or 19.

The premium varies according to the type of policy and the insurance company.

Another type of policy is one which brings in a lump sum when the child is 21 years old. An annual premium of £5, for instance, paid from the date of the birth of a child, would give a welcome twenty-first birthday present of about £120.

Index